Organellar Ion Channels and Transporters

Society of General Physiologists Series • Volume 51

Organellar Ion Channels and Transporters

Society of General Physiologists • 49th Annual Symposium

Edited by
David E. Clapham
Department of Pharmacology, Mayo Foundation, Rochester, Minnesota
and
Barbara E. Ehrlich
Departments of Medicine and Physiology, University of Connecticut,
Farmington, Connecticut

Marine Biological Laboratory
Woods Hole, Massachusetts

7–9 September 1995

© **The Rockefeller University Press**
New York

Contents

Preface

An international symposium on Organellar Ion Channels and Transporters was held in September, 1995, at the Marine Biological Laboratory in Woods Hole, Massachusetts, under the auspices of the Society of General Physiologists. The symposium focused on the biochemistry, molecular biology, structure/function, and physiology of ion channels and transporters found in intracellular membranes such as the endoplasmic reticulum, mitochondria, and nucleus. The overall aim of the symposium was to integrate the physiologic, biochemical, and genetic approaches to the study of this class of membrane proteins and to provide a focus for discussion of this exciting new frontier of membrane biology.

In addition to the keynote address, there were 24 lectures distributed in five sessions with the following themes: (1) Endoplasmic reticulum ion channels and transporters; (2) mitochondrial channels and transporters; (3) nuclear channels and transporters; (4) secretory mechanisms; and (5) organellar localization of calcium. The speakers organized their talks to address a broad audience whose interests ranged from protein chemistry to cell physiology. A late-breaking science session highlighted new measurements of Ca^{2+} microdomains and described laser inactivation of tagged proteins. The keynote address was delivered by Dr. Clara Franzini-Armstrong of the University of Pennsylvania, who discussed her pioneering work on skeletal muscle ultrastructure and its relationship to contractile function.

Intracellular calcium (Ca^{2+}) is the ubiquitous trigger of a vast array of cellular events. Calcium enters the cytoplasm from the extracellular medium through voltage- or ligand-gated channels, or from intracellular stores through Ca^{2+} (ryanodine receptors) or $InsP_3$-gated channels. The refilling of stores by Ca^{2+} release–activated channels has been described in detail, but little is known of the messenger between store and refilling channel. Intracellular Ca^{2+} control and release was a common theme of the meeting, and presentations ranged from the complex dependence of the Ca^{2+}-release channels on cytosolic ATP and $[Ca^{2+}]$ and direct recording of these channels on the nuclear endoplasmic reticular membranes, to observations of Ca^{2+} "sparks," reflecting quantized Ca^{2+} release.

The cell membrane as a lipid bilayer necessitated the evolution of specialized channels and transporters to ferry nutrients and ions into specific compartments. Detailed mutagenesis of the Ca-ATPase pump and early structural studies yielded significant insights into the molecular mechanisms of these transport processes. The biochemical and functional properties of the intracellular sugar and amino acid transporters, the mitochondrial transporters, mitochondrial (VDAC) channels, and one of the first mechanosensitive channels from bacteria were described.

Membrane fusion mediates endocytosis, constitutive secretion, recycling of membrane components, as well as regulated exocytosis of hormones, enzymes, and neurotransmitters. The assembly of the nuclear envelope and its control of transcription factor diffusion through the nuclear pores were dramatically illustrated. Model systems, such as hemagglutinin virus fusion to liposomes, and capacitance

Organellar Ion Channels and Transporters © 1996 by The Rockefeller University Press

and amperometry measurements of exocytosis in chromaffin and mast cells were used to describe some of the underlying physical parameters of fusion.

The symposium was largely supported by the Society of General Physiologists, the National Science Foundation, and the attendees. Other generous contributions were made by the National Institutes of Health (NIGMS), Burroughs Wellcome Corp., Merck Research Laboratories, Smith Kline Beecham Inc., Upstate Biotechnology Inc., BioSignals Inc., Adams and List Associates, Ltd., Warner Instruments Corp., and SOMA Scientific. Donations from Cape Cod Potato Chips and Ocean Spray Cranberry Juice made the poster sessions more palatable.

We are particularly grateful to the organization and persistence of Jane Leighton and Susan Judd in managing the symposium, to John Burris and the Marine Biological Laboratories for their support and hospitality, to The Rockefeller University Press, and to Lori Volkman for significant secretarial help in Rochester, MN.

David Clapham
Barbara Ehrlich

Chapter 1

**Ryanodine Receptors and Inositol
Trisphosphate Receptors**

Functional Significance of Membrane Architecture in Skeletal and Cardiac Muscle

Clara Franzini-Armstrong

Department of Cell and Developmental Biology, University of Pennsylvania School of Medicine, Philadelphia, Pennsylvania 19104-6058

Structure of Membranes Involved in e-c Coupling: General Considerations

Excitation-contraction (e-c) coupling, also termed *depolarization-contraction* coupling, involves a series of steps that link an initial depolarization of the surface membrane to the contraction of the actomyosin system in all types of muscle fibers. Two membrane systems are involved in e-c coupling: the plasma, or surface, membrane (and its invaginations, the transverse (T) tubules) and the sarcoplasmic reticulum (SR). The latter constitutes an internal network responsible for the sequestering and release of calcium. Special junctions at which the internal and exterior membrane systems come to close approximation allow interactions between surface membranes and SR. At these sites, a signal initiated by depolarization of the surface membrane results in release of calcium from the SR.

Feet and Tetrads

Two major structural components have been identified in the SR and T-tubule membranes participating in junctions (jSR and jT membranes, Fig. 1). The feet are components of the jSR that are arranged in orderly arrays within the narrow junctional gap separating the apposed membranes of the SR and T tubules. Feet span the entire width of the junctional gap, joining the two membranes to each other, and have a tetrameric (quatrefoil) structure (Ferguson et al., 1984). The feet have been identified with a large peptide, which is an intrinsic component of the SR membrane involved in triad formation (Kawamoto et al., 1986; 1988). The intact tetrameric foot was isolated and characterized by use of mild detergent extraction and a procedure that takes advantage of its high affinity for ryanodine, a plant alkaloid (Inui et al., 1987*a* and *b*; Lai et al., 1988; Block et al., 1988; Anderson et al., 1989). Ryanodine receptors (RyRs) are homotetramers (~2,000 kD) that function as the SR calcium-release channels (Smith et al., 1985; Lai et al., 1988). The unusually large cytoplasmic domains of RyRs, which constitute the feet, have a complex structure (Radermacher et al., 1994).

A second component of the junctions, the tetrad, belongs to the jT membrane and was first identified in fish muscle (Franzini-Armstrong and Nunzi, 1983; Block et al., 1988). Tetrads are also present in junctional domains of the plasma membrane (jPM). Tetrads are visualized in freeze-fracture images of T tubules, where they are arranged in two rows parallel to the long axis of the T tubule and overlap-

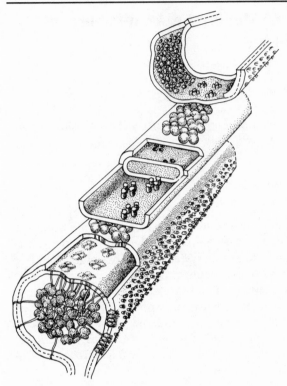

Figure 1. Three-dimensional reconstruction of a triad in skeletal muscle, illustrating the disposition of the main components of the junction. The cut-out view of the sarcoplasmic reticulum (*SR*), at the bottom, shows the enlarged junctional SR, with its content of calsequestrin, held in place by links to the membrane. The lateral surfaces of the SR are decorated by heads of the numerous calcium ATPase or calcium pump molecules. The T tubule is the central flattened tube. The cytoplasmic domains of the ryanodine receptors (or SR calcium-release channels) have a four leaf clover shape and are arranged in two rows in the narrow junctional gap between SR and T-tubule membranes. The intramembrane domains of RyRs, shown in the cut-off view of the SR membrane, are also tetrameric, but smaller than the cytoplasmic domains. Within the fractured T-tubule membrane are groups of four identical particles, called tetrads. Tetrads are thought to be groups of four dihydropyridine receptors. From Block et al., 1988.

ping the two rows of feet. Each tetrad is composed of four identical intramembrane particles arranged in a tetragonal disposition. It was proposed that the tetrads are composed of four dihydropyridine receptors, or DHPRs (Block et al., 1988). This hypothesis is supported by the following evidence. (*1*) DHPRs are located in the junctional T-tubule membrane and also in the surface membrane facing the SR at peripheral couplings (Jorgensen et al., 1989; Flucher et al., 1990; 1991; Yuan et al., 1991). This corresponds to the location of tetrads. (*2*) Tetrads are missing in myotubes from dysgenic mice (Franzini-Armstrong et al., 1991). Muscular dysgenesis is due to a point mutation in the gene coding for the $\alpha 1$ subunit of the DHPR (Chaudari, 1992), resulting in lack of the protein, block of excitation contraction coupling, and lack of charge movement and slow-activating calcium currents (Tanabe et al., 1988). In the absence of the α_1 subunit, the α_2 subunit has a diffuse location (Flucher et al., 1991). (*3*) Rescue of cultured dysgenic myotubes with cDNA for the DHPR restores the presence of tetrads (Takekura et al., 1994*b*).

Variety of Junctional Configurations

Junctions involved in e-c coupling have a variety of configurations (Fig. 2). In the majority of adult skeletal muscle fibers, as shown in the upper portion of the figure, junctions are formed by the apposition of two elements of the SR and a transverse portion of the T-tubule system. The group of three components is termed a *triad* (*three arrows*). A junction involving one, rather than two, SR elements, is called a *dyad* (*two arrows*). A junction between the SR and the surface membrane is called a *peripheral coupling* (*single arrow*), a term first introduced for cardiac muscle (Sommer and Johnson, 1979). During early embryonal development of skeletal muscle, T tubules are not present and peripheral couplings are the only junctions present (Kelly, 1971; Takehura et al., 1994*a*). T tubules develop after peripheral couplings, and the delay between the appearances of the two structures is variable (less than one hour in zebrafish myotomes, C. Franzini-Armstrong, unpublished observations; less than one day in mouse diaphragm, B. Flucher and C. Franzini-Armstrong, unpublished observations; up to 8–9 days in chicken leg muscles, Takekura et al., 1994*a*). T tubules initially develop at the periphery of the muscle fiber, where they have a predominantly longitudinal orientation and form randomly located triads and dyads (Flucher et al., 1993*a*). In chick and mouse leg muscles, peripheral couplings are lost within a few days of the initial development of T tubules. Other skeletal muscle fibers (e.g., slow tonic fibers in frog) maintain both peripheral couplings and triads/dyads in the adult. Transverse orientation of T tubules and triads is gradually achieved over late embryonal and early postnatal periods.

Despite their different overall disposition in the fiber, all junctions of skeletal muscle (triads, dyads, and peripheral couplings) have common features: They all involve a calsequestrin-containing SR sac, lined with feet, and closely apposed to a surface membrane membrane/T-tubule domain containing DHPRs/tetrads (Jor-

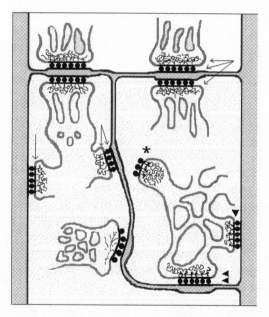

Figure 2. Schematic representation of all the observed dispositions of junctions between the sarcoplasmic reticulum and either the plasma membrane or the T tubules (e-c units). The long axis of the fiber is vertical. In adult skeletal muscle, transversely oriented T tubule networks and triads are most common (*Top, left and right, three arrows*). The *center left* of the image shows a longitudinal T tubule, a dyad (*two arrows*) and a peripheral coupling (*single arrow*). These components are most often found in developing skeletal muscle but also in some adult fibers. The lower right portion of the image shows e-c units in cardiac muscle: peripheral couplings (*single arrowhead*), dyads (*double arrowheads*), and triads (not shown). In addition, there is corbular or extended junctional SR (*asterisk*), which has feet but does not form a junction. Corbular SR functions as a calcium-release unit, but not as an e-c coupling unit in the strict sense (see text). In some arthropods (*lower left*), feet extend beyond the area of junction with T tubules. Note that junctional SR contains calsequestrin (or similar calcium binding proteins) in all cases, although less abundantly in invertebrate muscle. All specialized junctional domains of plasma membrane and T tubules contain DHPRs and face the feet.

gensen et al., 1989; Flucher et al., 1990; Yuan et al., 1991; Franzini-Armstrong and Nunzi, 1983; Block et al., 1988; Franzini-Armstrong and Kish, 1995). Triadin (Kim et al., 1990) is present at the junctions (Flucher et al., 1993*b*; Knudson et al., 1993). The association of arrays of feet with membrane domains containing DHPRs seems to be an obligatory feature of the skeletal muscle membrane system. It is possible that some RyRs are located at sites other than the junctional ones (Dulhunty et al., 1992). These however are few, they are not arranged in arrays, and it is not clear that they participate in e-c coupling.

The disposition of membranes in cardiac muscle has some similarities and one important difference with skeletal muscle (see *lower right*, Fig. 2). Peripheral couplings and dyads of cardiac muscle, like their counterparts in skeletal muscle, involve the interaction between the jSR membrane bearing an array of feet and a junctional domain of the surface membrane/T tubules bearing DHPRs (Jewett et al., 1971; Dolber and Sommer, 1984; Carl et al., 1995; Sun et al., 1995). Calsequestrin and triadin are also present in cardiac muscle junctions (Campbell et al., 1983; Brandt et al., 1993). In addition, however, cardiac muscle has SR domains that contain calsequestrin, store calcium (Jorgensen et al., 1988) and bear arrays of feet (identified as RyRs), but do not participate in junctions (*arrowheads*, Fig. 2; Jewett et al., 1971; Dolber and Sommer, 1984; Bossen et al., 1978; Jorgensen et al., 1993; Junker et al., 1994). The feet in this so-called extended junctional SR and corbular SR face the cytoplasm instead of facing a junctional domain of the surface membrane/T tubules. Thus a proximity between DHPRs and RyRs is not obligatory in cardiac muscle. It has been argued that in myocardial cells that do not have T tubules, but have extensive extended jSR, the latter must have a major role in e-c coupling (Sommer et al., 1995) since calcium release occurs across the whole fiber even where T tubules are not present (Berlin, 1995). If this is the case, then e-c coupling in cardiac muscle may involve two mechanisms—one requiring the interaction of feet-bearing SR with DHPR-bearing domains of surface membrane and T tubules, the other involving a saltatory conduction of Ca release from one internal group of feet to the other. Note that the relative content of extended junctional SR varies between different cardiac muscles from large (up to 70% in some birds, Jewett et al., 1971; Bossen et al., 1978) to nil, and thus the contribution of the two modes of activation may vary greatly from one cardiac muscle to another. This variation must be taken into consideration when one is discussing e-c coupling in this tissue.

In some muscles of invertebrates, feet-containing SR membrane is apposed to a junctional T-tubule membrane, but it also extends farther, so that some feet face the cytoplasm rather than the T tubules (Gilai and Parnas, 1972; Fig. 2, *between asterisks*). If these feet participate in e-c coupling, then they clearly are activated by mechanisms that depend indirectly on surface membrane (and T tubules) depolarization. In this respect, as well as in the need for extracellular calcium, cardiac muscle and muscle of invertebrates have similar requirements.

Spatial Relationships between RyRs and DHPRs in Skeletal and Cardiac Muscle

It is clear that there are important differences in some details of the e-c coupling process between skeletal and cardiac muscle. One major point of divergence is the

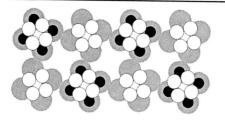

Figure 3. Diagram of the relationship between feet and tetrads in the triads of fish muscle. The long axis of the T tubule runs horizontally, from left to right, and the viewer is looking at the superimposed tetrads and feet. Each group of four *large shaded spheres* represents one foot; *small white spheres* are the intramembranous components of the RyR; *black spheres* are components of the tetrads. Tetrads are located over alternate feet. Note that feet and tetrads have a skewed position relative to the long axis of the T tubules. From Block et al., 1988.

requirement for extracellular calcium and for calcium currents through the DHPRs in cardiac but not in skeletal muscle. An immediate question is whether this is reflected in any obvious differences in the disposition of DHPRs relative to RYRs in the two types of muscles.

Skeletal Muscle

In skeletal muscle, presumed DHPRs are grouped into tetrads, and tetrads are arranged in orderly arrays. The location of the tetrads is clearly such that its four components are located immediately above the four subunits of feet, thus establishing a possible direct interaction between DHPRs and RyRs. An internal loop of the DHPR has been tentatively identified as a component that allows functional interaction of skeletal muscle DHPR with the feet, but some disagreement exists on the essential amino acids within the loop (Nakai et al., 1995; Lu et al., 1995).

In T tubules of fish muscle, a curious relationship between tetrads and feet was discovered (Franzini-Armstrong and Nunzi, 1983; Block et al., 1988): Tetrads are located above alternate feet (Fig. 3). We have recently determined the location of tetrads in peripheral couplings in frog slow fibers, developing mouse muscle, and cultured human muscle, the latter from images kindly donated by Dr. A.G. Engel

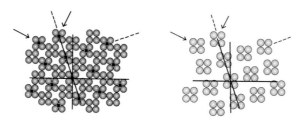

Figure 4. Diagram of the disposition of feet (*left*) and tetrads (*right*) in extended arrays such as those found at sites of peripheral couplings. Each group of four spheres is one foot in the left image and a tetrad in the right image. The arrays are built by the same principles as in Ferguson et al. (1984) and Block et al. (1988); see also Fig. 3. View of the arrays in the direction of the *arrows* is equivalent to views of a triad along the axis of the T tubule. The spacing between tetrads in this direction is twice the spacing between feet. The *continuous lines* demonstrate the skew angle also visible in Fig. 3. Measurements of tetrad spacings and skew angles in peripheral couplings of three vertebrate muscles agree well with the predictions of this model, an observation indicating that tetrads are disposed over alternate feet in these muscles (Franzini-Armstrong and Kish, 1995). The tetrads in this figure are drawn larger than the feet, in agreement with measurements from electron micrographs which indicate that the center-to-center distance between the four components of tetrads is due to a slightly peripheral positioning of the four tetrad components over the four feet subunits.

(Franzini-Armstrong and Kish, 1995). Alternate position of tetrads is present in all these cases (Fig. 4). Two of the muscles from this list have either a single RyR isoform in their skeletal muscle (toadfish swimbladder, O'Brien et al., 1993), or only a very small amount of a second isoform (mouse, Takeshima et al., 1994; Giannini et al., 1995). This indicates that the alternate disposition of tetrads is not due to the presence of two different RyR isoforms and that it may be a general phenomenon.

One possible clue to the basis for the alternate disposition of tetrads relative to feet comes from the observation that the center-to-center distance between the components of the tetrads is somewhat larger than the center-to-center distance between feet subunits (Franzini-Armstrong and Kish, 1995). The DHPRs seem to be located slightly off-center relative to the feet subunits, in a position that allows them to interact with the portion of the RyR's cytoplasmic domain that is tallest and thus is expected to reach closest to the T-tubule membrane (Radermacher et al., 1994). If tetrads occupy a membrane area larger than the feet, it is clear that they cannot be associated with immediately adjacent feet in the array. However, this simple steric hindrance is not sufficient to explain the formation of the observed exact alternate disposition of tetrads relative to feet.

The DHPR/RyR ratio predicted by the observed alternate disposition of tetrads is 2:1. However, tetrads are not always complete: In each array of tetrads, some (complete) tetrads have four subunits, other (incomplete) tetrads have three, two, or even one subunit. Finally, tetrads may be totally missing from their expected position. It is clear that some of the subunits are only apparently missing because they have been fractured in the middle and produce a short stump instead of a particle. Other subunits, however, may be really absent. Thus the actual DHPR/RyR ratio may be lower than predicted on the basis of an alternate array of tetrads in which all components are present.

The precise relationship between the location of tetrads and feet provides a strong support for the hypothesis of a direct interaction between T-tubule voltage sensors (DHPRs) and SR calcium-release channels (Schneider and Chandler, 1973). However, it is clear that two classes of RyRs exist: those that are associated with DHPRs and those that are not (Fig. 5). If both categories of RyRs participate in e-c coupling, some means of activating the orphan channels must exist (Rios and Gonzales, 1991).

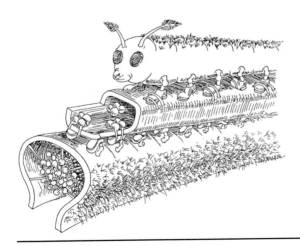

Figure 5. Functional representation of a triad, indicating a possible direct interaction of alternate tetrads with feet.

Cardiac Muscle

In cardiac muscle the situation is clearly different. At the light microscope level, immunolabeling for DHPRs shows co-localization with RyRs at peripheral couplings of guinea pig (Carl et al., 1995) and chicken (Sun et al., 1995), exactly as in developing skeletal muscle. At the electron microscope level, however, skeletal and cardiac muscles diverge (Sun et al., 1995). In chick myocardium, we find that junctional domains of surface membrane, at sites of peripheral couplings, are occupied by groups of large particles, of a size very similar to those composing the tetrads (Fig. 6). Since these particles are located in the same patch of membrane as DHPRs, and since they have the same appearance as the DHPRs in tetrads, we assume that they are also DHPRs. The relationship between feet and DHPRs in cardiac muscle is not the same as in skeletal muscle. In cardiac muscle there are no tetrads, and the disposition of large membrane particles does not show evidence of periodicity (Fig. 6). For the moment, we must assume that, although located in close proximity to RyRs, cardiac DHPRs may not be anchored to the feet and that a direct interaction between the cardiac DHPRs and RyRs may not be possible.

Figure 6. Freeze-fracture electron micrograph of the plasma membrane of avian myocardium. Groups of large particles at sites of peripheral couplings probably represent aggregates of DHPRs. Although located at the junctions, these DHPRs are not arranged in tetrads, and their spacing is not regular. The separation between the aggregates of DHPR is much larger than the distance between the DHPRs. *Bar:* 0.2 μm. Courtesy of F. Protasi, from Sun et al., 1995.

Steps in the Development of e-c Units

Clues to the formation of junctions in skeletal and cardiac muscle come from observations on developing and mutated muscles and from in vivo expression systems.

Skeletal type ryanodine receptors (RyR1), following expression in chinese hamster ovary cells, are found inserted in the endoplasmic reticulum membrane, where they form extensive, ordered arrays with the same spacing as in skeletal muscle (Takekura et al., 1995*b*). Thus the formation of arrays is a property of the RyR, independent of its interaction with other proteins of the junction. Indeed, isolated purified RyRs may be induced to aggregate into a semicrystalline arrangement that exactly mimicks the disposition of feet in the triads and peripheral couplings of skeletal muscle (T. Lai, personal communication).

Dihydropyridine receptors, on the other hand, do not spontaneously group into tetrads. In skeletal muscle from transgenic mice that lack the RyR (Takeshima et al., 1994), peripheral couplings and triads are formed, despite the obvious lack of feet (Takekura et al., 1995*a*). In peripheral couplings of the dyspedic muscle fibers, tetrads are missing and no aggregation of DHPRs is observed. The feet are missing because the mutation results in lack of the RyR1 isoform, and the alternate RyR3 present is in insufficient amount to substitute for it. Presumably, the tetrads are missing despite expression of the protein, because association with the feet is required for the formation of tetrads.

The formation of junctions (peripheral couplings, dyads and triads) in dysgenic and dyspedic mice (Franzini-Armstrong et al., 1991; Takeura et al., 1995*a*), in which either DHPRs are missing, or RyRs are missing and DHPRs are not associated with the junctions, indicate that the two proteins are not necessary for the docking of SR to the surface membrane, an action that initiates the formation of the junction. Indeed, it was noticed that during early muscle development and in the differentiation of cells in a muscle cell line, SR-to-surface junctions without feet are present.

We have studied the formation of peripheral coupling in developing chick myocardium from very early stages (day 2.5 of incubation) to the adult (Protasi et al., 1995) and noted the following. (*1*) During early development there are junctions that seem to have no feet (incomplete junctions), others that have only some feet (partially complete junctions), and others whose junctional gap is filled by a complete array of feet (complete junctions). The relative frequency of incomplete junctions rapidly declines during early development, while that of complete junctions increases. (*2*) Feet always group together on one side in incomplete junctions. On the average, the total length of the junction remains approximately constant throughout development, while the length of the junction occupied by feet increases until it becomes equal to the total length. (*3*) The size of the junctional domains of the surface membrane occupied by large particles increases with time. (*4*) The surface areas of junctional gap occupied by feet and that of surface membrane occupied by large particles remain approximately equal to each other, while increasing in parallel during development. From these observations, we deduce the following steps in the formation of junctions. First, the SR docks to the surface membrane. Second, feet reach the junction and begin to form a small array. As soon as that happens, DHPRs also become associated with the junction, thus forming a surface membrane junctional domain. The junctions become complete by accrual of RyRs and DHPRs, until the whole junctional gap is filled. Less-complete observations indicate that the same process occurs in skeletal muscle. One question remains: since DHPRs do not seem to be specifically associated with RyRs in cardiac muscle, what holds them associated with the junction?

e-c Units Are Discrete Structures

A detail that is common to all muscle fibers is the fact that while surface membrane, T tubules, and SR constitute continuous membrane systems, their junctional domains are always discrete, discontinuous structures (Fig. 2). This is true for all muscle fibers, but particularly for cardiac and smooth muscles, where the junctions are less frequent and relatively large distances separate junctional domains from each other. A junctional domain of the surface membrane or T tubule and its associated junctional SR elements is termed an *e-c coupling*, or *calcium release*, unit.

In skeletal muscle, the size of e-c coupling units can be shown by use of the Golgi stain, a silver-osmium impregnation technique that results in filling of the T tubules with a homogeneous, electron-dense precipitate (Franzini-Armstrong et al., 1988; Appelt et al., 1991). Fig. 7 illustrates the T tubules in toadfish swimbladder muscle. The tubules are composed of two types of segments: Some are wide and straight, others are narrow and sinuous (Fig. 7, *B* and *C*). The wider segments are the sites where the SR forms junctions with the T tubules and are associated with feet (Fig. 7 *A*, Appelt et al., 1991). Smaller, nonjunctional segments are intercalated.

The discontinuity of junctional domains has several possible functional implications. One is trivial: The T-tubule network needs to change shape during muscle contraction. The transversely oriented networks need to expand when the fibers shorten, the longitudinally arranged components need to lengthen when the fiber is stretched. The junctional segments of the T network seem to be rigidly associated to the SR, while the nonjunctional, free, segments are sinuous. The latter have the appropriate shape for lengthening and thus give flexibility to the T network. However, if necessity of length changes were the only reason for the existence of free T tubules, one would expect free segments to be more frequent (or longer) in fibers that have the longest length excursion in situ. This is not the case.

The extent and shape of the junctional regions is related to the activity pattern of the muscle fiber. In skeletal muscle, fast-acting fibers tend to have longer junctional T-tubule segments and less frequent nonjunctional segments in-between (Franzini-Armstrong et al., 1988). At the other extreme are slow, tonic fibers in which flat junctional T-tubule regions are separated from each other by long stretches of nonjunctional tubules. The direct effect of these differences is to vary the density of feet per fiber volume. Thus fibers that are faster tend to have a higher density of SR calcium-release channels, as might be expected (Eisenberg et al., 1987; Franzini-Armstrong et al., 1988; Appelt et al., 1991).

A second, e-c–coupling related, functional result of grouping feet (and DHPRs) into discontinuous junctions is that of allowing the possibility of some sort of interaction between feet, while keeping this activity from spreading through the whole muscle fiber. If activity of one, or few, RyRs in an e-c coupling unit somehow facilitates activity of its immediate neighbors, this would result in amplification of the

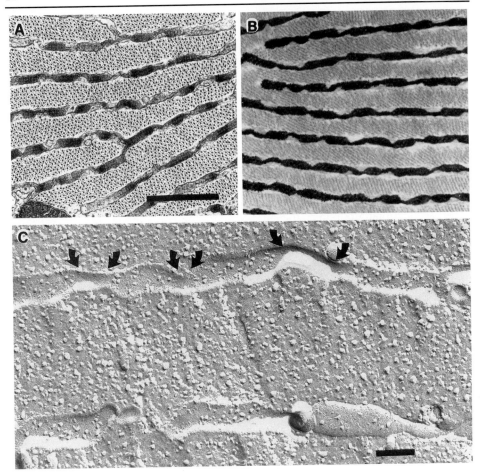

Figure 7. Transversely oriented thin section (*A*), semithin section following Golgi stain (*B*), and freeze-fracture (*C*) of a muscle fiber from the toadfish swimbladder. All sections are at the level of the T tubules. In *A*, feet are visible under the wide portions of T tubules, but not under the thinner ones. In *B* the junctional (wide) and thinner segments of the T tubule are clearly delineated by the electron-dense precipitate filling them. In freeze-fracture (*C*): short free T-tubule segments (between *arrows*) separate junctional segments with tetrads. The distance between adjacent e-c units is not much larger than the distance between tetrads (*small arrows*). In *B* and *C*, note that the nonjunctional segments are often quite short, as in other fast-twitch muscle fibers. *A*, *B*: from Appelt et al. (1991); *C*: from Block et al. (1988). *A*, *B*: Bar = 1 μm; *C*: Bar = 0.1 μm.

calcium release induced by surface membrane depolarization. The increment in release would depend on the size of the e-c units, which in turns determines how many feet are within interacting distance. The question posed by this consideration is whether in fact RyRs release in coordinated groups or independently. Recent advances in calcium detecting techniques, which have led to the observation of very small, localized calcium releases, promise some interesting insights into this question (see other reports in this symposium).

When one considers the possibility of interactions between the feet within an e-c coupling unit, and between e-c coupling units, it is useful to consider some measurements. The distance between feet is ~30 nm and the junctional gap is ~10 nm in both skeletal and cardiac muscle. These distances are sufficiently small that the RyRs should readily "see" both calcium entering through the DHPRs and calcium released from adjacent feet (see also Gyorke and Palade, 1993). If calcium-activated calcium release plays a role in opening RyRs, then it is probable that the effect, once initiated, would spread through the whole e-c unit. In frog semitendinosus and tibialis anterior, the average length of a junctional T-tubule segment is 0.29 μm, and it contains 20 feet on either side of the T tubule. In chick left ventricle, the average area of a junction is 24,000 nm^2, and thus it comprises approximately 28 feet. Thus the number of channels that are potentially available for simultaneous activation are not very different between the two types of muscles, and it should be possible for one to determine whether release events involve one, very few or all channels within a unit. Recent advances in calcium imaging promise just such a possibility, and the process of unmasking the behavior of single release sites has already started (Cheng et al., 1993; Cannell et al., 1995; Berlin, 1995; see also this volume).

The separation between e-c coupling units is an important determinant of whether one unit can interact with the next by the diffusion of an activating substance, for example, calcium (Stern, 1992). In chicken cardiac muscle, e-c units associated with the surface membrane (peripheral couplings) are separated by relatively large distances. The distance between the periphery of one unit and its nearest neighbour is ~472 nm (F. Protasi, personal communication). Thus it may be possible to have simultaneous activation of all or most of the feet within each cluster by calcium-activated calcium release (initiated by activity of the DHPR), while the spread of activity from one cluster to another is limited. A self-regenerating surge of calcium release through the peripheral couplings may be either avoided or limited to special circumstances (e.g., a well-loaded SR, Spencer and Berlin, 1995). This has been modeled by Stern, 1992, and experimentally observed by Cannell et al., 1995. However, most cardiac muscle fibers contain internal calcium release units that cannot be directly activated by events in the surface membrane/T tubules. As mentioned earlier, these must be activated by saltatory spread of activity from one unit to the other. The distance between each of these extended junctional SR domains and its nearest neighbor is, on the average, ~135 nm in chicken ventricle (F. Protasi, personal communication). The distance is probably even smaller in the finch muscle (Sommer, 1995). These small distances are appropriate if the internal calcium release units need to interact with each other. It would be interesting to see under what conditions spread of activation occurs in avian myocardium.

In fast-twitch fibers of skeletal muscle, the distances between e-c units are very small. In frog semitendinosus and ileofibularis and in toadfish swimbladder muscle, for example, the distance between the end of one unit and the beginning of its nearest neighbor is on the average 101 nm and 107 nm respectively, or about three-times the distance between feet (Fig. 7 and F. Protasi and R. Aggarwal, unpublished observations). With such a geometry, spread of activity from one junction to another would be relatively easy if the RyRs were quite sensitive to a diffusable agent, such as calcium. However, effect of T-tubule depolarization is clearly local in skeletal muscle, as demonstrated directly by the local stimulation experiments

(Huxley, 1971) and less directly but convincingly by Pape et al. (1995). Thus it must be assumed that skeletal muscle RyRs are not easily activated by indirect means, such as by calcium.

Finally, it is estimated that in a single cross section of a 100-μm diameter fiber there are $\sim$57,000 triads and 1.14×10^6 feet; thus results in a density of 65 feet/μm^3 (F. Protasi, unpublished observations). A stimulation close to threshold results in a release that is approximately 1/10,000 of the release following maximum stimulation (Pape et al., 1995). If one assumes that either all triads or all feet are activated when maximum release occurs, the low level of release would result from 6 triads (if they release as units) or 114 feet (if they release independently), for each cross section. Appropriate experiments might detect the difference between these two possibilities.

Acknowledgments

The work described in this review would not have been possible without the contribution of excellent postdoctoral fellows (Drs. G. Nunzi, E. Varriano-Marston, D.G. Ferguson, B. Block, H. Takekura, F. Protasi) and undergraduate, medical, and graduate students (H. Schwartz, L. Kenney, B. Buenviaje, V. Shen, J. Kish). Mrs. D. Appelt, C. Champ, and X.-H. Sun have also actively participated in the projects. I thank Mrs. Nosta Glaser for most of the art work.

References

Anderson, K., F.A. Lai, Q.-Y. Liu, E. Rousseau, H.P. Erickson, and G. Meissner. 1989. Structural and functional characterization of the purified cardiac ryanodine receptor-Ca^{2+} release channel complex. *J. Biol. Chem.* 264:1329–1335.

Appelt, D., V. Shen, and C. Franzini-Armstrong. 1991. Quantitation of Ca ATPase, feet and mitochondria in super fast muscle fibres from the toadfish, Opsanus tau. *J. Muscle Res. Cell Motil.* 12:543–552.

Berlin, J.R., 1995. Spatiotemporal changes of Ca^{2+} during electrically evoked contractions in atrial and ventricular cells. *Am. J. Physiol.* 269:H1165–H1170.

Block, B.A., T. Imagawa, K.P. Campbell, and C. Franzini-Armstrong. 1988. Structural evidence for direct interaction between the molecular components of the transverse tubule/sarcoplasmic reticulum junction in skeletal muscle. *J. Cell Biol.* 107:2587–2600.

Bossen, E.H., J.R. Sommer, and R.A. Waugh. 1978. Comparative stereology of the mouse and finch left ventricle. *Tissue & Cell.* 10:773–779.

Brandt, N.R., A.H. Caswell, S.A. Carl, D.G. Ferguson, T. Brandt, J.P. Brunschwig, and A.L. Bassett. 1993. Detection and localization of triadin in rat ventricular muscle. *J. Membr. Biol.* 131:219–228.

Cannell, M.B., H. Cheng, and W.J. Lederer. 1995. The control of calcium release in heart muscle. *Science (Wash. DC).* 268:1045–1049.

Campbell, K.P., D.H. MacLennan, A.D. Jorgensen, and A.C. Mintzer. 1983. Purification and characterization of calsequestrin from canine cardiac sarcoplasmic reticulum and identification of 53,000 dalton glycoprotein. *J. Biol. Chem.* 258:1197–1204.

Carl, S.L., K. Felix, A.H. Caswell, N.R. Brandt, W.J. Ball, P.L. Vaghy, G. Meissner, and D.G. Ferguson. 1995. Immunolocalization of sarcolemmal dihydropyridine receptor and sarcoplasmic reticular triadin and ryanodine receptor in rabbit ventricle and atrium. *J. Cell Biol.* 129:673–682.

Chaudari, N. 1992. A single nucleotide deletion in skeletal muscle specific calcium channel transcript of muscular dysgenesis (mdg) mice. *J. Biol. Chem.* 267:636–639.

Cheng, H., W.J. Lederer, and M.B. Cannell. 1993. Calcium sparks: Elementary events underlying excitation-contraction coupling in heart muscle. *Science (Wash. DC).* 262:740–743.

Dolber, P.C., and J.R. Sommer. 1984. Corbular sarcoplasmic reticulum of rabbit cardiac muscle. *J. Ultrastruct. Res.* 87:190–196.

Dulhunty, A.F., P.R. Junankar, and C. Stanhope. 1992. Extra-junctional ryanodine receptors in the terminal cisternae of mammalian skeletal muscle fibres. *Proc. R. Soc. Lond. Ser. B.* 247:69–75.

Eisenberg, B.R., D.J. Dix, Z.W. Lin, and M.P. Wenslroth. 1987. Relationship of membrane systems in muscle to isomyosin content. *Can. J. Physiol. Pharmacol.* 65:598–605.

Ferguson, D.G., H.W. Schwartz, and C. Franzini-Armstrong. 1984. Subunit structure of junctional feet in triads of skeletal muscle: A freeze-drying, rotary-shadowing study. *J. Cell Biol.* 99:1735–1742.

Flucher, B.E., M.E. Morton, S.C. Froehner, and M.P. Daniels. 1990. Localization of the α_1 and α_2 subunits of the dihydropyridine receptor and ankyrin in skeletal muscle triads. *Neuron.* 5:339–351.

Flucher, B.E., J.L. Phillips, and J.A. Powell. 1991. Dihydropyridine receptor alpha subunits in normal and dysgenic muscle in vitro: Expression of $alpha_1$ is required for proper targeting and distribution of alpha. *J. Cell Biol.* 115:1345–1351.

Flucher, B.E., H. Takakura, and C. Franzini-Armstrong. 1993*a*. Development of the excitation-contraction coupling apparatus in skeletal muscle: Association of sacroplasmic reticulum and transverse tubules with myofibrils in developing muscle fibers. *Dev. Biol.* 160:135–147.

Flucher, B.E., S.B. Andrews, S. Fleischer, A.R. Marks, A. Caswell, and J.A. Powell. 1993*b*. Triad formation: Organization and function of the sarcoplasmic reticulum calcium release channel and triadin in normal and dysgenic myotubes. *J. Cell Biol.* 123:1161–1169.

Franzini-Armstrong, C., and G. Nunzi. 1983. Junctional feet and particles in the triads of fast-twitch muscle fibers. *J. Muscle Res. Cell Motil.* 4:233–252.

Franzini-Armstrong, C., and C.W. Kish. 1995. Alternate disposition of tetrads in peripheral couplings of skeletal muscle. *J. Muscle Res. Cell Motil.* 16:319–324.

Franzini-Armstrong, C., D.G. Ferguson, and C. Champ. 1988. Discrimination between fast- and slow-twitch fibres of guinea pig skeletal muscle using the relative surface density of junctional transverse tubule membrane. *J. Muscle Res. Cell Motil.* 9:403–414.

Franzini-Armstrong, C., M. Pincon-Raymond, and F. Rieger. 1991. Muscle fibers from dysgenic mouse *in vivo* lack a surface component of peripheral couplings. *Dev. Biol.* 146:364–376.

Giannini, G., A. Conti, S. Mammarella, M. Scrobogna, and V. Sorrentino. 1995. The ryanodine receptor calcium channel genes are differentially expressed in murine brain and peripheral tissue. *J. Cell Biol.* 128:893–904.

Gilai, A., and I. Parnas. 1972. Electromechanical coupling in tubular muscle fibers. I. The organization of tubular muscle fibers in the scorpion Leisurus quinquestriatus. *J. Cell Biol.* 52:626–640.

Gyorke, S., and P. Palade. 1993. Role of local Ca^{2+} domains in activation of Ca^{2+}-induced Ca^{2+} release in crayfish muscle fibers. *Am. J. Physiol.* 264:C1505–1512.

Huxley, A.F. 1971. The activation of striated muscle and its contractile response. *Proc. R. Soc. Lond. Ser. B.* 178:1–27.

Inui, M., A. Saito, and S. Fleischer. 1987*a*. Purification of the ryanodine receptor and identity with feet structures of junctional terminal cisternae of sarcoplasmic reticulum from fast skeletal muscle. *J. Biol. Chem.* 262:1740–1747.

Inui, M., A. Saito, and S. Fleischer. 1987*b*. Isolation of the ryanodine receptor from cardiac sarcoplasmic reticulum and identity with the feet structure. *J. Biol. Chem.* 262:15637–15642.

Jewett, P.H., J.R. Sommer, and E.A. Johnson. 1971. Cardiac muscle: Its ultrastructure in the finch and hummingbird with special reference to the sarcoplasmic reticulum. *J. Cell Biol.* 49:50–65.

Jorgensen, A.O., R. Broderick, A.P. Somlyo, and A.V. Somlyo. 1988. Two structurally distinct calcium storage sites in rat cardiac sarcoplasmic reticulum: An electron microprobe analysis study. *Circ. Res.* 63:1060–1069.

Jorgensen, A.O., A.C.-Y. Shen, W. Arnold, A.T. Leung, and K.P. Campbell. 1989. Subcellular distribution of the 1,4-dihydropyridine receptor in rabbit skeletal muscle in situ: An immunofluorescence and immunocolloidal gold-labeling study. *J. Cell Biol.* 109:135–147.

Jorgensen, A.O., A.C.-Y. Shen, W. Arnold, P.S. McPherson, and K.P. Campbell. 1993. The Ca^{2+} release channel/ryanodine receptor is localized in junctional and corbular sarcoplasmic reticulum in cardiac muscle. *J. Cell Biol.* 120:969–980.

Junker, J., J.R. Sommer, M. Sar, and G. Meissner. 1994. Extended junctional sarcoplasmic reticulum of avian cardiac muscle contains functional ryanodine receptors. *J. Biol. Chem.* 269:1627–1634.

Kawamoto, R.M., J.-P. Brunschwig, K.C. Kim, and A.H. Caswell. 1986. Isolation, characterization and localization of the spanning protein from skeletal muscle triads. *J. Cell Biol.* 103:1405–1414.

Kawamoto, R.M., J.-P. Brunschwig, and A.H. Caswell. 1988. Localization by immunoelectron microscopy of spanning protein of triad junction in terminal cisternae/triad vesicles. *J. Muscle Res. Cell Motil.* 9:334–343.

Kelly, A.M. 1971. Sarcoplasmic reticulum and transverse tubules in differentiating rat skeletal muscle. *J. Cell Biol.* 49:335–344.

Kim, K.C., A.H. Caswell, J.A. Talvenheimo, and N.R. Brandt. 1990. Isolation of a terminal cisterna protein which may link the dihydropyridine receptor to the junctional foot protein in skeletal muscle. *Biochemistry.* 29:9283–9289.

Knudson, C.M., K.K. Stang, A.O. Jorgensen, and K.P. Campbell. 1993. Biochemical characterization and ultrastructural localization of a major junctional sarcoplasmic reticulum glycoprotein (triadin). *J. Biol. Chem.* 268:12637–12642.

Lai, F.A., H.P. Erickson, E. Rosseau, Q.-Y. Liu, and G. Meissner. 1988. Purification and reconstitution of the calcium release channel from skeletal muscle. *Nature (Lond.).* 331:315–319.

Lu, X., L. Xu, and G. Meissner. 1995. Identification of amino acid sequences in the dihydropyridine receptor cytoplasmic II-III loop that activate the skeletal muscle calcium release channel. *Biophys. J.* 68:A372.

Nakai, J., T. Tanabe, and K.G. Beam. 1995. Localization of the sequence important in skeletal-type e-c coupling in the II-III loop of the DHP receptor. *Biophys. J.* 68:A14.

O'Brien, J., G. Meissner, and B.A. Block. 1993. The fastest contracting muscles of nonmammalian vertebrates express only one isoform of the ryanodine receptor. *Biophys. J.* 65:2418–2425.

Pape, P.C., D.-S. Jong, and W.K. Candler. 1995. Calcium release and its voltage dependence in frog cut muscle fibers equilibrated with 20 mM EGTA. *J. Gen. Physiol.* 106:259–336.

Protasi, F., X.-H. Sun, and C. Franzini-Armstrong. 1995. Formation and maturation of the calcium release apparatus in developing and adult avian myocardium. *Dev. Biol.* 73:265–278.

Radermacher, M., V. Rao, R. Grassucci, J. Frank, A.P. Timmerman, S. Fleischer, and T. Wagenknecht. 1994. Cryo-electron microscopy and three-dimensional reconstruction of the calcium release channel/ryanodine receptor from skeletal muscle. *J. Cell Biol.* 127:411–423.

Rios, E., J. Ma, and A. Gonzalez. 1991. The mechanical hypothesis of excitation-contraction coupling. *J. Muscle Res. Cell Motil.* 12:127–135.

Schneider, M.F., and W.K. Chandler. 1973. Voltage dependence charge movement in skeletal muscle: A possible step in excitation contraction coupling. *Nature (Lond.).* 242:244–246.

Smith, J.S., R. Coronado, and G. Meissner. 1985. Sarcoplasmic reticulum contains adenine nucleotide activated calcium channels. *Nature (Lond.).* 316:446–450.

Sommer, J.R., and E.A. Johnson. 1979. Ultrastructure of cardiac muscle. *In* Handbook of Physiology. Volume 1. The Heart. R.M. Berne, N. Sperelakis, and S.R. Geiger, editors. American Physiological Society, Bethesda. 113–187.

Sommer, J.R., T. High, and I. Taylor. 1995. The geometry of the EJSR Z-rete in avian cardiac muscle. *In* Microscopy and Microanalysis. G.W. Beiley, M.H. Ellisman, R.A. Hemigor, and N.Y. Zaluzec, editors. Jones and Begell, NY. 940–941.

Spencer, C.I., and J.R. Berlin. 1995. Control of sarcoplasmic reticulum calcium release during calcium loading in the isolated rat ventricular myocytes. *J. Physiol. (Lond).* 488:267–273.

Stern, M.D. 1992. Excitation-contraction coupling in cardiac muscle. *Biophys. J.* 63:497–517.

Sun, X.-H., F. Protasi, M. Takahashi, H. Takeshima, D.G. Ferguson, and C. Franzini-Armstrong. 1995. Molecular architecture of membranes involved in excitation-contraction coupling of cardiac muscle. *J. Cell Biol.* 129:659–671.

Takekura, H., X.-H. Sun, and C. Franzini-Armstrong. 1994a. Development of the excitation-contraction coupling apparatus in skeletal muscle. Peripheral and internal calcium release units are formed sequentially. *J. Muscle Res. Cell Motil.* 15:102–118.

Takekura, H., L. Bennet, T. Tanabe, K.G. Beam, and C. Franzini-Armstrong. 1994b. Restoration of junctional tetrads in dysgenic myotubes by dihydropyridine receptor cDNA. *Biophys. J.* 67:793–804.

Takakura, H., M. Nishi, T. Noda, H. Takeshima, and C. Franzini-Armstrong. 1995a. Peripheral couplings and triads lack feet and tetrads in dyspedic mice with a targeted mutation of the gene for skeletal muscle ryanodine receptor. *Proc. Natl. Acad. Sci. USA.* 92:3381–3385.

Takekura, H., H. Takeshima, S. Nishimura, K. Imoto, M. Takahashi, T. Tanabe, V. Flockerzi, F. Hofmann, and C. Franzini-Armstrong. 1995*b*. Co-expression in CHO cells of two muscle proteins involved in excitation-contraction coupling. *J. Muscle Res. Cell Motil.* 16:465–480.

Takeshima, H., M. Iino, H. Takekura, M. Nishi, J. Kuno, O. Minowa, H. Takano, and T. Noda. 1994. Excitation-contraction uncoupling and muscular degeneration in mice lacking junctional skeletal muscle ryanodine-receptor gene. *Nature (Lond.).* 36:556–559.

Tanabe, T., K.G. Beam, J.A. Powell, and S. Numa. 1988. Restoration of excitation-contraction coupling and slow calcium current in dysgenic muscle by dihydropyridine receptor complementary DNA. *Nature (Lond.).* 336:134–139.

Yuan, S., W. Arnold, and A.O. Jorgensen. 1991. Biogenesis of transverse tubules and triads: Immunolocalization of the 1,4-dihydropyridine receptor, TS28, and the ryanodine receptor in rabbit skeletal muscle developing in situ. *J. Cell Biol.* 112:289–301.

Triadin, a Linker for Calsequestrin and the Ryanodine Receptor

Wei Guo,* Annelise O. Jorgensen,‡ and Kevin P. Campbell*

*Howard Hughes Medical Institute, Department of Physiology and Biophysics, University of Iowa College of Medicine, Iowa City, Iowa 52242, and ‡Department of Anatomy and Cell Biology, University of Toronto, Toronto, Ontario, Canada M5S 1A8

Introduction

Protein components of the triad junction play essential roles in muscle excitation-contraction coupling (EC coupling). Considerable research has been performed on the identification and characterization of proteins that regulate calcium storage and release from the sarcoplasmic reticulum (McPherson and Campbell, 1993; Franzini-Armstrong and Jorgensen, 1994). Key proteins characterized include the dihydropyridine receptor; the voltage sensor and L-type calcium channel in t-tubules; the ryanodine receptor/Ca^{2+}-release channel in the terminal cisternae of the sarcoplasmic reticulum; and calsequestrin, a moderate-affinity, high-capacity calcium-binding protein located in the lumen of the junctional sarcoplasmic reticulum. Study of these proteins has been instrumental to our understanding of the molecular mechanisms of EC coupling. Recent research from our laboratory has focused on triadin, an abundant transmembrane protein in the junctional sarcoplasmic reticulum. Here, we briefly review recent results on the structure of triadin and its interactions with other protein components of the junctional complex in skeletal and cardiac muscle.

Identification of Triadin

Using purified skeletal muscle triads, we generated a library of monoclonal antibodies against different proteins of the junctional sarcoplasmic reticulum (Campbell et al., 1987). Several monoclonal antibodies recognize a protein of 94 kD (now called triadin) on reducing SDS-PAGE (Fig. 1 *A*). Triadin is highly enriched in the junctional membrane preparations including heavy sarcoplasmic reticulum, triads, and junctional face membranes, but it is not detectable in longitudinal sarcoplasmic reticulum (SR) or T-tubules. Triadin migrates just slightly faster than the Ca^{2+}/ATPase, the mobility of which prevents the identification on Coomassie blue-stained gels. However, triadin is clearly detected in the junctional face membrane preparation, which is deplete of most of the Ca^{2+}/ATPase (Knudson et al., 1993*a*). The migration of this protein and its localization in the junctional membrane fractions closely resembles a 95-kD protein characterized by Brandt et al. (1990) and Caswell et al.

Organellar Ion Channels and Transporters © 1996 by The Rockefeller University Press

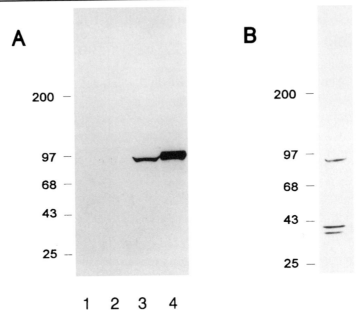

Figure 1. Identification of triadin in skeletal and cardiac muscle sarcoplasmic reticulum. (*A*) Immunoblot of light sarcoplasmic reticulum (*lane 1*), T-system (*lane 2*), triads (*lane 3*), and junctional face membrane (*lane 4*) stained with monoclonal antibodies XIIH11-2 and IIG12 against skeletal muscle triadin. (*B*) Identification of cardiac triadin isoforms in rabbit cardiac muscle microsomes by use of polyclonal antibody GP57.

(1991). This protein was named *triadin* (Brandt et al., 1990) because of specific association with isolated triads.

Localization of Triadin by Immunofluorescent Staining

The localization of triadin in skeletal muscle was carried out by immunofluorescence staining (Knudson et al., 1993*a*; Flucher et al., 1993). Labeling of transverse cryosections with anti-triadin antibodies showed a polygonal pattern throughout the cytoplasm of the myofibers. The staining pattern observed in longitudinal cryosections appeared as transversely oriented rows of discrete foci. The distribution of the rows corresponded to the interface between the A-band and the I-band. This pattern corresponds to the location of triads in skeletal muscle. To determine more precisely whether triadin is confined to the terminal cisternae, its subcellular distribution was determined by immunocolloidal gold labeling and compared with the ryanodine receptor/calcium release channel. Triadin was distributed predominantly over the terminal cisternae, and the labeling was generally indistinguishable from the ryanodine receptor. This nearly identical pattern of staining suggests these two proteins colocalize at the junctional face membrane and may interact with each other. Triadin was also examined in dysgenic mice (Flucher et al., 1993). Dysgenic myotubes with a deficiency in the α_1 subunit of the dihydropyridine receptor show

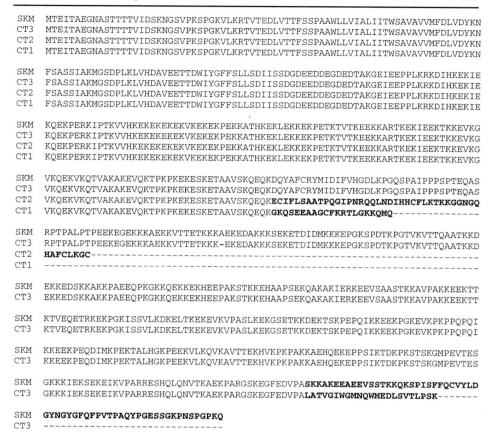

```
SKM   MTEITAEGNASTTTTVIDSKNGSVPKSPGKVLKRTVTEDLVTTFSSPAAWLLVIALIITWSAVAVVMFDLVDYKN
CT3   MTEITAEGNASTTTTVIDSKNGSVPKSPGKVLKRTVTEDLVTTFSSPAAWLLVIALIITWSAVAVVMFDLVDYKN
CT2   MTEITAEGNASTTTTVIDSKNGSVPKSPGKVLKRTVTEDLVTTFSSPAAWLLVIALIITWSAVAVVMFDLVDYKN
CT1   MTEITAEGNASTTTTVIDSKNGSVPKSPGKVLKRTVTEDLVTTFSSPAAWLLVIALIITWSAVAVVMFDLVDYKN

SKM   FSASSIAKMGSDPLKLVHDAVEETTDWIYGFFSLLSDIISSDGDEEDDEGDEDTAKGEIEEPPLKRKDIHKEKIE
CT3   FSASSIAKMGSDPLKLVHDAVEETTDWIYGFFSLLSDIISSDGDEEDDEGDEDTAKGEIEEPPLKRKDIHKEKIE
CT2   FSASSIAKMGSDPLKLVHDAVEETTDWIYGFFSLLSDIISSDGDEEDDEGDEDTAKGEIEEPPLKRKDIHKEKIE
CT1   FSASSIAKMGSDPLKLVHDAVEETTDWIYGFFSLLSDIISSDGDEEDDEGDEDTAKGEIEEPPLKRKDIHKEKIE

SKM   KQEKPERKIPTKVVHKEKEKEKEKVKEKEKPEKKATHKEKLEKKEKPETKTVTKEEKKARTKEKIEEKTKKEVKG
CT3   KQEKPERKIPTKVVHKEKEKEKEKVKEKEKPEKKATHKEKLEKKEKPETKTVTKEEKKARTKEKIEEKTKKEVKG
CT2   KQEKPERKIPTKVVHKEKEKEKEKVKEKEKPEKKATHKEKLEKKEKPETKTVTKEEKKARTKEKIEEKTKKEVKG
CT1   KQEKPERKIPTKVVHKEKEKEKEKVKEKEKPEKKATHKEKLEKKEKPETKTVTKEEKKARTKEKIEEKTKKEVKG

SKM   VKQEKVKQTVAKAKEVQKTPKPKEKESKETAAVSKQEQKDQYAFCRYMIDIFVHGDLKPGQSPAIPPPSPTEQAS
CT3   VKQEKVKQTVAKAKEVQKTPKPKEKESKETAAVSKQEQKDQYAFCRYMIDIFVHGDLKPGQSPAIPPPSPTEQAS
CT2   VKQEKVKQTVAKAKEVQKTPKPKEKESKETAAVSKQEQK**ECIFLSAATPQGIPNRQQLNDIHHCFLKTKKGGNGQ**
CT1   VKQEKVKQTVAKAKEVQKTPKPKEKESKETAAVSKQEQK**GKQSEEAAGCFKRTLGKKQMQ**---------------

SKM   RPTPALPTPEEKEGEKKKAEKKVTTETKKKAEKEDAKKKSEKETDIDMKKKEPGKSPDTKPGTVKVTTQAATKKD
CT3   RPTPALPTPEEKEGEKKKAEKKVTTETKKK-EKEDAKKKSEKETDIDMKKKEPGKSPDTKPGTVKVTTQAATKKD
CT2   **HAFCLKGC**-------------------------------------------------------------------
CT1   -------------------------------------------------------------------------

SKM   EKKEDSKKAKKPAEEQPKGKKQEKKEKHEEPAKSTKKEHAAPSEKQAKAKIERKEEVSAASTKKAVPAKKEEKTT
CT3   EKKEDSKKAKKPAEEQPKGKKQEKKEKHEEPAKSTKKEHAAPSEKQAKAKIERKEEVSAASTKKAVPAKKEEKTT

SKM   KTVEQETRKEKPGKISSVLKDKELTKEKEVKVPASLKEKGSETKKDEKTSKPEPQIKKEEKPGKEVKPKPPQPQI
CT3   KTVEQETRKEKPGKISSVLKDKELTKEKEVKVPASLKEKGSETKKDEKTSKPEPQIKKEEKPGKEVKPKPPQPQI

SKM   KKEEKPEQDIMKPEKTALHGKPEEKVLKQVKAVTTEKHVKPKPAKKAEHQEKEPPSIKTDKPKSTSKGMPEVTES
CT3   KKEEKPEQDIMKPEKTALHGKPEEKVLKQVKAVTTEKHVKPKPAKKAEHQEKEPPSIKTDKPKSTSKGMPEVTES

SKM   GKKKIEKSEKEIKVPARRESHQLQNVTKAEKPARGSKEGFEDVPA**SKKAKEEAEEVSSTKKQKSPISFFQCVYLD**
CT3   GKKKIEKSEKEIKVPARRESHQLQNVTKAEKPARGSKEGFEDVPA**LATVGIWGMNQWMEDLSVTLPSK**-------

SKM   **GYNGYGFQFPVTPAQYPGESSGKPNSPGPKQ**
CT3   ----------------------------
```

Figure 2. Protein sequences of skeletal and cardiac muscle triadin isoforms. Amino acid sequences of skeletal muscle triadin (SKM) and cardiac muscle triadin (CT1, CT2, and CT3) are aligned. The residues that are different among these isoforms are indicated with bold characters.

reduced expression of the ryanodine receptor and triadin. However, both proteins are still capable of forming clusters and attaining mature cross-striated distribution.

Biochemical Characterization of Triadin

Triadin has been thoroughly characterized by biochemical methods (Caswell et al., 1991; Knudson et al., 1993*a*). Endo H treatment shifts the mobility of triadin by approximately 2 kD; this suggests that it is a glycoprotein. In addition, ConA directly binds to triadin. Furthermore, this protein labeled by ^{125}I-TID, a compound that binds to the hydrophobic domains of proteins. The membrane topology of triadin was also examined by the vesicle-protection assay. The result suggests that only a small portion of triadin is cytoplasmic, while the bulk of this protein is located in the lumen of the sarcoplasmic reticulum.

Another major characteristic of skeletal muscle triadin is that it may form disulfide-linked oligomers (Caswell et al., 1991; Knudson et al., 1993*a*). This protein

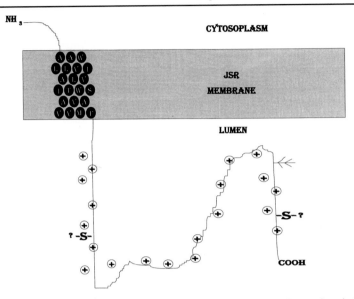

Figure 3. Proposed model for the membrane topology of skeletal muscle triadin. Amino acids 48–68 of triadin are represented in the membrane domain of the protein. The approximate locations of the 2 cysteines that are located at positions 270 and 671 and are likely disulfide-linked are represented by an *S* and a *question mark*. The basic nature of the luminal domain of triadin is depicted by the positive charge symbols (+). Possible glycosylation site is depicted by the *glycosylation symbol*.

requires strong sulfhydryl reducing agents to migrate at 94 kD on SDS-PAGE. In the presence of non-reducing reagents such as *N*-ethylmaleide and absence of reducing agents, triadin migrates as a series of high-molecular-mass multimers. The functional implications of this biochemical characteristic have been investigated, and it was suggested that these disulfide groups may be important in the regulation of calcium release by the sarcoplasmic reticulum (Liu et al., 1994).

Primary Structure of Triadin

The full-length cDNA encoding the rabbit skeletal muscle triadin was obtained by library screening using anti-triadin monoclonal antibodies (Knudson et al., 1993*b*), and the primary structure of the protein was deduced from the cDNA sequence (Fig. 2). This protein is composed of 706 amino acid residues. On the basis of hydrophobicity analysis, triadin contains a single transmembrane domain that separates it into cytoplasmic and luminal segments (Fig. 3). Only the NH$_2$-terminal 47 amino acids are cytoplasmic; the rest of the protein including the C-terminus is located in the lumen of the sarcoplasmic reticulum. This membrane topology is consistent with the results of the vesicle-protection assay (Knudson et al., 1993*b*). The amino acid content of the luminal domain of triadin is remarkable for a very high abundance of charged residues. The relative abundance of the basic residues over acidic residues results in a predicted isoelectric point of 10.18. The positively charged luminal domain may interact with the negatively charged calsequestrin in the lumen of the junctional sarcoplasmic reticulum (Knudson et al., 1993*b*).

Triadin in Cardiac Muscle Sarcoplasmic Reticulum

Results from Western blot analysis with a combination of monoclonal antibodies and Northern blot analysis using partial DNA sequence of skeletal muscle triadin suggested that triadin is specific for skeletal muscle (Knudson et al., 1993*b*). However, several recent reports suggested that triadin is also present in cardiac muscle (Brandt et al., 1993; Peng et al., 1994; Sun et al., 1995; Carl et al., 1995). Peng et al. (1994) were able to detect several messages of triadin in cardiac muscle using Northern blot analysis. Recently, we generated polyclonal antibodies against the luminal domain of triadin-glutathione *S*-transferase (GST) fusion proteins. All the polyclonal antibodies recognize proteins in cardiac muscle microsomes as well as skeletal muscle (Guo et al., 1996). In fact, three isoforms of triadin were detected with these antibodies. One migrates at a molecular mass of about 92 kD, slightly smaller than the skeletal muscle counterpart. The two other isoforms correspond to the doublet of about 35 kD (Fig. 1 *B*). It is of interest that none of the monoclonal antibodies that were used to isolate the skeletal muscle triadin cDNA recognized these proteins (Guo et al., 1996).

Using RT-PCR and library screening, three cDNAs encoding cardiac triadin isoforms were obtained (Fig. 2). The deduced amino acid sequences show that these proteins are identical in their NH$_2$-terminal sequences, whereas the COOH-terminal sequences are distinct from each other and from that of skeletal muscle triadin. In fact, the NH$_2$-terminal sequence identity is also shown at the nucleotide level. The isoforms of triadin in skeletal and cardiac muscle are probably encoded by the same gene by alternative splicing. Recently, we have localized the human triadin gene to chromosome 6 (data not shown).

Immunofluorescence staining of rabbit cardiac muscle shows that cardiac triadin is primarily confined to the I-band region of cardiac myocytes where the ryanodine receptor and calsequestrin-containing junctional and corbular sarcoplasmic reticulum are localized (Guo et al., 1996; Jorgensen et al., 1984, 1993). Immunoelectron microscopical studies will be required to determine whether one or more of the three isoforms of cardiac triadin is confined to either corbular or junctional sarcoplasmic reticulum.

Molecular Interactions of Triadin

Molecular interactions of triadin in skeletal muscle were first examined by a protein overlay assay and by affinity chromatography. Both the solubilized ryanodine receptor and the α_1 subunit of the dihydropyridine receptor were found to bind triadin (Brandt et al., 1990; Kim et al., 1990). It was therefore thought that triadin was a coupling protein spanning the triad junction that mediates the signal transduction between the two calcium channels. However, membrane analysis of triadin has led to some controversy regarding the ability of triadin to interact with the dihydropyridine receptor (Knudson et al., 1993*b*). Only 47 amino acids of triadin are located in the cytosol. This segment may be too small to cross the triad cleft to interact directly with the dihydropyridine receptor that is located in the T-tubule membrane. Instead, since the bulk of this protein is intraluminal, triadin probably exerts its function in the lumen of the sarcoplasmic reticulum.

The molecular interactions of skeletal muscle triadin were also examined by Guo and Campbell (1995). Domains of skeletal muscle triadin that are localized in the cytoplasm or the lumen of the sarcoplasmic reticulum were expressed as GST–fusion proteins and immobilized on glutathione Sepharose to form an affinity column. Detergent-solubilized homogenates were prepared from rabbit skeletal muscle and applied to the columns. Two proteins of ~63 kD and ~550 kD bound to the Sepharose that conjugated with the luminal domain of triadin (L-triadin Sepharose). These two proteins were identified as the ryanodine receptor and calsequestrin. The ryanodine receptor and calsequestrin are minor components in the solubilized whole-muscle homogenates; however, they are the major proteins from the homogenates that bind to the L-triadin Sepharose. This demonstrates the specificity of the interactions.

The association of the ryanodine receptor with triadin was demonstrated further in [^{3}H]ryanodine receptor–binding experiments. The luminal portion fusion protein bound the labeled ryanodine receptor in a dose-dependent manner. Using the same beads assay, we examined the possible interaction of triadin Sepharose with the [^{3}H]PN-200-110 labeled dihydropyridine receptor. However, neither the cytoplasmic nor the luminal portion of triadin was able to bind to the [^{3}H]PN-200-110 labeled receptor in the muscle homogenate. These results demonstrate a specific interaction between triadin and the ryanodine receptor that occurs in the lumen of the sarcoplasmic reticulum; and we have obtained no evidence for an interaction of triadin with the dihydropyridine receptor.

Calsequestrin binds Ca^{2+} with moderate affinity and high capacity (MacLennan et al., 1983), and the binding of Ca^{2+} leads to dramatic conformational change of this luminal protein (Mitchell et al., 1988; He et al., 1993). We therefore examined the effect of Ca^{2+} on the interaction between calsequestrin and triadin. In the presence of $CaCl_2$, L-triadin Sepharose was able to bind calsequestrin. However, when EDTA was present, the interaction was inhibited. Thus, calsequestrin binds to the luminal domain of triadin in a Ca^{2+}-dependent manner.

Calsequestrin is a soluble protein that remains associated with the luminal side of the junctional membrane of the sarcoplasmic reticulum through its interaction with a previously unidentified membrane protein (Franzini-Armstrong et al., 1987). To test whether triadin is the anchoring protein for calsequestrin, we examined whether the triadin-luminal-domain-GST fusion protein was capable of inhibiting the reassociation of calsequestrin with the junctional face membrane. When calsequestrin was incubated with the junctional face membrane, calsequestrin reassociated with the junctional face membrane. However, when increasing amounts of triadin-GST fusion protein were added to the incubation buffer, less calsequestrin reassociated to the junctional face membrane. This result suggests that one function of triadin is to anchor calsequestrin to the luminal side of the junctional sarcoplasmic reticulum in proximity to the "SR feet" (ryanodine receptor), where calsequestrin stores calcium that is available for release (Franzini-Armstrong, 1970; Franzini-Armstrong et al., 1987).

Since different isoforms of triadin also exist in cardiac muscle, we examined whether the cardiac triadin binds to the ryanodine receptor and calsequestrin in cardiac muscle. Our results indicate that the segment of the luminal domain of triadin, which is homologous among all the isoforms in the two tissues, is able to interact with both the ryanodine receptor and calsequestrin.

Calsequestrin is a soluble protein that remains associated with the luminal side of the junctional membrane of the sarcoplasmic reticulum through its interaction with a previously unidentified membrane protein (Franzini-Armstrong et al., 1987). Calsequestrin can be extracted from the junctional face membrane by treatment with EDTA or high concentrations of NaCl (Ikemoto et al., 1991; Costello et al., 1986); this indicates that the interaction between calsequestrin and its membrane-anchoring protein can be inhibited by EDTA and is disruptable by high ionic strength. Notably, the association between calsequestrin and triadin-GST fusion protein is also inhibited by EDTA. Futhermore, high salt concentration can elute calsequestrin from L-triadin Sepharose. These binding properties resemble those of the interaction of calsequestrin with its anchoring protein in the junctional face membrane. In addition, like calsequestrin, triadin is an abundant protein that is specifically localized in the junctional region, with the bulk of this protein in the lumen of the sarcoplasmic reticulum (Knudson et al., 1993a, b). Together, these characteristics strongly suggest that triadin is the physiological anchoring protein for calsequestrin at the junctional face of sarcoplasmic reticulum. This hypothesis was further confirmed in the calsequestrin/junctional face membrane reassociation experiment.

It is known that the intraluminal Ca^{2+}-binding protein, calsequestrin, and the ryanodine receptor/Ca^{2+}-release channel are functionally coupled (Ikemoto et al., 1991; Ikemoto et al., 1989; Gilchrist et al., 1992; Kawasaki et al., 1994; Donoso et al., 1995). The ryanodine receptor, when activated by Ca^{2+}-release agents, such as caffeine, induces dissociation of calcium from calsequestrin (Ikemoto et al., 1991). Conversely, changes in luminal Ca^{2+} concentration lead to conformational changes in calsequestrin, and this information can be transmitted to the ryanodine receptor, thus affecting the activation of the ryanodine receptor/Ca^{2+}-release channel (Ikemoto et al., 1989; Gilchrist et al., 1992; Kawasaki et al., 1994; Donoso et al., 1995). However, despite the biophysical evidence for functional coupling between the ryanodine receptor and calsequestrin, there is no biochemical evidence for direct interaction between the two proteins. It is thought that the interaction is mediated by a third protein. Our data and previous studies suggest that triadin binds to the ryanodine receptor (Caswell et al., 1991; Liu et al., 1994) and the luminal domain of triadin also interacts with calsequestrin. Together, these results suggest that triadin anchors calsequestrin to the junctional face membrane and thus may be involved in the functional coupling between calsequestrin and the ryanodine receptor/Ca^{2+}-release channel in the lumen of the sarcoplasmic reticulum. A model illustrating the molecular interactions of triadin in the lumen of the sarcoplasmic reticulum is presented (Fig. 4).

These results have provided biochemical evidence for a structural and/or functional role of triadin in the lumen of the junctional sarcoplasmic reticulum. However, many questions still await further investigations. For example, what are the cDNA sequences for the different isoforms of triadin in skeletal muscle? What is the function of the different isoforms of triadin? How does triadin mediate the functional coupling between the ryanodine receptor and calsequestrin? Answers to

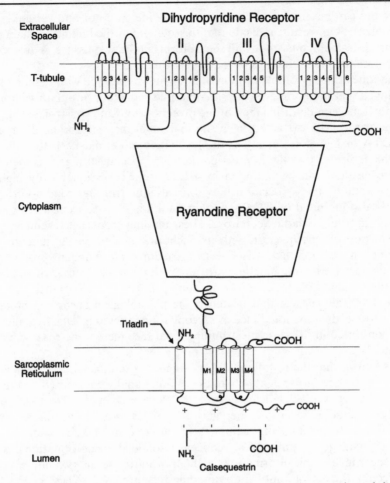

Figure 4. Proposed model for the interactions of triadin with calsequestrin and the ryanodine receptor/calcium release channel in triads.

these questions will help us understand the triad structure and EC coupling at a new level.

Acknowledgments

We thank Dr. Larry R. Jones for his helpful comments on this manuscript.
    K.P. Campbell is an Investigator of the Howard Hughes Medical Institute.

References

Brandt, N.R, A.H. Caswell, S.W. Wen, and J.A. Talvenheimo. 1990. Molecular interactions of the junctional foot protein and dihydropyridine receptor in skeletal muscle triads. *J. Membr. Biol.* 113:237–251.

Brandt, N.R., A.H. Caswell, S.A.L. Carl, D.G. Ferguson, T. Brandt, J-P. Brunschwig, and A.L. Bassett. 1993. Detection and localization of triadin in rat ventricular muscle. *J. Membr. Biol.* 131:219–228.

Campbell, K.P., C.M. Knudson, T. Imagawa, A.T. Leung, J.L. Sutko, S.D. Kahl, C.R. Raab, and L. Madson. 1987. Identification and characterization of the high affinity [^{3}H]ryanodine receptor of the junctional sarcoplasmic reticulum Ca^{2+} release channel. *J. Biol. Chem.* 262:6460–6463.

Carl, S.L., K. Felix, A.H. Caswell, N.R. Brandt, W.J. Ball, Jr., P.L. Vaghy, G. Meissner, and D.G. Ferguson. 1995. Immunolocalization of sarcolemmal dihydropyridine receptor and sarcoplasmic reticular triadin and ryanodine receptor in rabbit ventricle and atrium. *J. Cell Biol.* 129:673–682.

Caswell, A.H., N.R. Brandt, J.P. Brunschwig, and S. Purkerson. 1991. Localization and partial characterization of the oligomeric disulfide-linked molecular weight 95,000 protein (triadin) which binds the ryanodine receptor and dihydropyridine receptors in skeletal muscle triadic vesicles. *Biochem.* 30:7507–7513.

Costello, B., C. Chadwick, A. Saito, A. Chu, A. Maurer, and S. Fleischer. 1986. Characterization of the junctional face membrane from terminal cisternae of sarcoplasmic reticulum. *J. Cell Biol.* 103:741–753.

Donoso, P., H. Prieto, and C. Hidalgo. 1995. Luminal calcium regulates calcium release in triads isolated from frog and rabbit skeletal muscle. *Biophys. J.* 68:507–515.

Flucher, B.E., S.B. Andrews, S. Fleischer, A.R. Marks, A. Caswell, and J.A. Powell. 1993. Triad formation: Organization and function of the sarcoplasmic reticulum calcium release channel and triadin in normal and dysgenic muscle in vitro. *J. Cell Biol.* 123:1161–1174.

Franzini-Armstrong, C. 1970. Studies of the triad I. structure of the junction in frog twitch fibers. *J. Cell Biol.* 47:488–499.

Franzini-Armstrong, C., L.J. Kenney, and E. Varriano-Marston. 1987. The structure of calsequestrin in triads of vertebrate skeletal muscle: A deep-etch study. *J. Cell Biol.* 105:49–56.

Franzini-Armstrong, C., and A.O. Jorgensen. 1994. Structure and development of E-C coupling units in skeletal muscle *Annu. Rev. Physiol.* 56:509–534.

Gilchrist, J.S., A.N. Belcastro, and S. Katz. 1992. Intraluminal calcium dependence of calcium and ryanodine-mediated regulation of skeletal muscle sarcoplasmic reticulum calcium release. *J. Biol. Chem.* 267:20850–20856.

Guo, W., and K.P. Campbell. 1995. Association of triadin with the ryanodine receptor and calsequestrin in the lumen of the junctional sarcoplasmic reticulum. *J. Biol. Chem.* 270:9027–9030.

Guo, W., A.O. Jorgensen, L.R. Jones, and K.P. Campbell. 1996. Biochemical characterization and molecular cloning of cardiac triadin. *J. Biol. Chem.* 271:458–465.

He, Z., A.K. Dunker, C.R. Wesson, and W.R. Trumble. 1993. Calcium-induced folding and aggregation of skeletal muscle sarcoplasmic reticulum calsequestrin. *J. Biol. Chem.* 268:24635–24641.

Ikemoto, N., M. Ronjat, L.G. Meszaro, and M. Koshita. 1989. Postulated role of calsequestrin in the regulation of calcium release from the sarcoplasmic reticulum. *Biochem.* 28:6764–6771.

Ikemoto, N., B. Antoniu, J.J. Kang, L.G. Meszaros, and M. Ronjat. 1991. Intravesicular calcium transient during calcium release from sarcoplasmic reticulum. *Biochem.* 30:5230–5327.

Imagawa, T., J.S. Smith, R. Coronado, and K.P. Campbell. 1987. Purified ryanodine receptor from skeletal muscle sarcoplasmic reticulum is the Ca^{2+}-permeable pore of the calcium release channel. *J. Biol. Chem.* 262:16636–16643.

Jorgensen, A.O., A.C-Y. Shen, W. Arnold, P.S. McPherson, and K.P. Campbell. 1993. The Ca^{2+} release channel/ryanodine receptor is localized in junctional and corbular sarcoplasmic reticulum in cardiac muscle. *J. Cell Biol.* 120:969–980.

Jorgensen, A.O., and K.P. Campbell. 1984. Evidence for the presence of calsequestrin in two structurally different regions of myocardial sarcoplasmic reticulum. *J. Cell Biol.* 98:1597–1602

Kawasaki, T., and M. Kassai. 1994. Regulation of calcium channel in sarcoplasmic reticulum by calsequestrin. *Biochem. Biophysics Res. Commun.* 199:1120–1127.

Kim, K.C., A.H. Caswell, J.A. Talvenheimo, and N.R. Brandt. 1990. Isolation of a terminal cisterna protein which may link the dihydropyridine receptor to the junctional foot protein in skeletal muscle. *Biochem.* 29:9281–9289.

Knudson, C.M., K.K. Stang, A.O. Jorgensen, and K.P. Campbell. 1993a. Biochemical characterization and ultrastructural localization of a major junctional sarcoplasmic reticulum glycoprotein (triadin). *J. Biol. Chem.* 268:12637–12645.

Knudson, C.M., K.K. Stang, C.R. Moomaw, C. Slaughter, and K.P. Campbell. 1993b. Primary structure and topological analysis of a skeletal muscle-specific junctional sarcoplasmic reticulum glycoprotein (triadin). *J. Biol. Chem.* 268:12646–12654.

Liu, G., and I.N. Pessah. 1994. Molecular interaction between ryanodine receptor and glycoprotein triadin involves redox cycling of functionally important hyperactive sulfhydryls. *J. Biol. Chem.* 269:33028–33034.

MacLennan, D.H., K.P. Campbell, and R.A.F. Reithmeier. 1983. Calsequestrin. *Calcium Cell Function.* 4:151–173.

McPherson, P.S., and K.P. Campbell. 1993. The ryanodine receptor/Ca^{2+} release channel. *J. Biol. Chem.* 268:13765–13768.

Mitchell, R.D., H.K.B. Simmerman, and L.R. Jones. 1988. Ca^{2+} binding effects on protein conformation and protein interactions of canine cardiac calsequestrin. *J. Biol. Chem.* 263:1376–1381.

Peng, M., H. Fan, T.L. Kirley, A.H. Caswell, and A. Schwartz. 1994. Structural diversity of Triadin in skeletal muscle and evidence of its existence in heart. *FEBS Lett.* 348:17–20.

Sun, X., F. Protasi, M. Takahashi, H. Takashima, D.G. Ferguson, and C. Franzini-Armstrong. 1995. Molecular architecture of membranes involved in excitation contraction coupling of cardiac muscle. *J. Cell Biol.* 129:659–671.

Single Channel Properties and Calcium Conductance of the Cloned Expressed Ryanodine Receptor/Calcium-Release Channel

Karol Ondrias,* Anne-Marie B. Brillantes,* Andrew Scott,* Barbara E. Ehrlich,‡ and Andrew R. Marks*

*Cardiovascular Institute, Department of Medicine, and Brookdale Center for Molecular Biology, Mount Sinai School of Medicine, New York 10029; and ‡Departments of Medicine and Physiology, University of Connecticut, Farmington, Connecticut 06030

The calcium-release channel/ryanodine receptor of the sarcoplasmic reticulum is a 2.3 million–D structure required for intracellular calcium release during excitation-contraction coupling in skeletal muscle. This structure is the largest ion channel characterized to date and is composed of four 565,000-D ryanodine receptors plus four molecules of FKBP12. In the present study we describe the single channel properties of the cloned expressed ryanodine receptor, with and without FKBP12, reconstituted into planar lipid bilayers with Ca as the charge carrier. The conductance for Ca (luminal, 53 mM/cytoplasmic, 10 μM) was 103 pS for the cloned expressed RyR and for the native channel from rabbit skeletal muscle. Conductance through the channel was Ca dependent: A decrease in the Ca gradient to luminal 10.6/cytoplasmic 10 μM reduced conductance to 68 pS for both the cloned and native RyR. The recombinant ryanodine receptor consistently behaved like the native skeletal muscle channel in terms of activation by caffeine, calcium, and ATP; inhibition by ruthenium red; and modulation by ryanodine. In the absence of FKBP12, the cloned expressed RyR exhibited multiple subconductance states and addition of FKBP12 reduced the frequency of subconductance states. These results show that with Ca as the charge carrier, the single channel properties of the cloned expressed RyR plus FKBP12 are essentially the same as those of the native channel.

Introduction

Intracellular Ca release channels participate in numerous signaling pathways including fertilization, neurotransmitter release, hormonal activation, T cell activation, and muscle contraction. The ryanodine receptor (RyR) is required for excitation-contraction (E-C) coupling in striated muscle. The RyR is a tetrameric structure (Franzini-Armstrong and Nunzi, 1983) composed of four 565,000-D subunits and at least one other protein, the 12,000-D FKBP12 (Brillantes et al., 1994; Jayaraman et al., 1992). The entire structure comprising the Ca-release channel is approximately 2.3 million–D; thus it is the largest ion channel characterized to date. Hydropathy plots (Takeshima et al., 1989; Zorzato et al., 1990) and protease sensitivity mapping (Marks et al., 1990) of the RyR have suggested that the transmembrane portions of the channel are clustered near the carboxy terminus and that the cytoplasmic "foot structure" is encoded by the amino terminal two-thirds of the molecule. The role of the foot structure in skeletal muscle and the location of critical functional domains of the RyR/Ca-release channel remain to be elucidated.

Excitation-contraction coupling in striated muscles requires the activation of the Ca release channel in the sarcoplasmic reticulum (SR) (reviewed in Catterall, 1991). In the heart, Ca influx via the voltage-gated Ca channel of the transverse tubule triggers the release of Ca from the SR into the cytosol via the RyR/Ca-release channel. This phenomenon is referred to as Ca-induced Ca release (Fabiato, 1983; Fabiato and Fabiato, 1984). In skeletal muscle the mechanism of activation of the RyR/Ca-release channel is less well-understood, although it has been proposed that a direct interaction with the voltage-gated Ca channel activates the RyR/Ca-release channel (Lu et al., 1994). Both the cardiac and skeletal muscle RyRs are activated and inactivated by Ca in micromolar to millimolar range (Chu et al., 1991; Tinker and Williams, 1992).

Abnormal Ca homeostasis has been demonstrated in failing human myocardium (Gwathmey et al., 1987; Morgan et al., 1990). We have previously shown that RyR expression is decreased and inositol 1,4,5-trisphosphate receptor/Ca-release channel (IP3R) expression is increased in failing human myocardium (Brillantes et al., 1992; Go et al., 1995). While these earlier studies have examined the regulation of expression of the intracellular Ca-release channels in the failing heart, little is known regarding the physiology of these channels in diseased muscle. We have recently developed a model system for heterologous expression of the cloned RyR/Ca-release channel in insect cells (Brillantes et al., 1994). Using this model we have characterized the single channel properties of the cloned RyR using cesium (Cs) as the charge carrier (Brillantes et al., 1994). As a basis for better understanding of the physiologic regulation of SR Ca release we now report the single channel properties of the cloned expressed RyR/Ca-release channel with Ca as the charge carrier. The properties of the cloned expressed RyR/Ca-release channel are similar to those of the native channel for the physiologic charge carrier, Ca. Significantly, for both the cloned and native channels, Ca conductance is dependent on the luminal-to-cytoplasmic Ca gradient. This finding indicates that decreased SR Ca loading, as observed in the failing heart, combined with decreased levels of RyR/Ca-release-channel expression, should have adverse effects on SR Ca release resulting in decreased contractility.

Materials and Methods
Cloning the Complete Skeletal Muscle RyR cDNA

Recombinant DNA manipulations were carried out by use of standard procedures (Sambrook et al., 1989). The cloning of cDNA encoding the rabbit skeletal muscle ryanodine receptor was as described (Marks et al., 1939). Seven overlapping cDNA clones were isolated and subcloned into the EcoR1 site in the pBluescript vector and used for construction of the full-length plasmid, pSK-RyR (Fig. 1). The Sfi (10870)/Xba (vector) of RyR3 was ligated to pRyR2 to yield pMID-RyR. The SGRA (13380)/Xba (vector) fragment of RyR4 was ligated to pRyYR5 to yield pRyR6. pRyR6 was digested with HincII (12797) and XhoI (vector) and ligated to

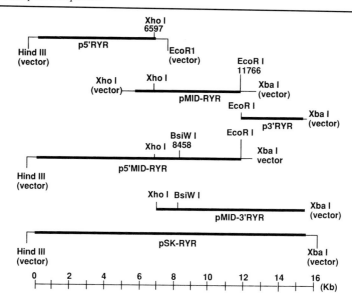

Figure 1. Ligation strategy for the ryanodine receptor cDNA. The complete 15.2-kb RyR cDNA was constructed from overlapping cDNAs by use of the strategy depicted in this figure. The cDNAs were isolated as previously described (Marks et al., 1989). p5'RyR was previously constructed from three smaller overlapping cDNAs isolated from a random primed cDNA library (Marks et al., 1989).

RyR7. The product was digested with XhoI and ligated to the pRyR8 to form p3'-RyR. pMID-3'RyR was then constructed as follows. The XhoI (vector)/XhoI (6467) fragment of pMID-RyR was removed and the linearized plasmid was recircularized. It was then linearized with EcoRI and ligated to p3'RyR. p5'MID-RyR was constructed by ligating the XhoI (6597)/XhoI (12149) fragment of pMID-3'RyR to p5'-RyR that had been linearized with XhoI (6597). Finally, the BsiW1 (8458)/Xba (vector) fragment of pMID-3'RyR was ligated to p5'MID-RyR to yield the full-length pSK-RyR.

Construction of Recombinant Vectors

Materials and methods for manipulating Baculovirus DNA (AcNPV) and Sf9 cells were performed as described by the manufacturers of the Baculogold expression system (Pharmingen) with the following modifications. The baculovirus transfer vector, pVL941, was modified by incorporating a poly-cloning site. The pVL941 vector was digested with BamH1 and ligated to preannealed oligonucleotide linkers (sense and antisense linkers were combined in equimolar amounts, incubated at 95°C for 5 min, and allowed to cool slowly to room temperature) with the following sequences: sense: 5'-GATCCGCGAATTCTCACTAGTCGACGCGTGATCTA-GACGGAATTCGCG-3' and antisense: 5'-GATCCGCGAATTCCGTCTAGAT-CACGCGTCGACTAGTGAGAATTCGCG-3', to yield pVL941-Link. The ~15.2-kb Spe1 fragment of pSK-RyR containing the RyR cDNA coding sequence was inserted into pVL941-Link after linearization with Spe1; this resulted in the plasmid pSKRyR. pSKRyR was co-transfected with Baculovirus gold DNA into Sf9 cells in 25-mm dishes. Three days after transfection, Sf9 clones containing recombinant baculovirus/RyR were isolated either by plaque assays or by dilutional cloning. Sf9 clones containing Baculovirus expressing full-length RyR mRNA were identified by Northern hybridizations. Individual viral isolates were subsequently amplified and used to reinfect Sf9 cultures. Sf9 cells were maintained in monolayer culture at 27°C in TNM-FH medium supplemented with 10% fetal calf serum, 2.5 μg/ml Fungizone (GIBCO) and 50 μg/ml gentamycin. Cells were harvested from 1 to 7 days after infection to assay levels of RyR protein and mRNA expression.

Isolation of Sf9 RNA and Northern Hybridizations

Total Sf9 RNA was prepared from Sf9 cells or from tissue by use of the guanidinium isothiocyanate/cesium chloride centrifugation method as previously described (Marks et al., 1989). Cells were harvested, resuspended in 8 ml of lysis buffer (2 M guanidinium isothiocyanate, 0.1% lauryl sarcosyl, and 0.01% 2-mercaptoethanol) and sheared by several passages through a 22-gauge needle. The suspension was then layered over 5.7 M cesium chloride and centrifuged overnight at 40,000 g at 40°C. The resulting RNA pellet was precipitated with ethanol and resuspended in DEPC-treated water. All operations were done on ice. RNA was quantitated by spectrophotometry at 260 nm.

Northern hybridizations of uninfected and infected Sf9 total RNA were performed with rabbit skeletal muscle RyR cDNA probes as previously described (Marks et al., 1989). Total cellular RNA (20 μg) was size-fractionated on formaldehyde-agarose gels run at 30 mA overnight to provide resolution of high–molecular weight mRNAs. RNA was transferred onto nitrocellulose filters overnight with 10× SSC transfer buffer. Filters were baked, prehybridized overnight in buffer containing 1× Denhardt's solution (0.02% polyvinylpyrrolidone/0.02% Ficoll/0.02% bovine serum albumin), 5× SSC (1× = 0.15 M NaCl/0.015 M sodium citrate, pH 7.0), 0.025 M sodium phosphate (pH 7.4), sonicated calf thymus DNA (50 mg/ml), 0.1% SDS, and 50% (vol/vol) formamide, and hybridized with cDNA probes in the same buffer mixture overnight at 42°C. Blots were then washed to a final stringency of 0.2× SSC/0.1% SDS at 65°C for 15 min. Filters were exposed at −80°C on X-ray films (X-OMAT, AR, Eastman KODAK) with a single intensifying screen or at room temperature on a storage phosphorscreen (Molecular Dynamics).

Isolation of Sf9 Membranes

Sf9 cells were harvested, centrifuged for 2 min at 1,000 rpm on a desktop centrifuge, and resuspended at a concentration of 1×10^7 cells/ml in 50 mM Tris-Cl (pH 7.25), 250 mM sucrose. Cells were homogenized with 30 strokes in a Dounce homogenizer, and the suspension was then centrifuged at 4,500 g for 15 min. The supernatant was centrifuged at 142,000 g for 45 min. The resulting membrane pellet was resuspended at a final concentration of 5–10 mg/ml in 20 mM Tris-Cl (pH 7.25) and 300 mM sucrose. All operations were carried out on ice and all solutions contained the following protease inhibitors: 0.1 mM phenylmethylsulfonyl fluoride (PMSF), 1 mM aprotinin, 10 μg/ml pepstatin, 10 μg/ml leupeptin, and 10 μg/ml aprotinin.

Sucrose Gradient Purification of Recombinant RyR Proteins

Purification was carried out as described (Lindsay and Williams, 1991). Pelleted membranes from infected and uninfected Sf9 cells were solubilized in buffer A (0.5% CHAPS, 1 M NaCl, 150 μM $CaCl_2$, 100 μM EGTA, 25 mM Pipes-Na, pH 7.4, 0.25% phosphatidylcholine) and the following protease inhibitor cocktail: 0.25 mM PMSF, 1 mM benzamidine, 1 mM iodoacetamide, 1 μg/ml leupeptin, 1 μg/ml pepstatin A, 1 μg/ml aprotinin. The suspensions were incubated for 1 h at 0°C, both with and without the addition of 2 nM [^{3}H]ryanodine, then centrifuged at 100,000 g for 45 min at 4°C. The supernatant was layered over a 10–30% (wt/vol) linear sucrose gradient containing 0.5% CHAPS, 1 M NaCl, 150 μM $CaCl_2$, 100 μM EGTA, 25 mM Pipes-Na (pH 7.4), 0.25% phosphatidylcholine, 0.1 mM dithiothreitol, 0.25 mM PMSF, and 1 μg/ml leupeptin, and centrifuged at 26,000 rpm in a Beckman SW-41 rotor for 17 h at 4°C. Fractions of 1 ml were collected from both labeled and unlabeled samples. Labeled samples were then diluted with 1 vol of buffer A and dialyzed overnight at 4°C against 4 × 1 liter of 0.1 M NaCl, 150 μM $CaCl_2$, 100 μM EGTA, and 25 mM Pipes-Na (pH 7.4). At the end of dialysis, an equal volume of 0.4 M sucrose was added to vesicles before snap-freezing in liquid nitrogen. Vesicles were aliquoted and stored at −80°C.

Immunoblots and Antibodies

A site-specific anti-peptide polyclonal α-RyR antibody was prepared as previously described (Jayaraman et al., 1992). Proteins were size fractionated by electrophoresis through a 5% SDS-polyacrylamide gel and transferred overnight onto nitrocellulose (Schleicher & Schuell) with Towbin transfer buffer (20 mM Tris, 150 mM glycine, 20% methanol, and 0.1% SDS). Nitrocellulose blots were blocked in PBS-T, pH 7.5 (80 mM disodium hydrogen orthophosphate anhydrous, 20 mM sodium dihydrogen orthophosphate, 100 mM sodium chloride, 0.1% Tween-20) and 5% (wt/vol) nonfat dry milk for overnight at 4°C. Primary antibody (1:500 dilution) in blocking solution was bound at 4°C for overnight. After three 15-min washes in PBS-T, horseradish peroxidase–labeled goat anti-rabbit secondary antibody (1:5,000 dilution) in PBS-T, and 5% (wt/vol) non-fat dry milk was bound at 4°C for 2 h, and blots were then washed 2 × 30 min. Detection was with ECL Western blotting reagents (Amersham), and blots were exposed for autoradiography.

Single Channel Bilayer Recordings

Planar lipid membranes were formed across a hole (diameter 0.05–0.3 mm) separating *cis* and *trans* chambers in heart phosphatidylethanolamine in decane (20 mg/ml, Avanti Polar Lipids). After formation of the planar lipid membranes, native membrane vesicles or sucrose-gradient purified RyR protein incorporated into liposomes or purified RyR as solubilized proteins were added to the *cis* chamber while stirring. A KCl gradient was used to induce fusion of the membrane vesicles, proteoliposomes, or proteins with the bilayer. After incorporation of the channel into the bilayer, the *cis* and *trans* chambers were perfused with the desired solutions. The *cis* chamber contained: 250 mM Hepes, ∼125 mM Tris, and 0.15–100 μM $CaCl_2$, pH 7.35. The *trans* chamber contained: 53 mM $Ca(OH)_2$, and 250 mM Hepes, pH 7.35. For recordings using cesium as the charge carrier, the *cis* chamber contained 250 mM CsCl, 10 mM Hepes-Tris, pH 7.4, and 12 μM Ca (free); *trans* chamber contained 50 mM CsCl and 10 mM Hepes-Tris, pH 7.4, and 12 μM Ca (free). The traces at each condition are representative of data collected over a minimum of 3 min. In all cases one of at least three similar experiments is shown. The holding potential was 0 mV unless otherwise indicated. The dashed lines to the left of each set of tracings indicate the closed level. Single channel currents were continuously monitored with an Axopatch 200 (Axon Instruments) and recorded with a Digital Audio Tape (Dagan Corp.) and/or with a chart recorder (Gould). Recordings were filtered through a low-pass Bessel filter (Frequency Devices) at 0.5 or 2 kHz and digitized at 2 or 10 kHz, respectively. Single channel properties were evaluated using PClamp 6.2.

Results

Ryanodine Receptor Expression in Insect Cells

Multiple partial cDNAs encoding the complete rabbit skeletal muscle RyR were isolated as previously described (Marks et al., 1989). A summary of the strategy for ligation of these partial cDNAs to form the cDNA used for functional expression of the RyR is shown in Fig. 1. The ligations illustrated in Fig. 1 show the locations for critical restriction sites that permitted the construction of the final 15.2-kb cDNA. The complete RyR cDNA was then cloned into a baculovirus transfer vector and used to infect Sf9 cells as described above. Fig. 2 shows a time course for RyR mRNA detected by Northern hybridization in infected Sf9 cells. No RyR mRNA was detected in uninfected Sf9 cells. A single ~16-kb specific RyR mRNA was detected within 72 h after infection with recombinant baculovirus (Fig. 2) by use of a rabbit skeletal muscle specific cDNA probe (Marks et al., 1989). A time course revealed an increasing accumulation of specific RyR mRNA in infected Sf9 cells up

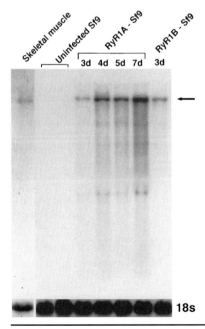

Figure 2. Expression of ryanodine receptor mRNA in insect cells infected with recombinant baculovirus. Insect cells were infected with recombinant baculovirus containing the complete cDNA encoding the skeletal RyR. Total Sf9 cellular RNA was isolated at the indicated time points (in days) after infection and from uninfected cells. In each lane 15 μg of total RNA was loaded. RNA loading was controlled by ethidium bromide staining of ribosomal RNA (staining of the 18s rRNA is shown). The *first lane* contains 15 μg of rabbit skeletal muscle total RNA. After transfer to nitrocellulose, hybridization was performed by use of a 2-kb cDNA encoding the 3′ region of the skeletal muscle RyR. Exposure was for 10 h with a single intensifying screen. The specific RyR mRNA was detected as a single band migrating at ~16 kb. No RyR mRNA was detected in uninfected Sf9 cells even after prolonged exposure (>two weeks).

to 7 days, at which point the cells were no longer viable because of extensive viral infection. Multiple infected Sf9 cell clones were plaque purified and analyzed; two examples are shown in Fig. 2.

Several of the isolated Sf9 clones, none of which were used for functional experiments, expressed partial RyR transcripts (Fig. 3) that were presumably the result of deletions in the RyR cDNA that occurred during homologous recombination between baculovirus genomic DNA and the transfer vector. Fig. 3 demonstrates the variability of expression of RyR mRNA in infected Sf9 cells. We initially followed previously published protocols for recombinant baculovirus expression in Sf9 cells. These protocols generally called for the isolation of a single clone after multiple rounds of amplification of virally infected insect cells. After these procedures we obtained truncated RyR mRNAs such as that shown in Fig. 3 (labeled *RyR1I-Sf9*). We reasoned that this might result from selection of a population of cells expressing a truncated RyR mRNA that had a growth advantage and therefore would be selected during multiple rounds of amplification. When samples were taken from the first transfection, before amplification, high levels of full length (~16-kb) RyR mRNA were expressed (Fig. 3, *lanes RyR1A-Sf9, RyR1B-Sf9, RyR1H-Sf9*). Other

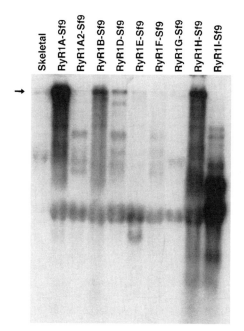

Figure 3. Expression of full length and truncated RyR mRNA in Sf9 cells. Northern hybridization showing expression of the ~16-kb RyR mRNA (*arrow*) in total RNA isolated from rabbit skeletal muscle (*Skeletal*) and Sf9 cells infected with recombinant baculovirus containing the complete RyR cDNA. *RyR1A-Sf9* shows high-level RyR mRNA expression in cells harvested after infection with recombinant baculovirus (titer = 10^7 pfu/ml) followed by a single round of amplification (see **Materials and Methods**). *RyR1A2-Sf9* shows very low level RyR mRNA expression in cells harvested after two rounds of amplification following infection with a 10-fold higher titer of baculovirus (10^8 pfu/ml). *RyR1B-Sf9 through RyR1G-Sf9* show RyR mRNA expression with progressive increase in the viral titer from 10^6 to 10^{10} pfu/ml. *RyR1H-Sf9* shows high level RyR mRNA expression in cells harvested after infection with recombinant baculovirus (titer = 10^6 pfu/ml) followed by a single round of amplification. Expression of a markedly truncated RyR mRNA is shown in the lane labeled *RyR1I-Sf9* loaded with total RNA isolated from cells infected with recombinant baculovirus (titer = 10^6 pfu/ml) from the same transfection as in lane *RyR1H-Sf9* but harvested after three rounds of amplification. 15 μg of total RNA was loaded in each lane. After transfer to nitrocellulose, hybridization was performed by use of a 2-kb cDNA encoding the 3′ region of the skeletal muscle RyR. Exposure was for 2 h with a single intensifying screen. Specific RyR mRNA was detected as a single band migrating at ~16 kb, additional lower molecular weight bands are due to non-specific binding to ribosomal RNAs, to degradation of the full length RyR mRNA, or expression of truncated RyR mRNA as in *RyR1HSf9*.

infections at higher titers of Baculovirus (see Fig. 3 legend for details) yielded lower levels of expression of RyR mRNA, presumably because the cells were not healthy as evidenced by a higher percentage of cell death.

Fig. 4 shows a representative sucrose gradient purification from infected Sf9 cells, control uninfected Sf9 cells, and skeletal muscle heavy sarcoplasmic reticulum. A 53-fold purification was achieved by this procedure starting with total cellular membranes. Approximately 4 μg of purified RyR were isolated from 84 mg of Sf9 total cell membranes, equivalent to the amount of RyR purified from 0.5 mg of heavy sarcoplasmic reticulum. No high molecular weight [³H]ryanodine binding proteins were isolated from the cytosol fraction of infected cells or from control, uninfected Sf9 cells. The *inset* in Fig. 4 shows an immunoblot analysis of recombinant RyR purified from Sf9 cells. A polyclonal anti-RyR peptide antisera (SKRyR5029) that recognizes the last nine amino acids of the carboxy terminus of the skeletal muscle RyR, was used for immunodetection (Jayaraman et al., 1992). The only specific band detected by immunoblot in infected Sf9 (*right lane*) but not in uninfected cells (*middle*) corresponded to recombinant RyR that migrated with the same mobility as the purified 565,000-dalton rabbit skeletal muscle RyR shown in the *first lane* (Fig. 4). No band was detected in this size range in uninfected Sf9 cells (*middle lane*) even after longer exposure to bring out faint bands (not shown). Immunodetection by use of an antibody directed against the carboxy terminal nine amino acids helped to insure that the complete RyR protein was expressed. In addition to the high–molecular weight band corresponding to the RyR (~600 kD) seen in infected but not in uninfected Sf9 cells, five other bands were observed in both infected and uninfected cells. The sizes of these bands were ~400 kD, ~300 kD, ~200 kD, ~180

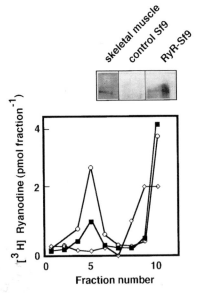

Figure 4. Sucrose gradient purification of ryanodine receptor from insect cells infected with recombinant baculovirus and from rabbit skeletal muscle. Rabbit skeletal muscle heavy sarcoplasmic reticulum (1.5 mg, *open circles*), infected Sf9 cells (84 mg of total cellular membranes, *filled squares*) and uninfected Sf9 cells (75 mg of total cellular membranes, *open diamonds*) were used for RyR isolation as detailed under **Materials and Methods**. Note that the cloned expressed RyR sedimented in the same fraction (#5, 22% sucrose) as the skeletal muscle RyR and no RyR was purified from uninfected Sf9 cells. The *inset* shows an immunoblot of the skeletal muscle RyR isolated from rabbit skeletal muscle sarcoplasmic reticulum (1 μg), membrane fraction #5 from uninfected Sf9 cells (50 μg), and the same fraction (#5) from Sf9 cells expressing recombinant RyR protein. Only the top portion of the blot is shown, no other specific bands were visualized. Protein samples were size fractionated on a 4% SDS-polyacrylamide gel, transferred to nitrocellulose, hybridized to a polyclonal site-specific antisera directed against the final 9 carboxy terminal amino acids, detection was with the ECL chemiluminescence system (see under **Materials and Methods** for details). No RyR band was detected in uninfected cells even after prolonged exposure.

kD, ~60 kD. The only band seen in the infected Sf9 cells that was not present in the uninfected cells was the highest molecular weight band on the gel that comigrated with the purified skeletal muscle RyR (Fig. 4).

Single Channel Properties of Recombinant Ryanodine Receptor

The single channel properties of purified, recombinant RyR reconstituted into liposomes were determined by use of cloned expressed material from Sf9 cell cultures infected with three independent Baculovirus recombinants and compared with those of the native RyR purified from rabbit skeletal muscle sarcoplasmic reticulum. Channels conducting either cesium (Cs) or Ca were examined and compared. Fig. 5 shows a comparison of purified native rabbit skeletal muscle RyR (*left pan-*

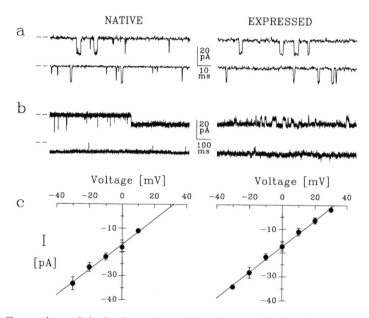

Figure 5. Comparison of single channel recordings from purified native RyR and recombinant RyR expressed in insect cells. Native and cloned expressed RyR were isolated under identical conditions by use of sucrose gradient density purification, incorporated into liposomes, and fused to planar lipid bilayers. (*a*) Channels with typically high conductances for Cs were observed in both native and cloned expressed preparations. (*b*) Both native and expressed RyRs were modulated by ryanodine (0.5 μM). Note in the top trace of *b* for the native RyR that the channel starts out closed then opens midway through this trace to the one-half conductance state characteristically induced by ryanodine. The amplitude of the single channel currents at 0 mV was 18.3 ± 1.3 pA before the addition of ryanodine and 9 ± 0.4 pA after the addition of ryanodine. Channel opening and closing kinetics were slowed after the addition of ryanodine (note that the time scale is decreased 10-fold in the presence of ryanodine). (*c*) The current-voltage relationship of the Cs current through the native and purified recombinant RyR reconstituted into bilayers. The slope conductances were 508 ± 35 ps for the native channel and 540 ± 48 ps for the expressed channel. The reversal potential calculated for Cs in both cases was 32 mV ($P_{Cs}:P_{Cl} = 11:1$). The conditions used for recording the cloned expressed channels were as described under **Materials and Methods**. In all cases *dashed lines* on the left of each tracing represent the closed state, channel openings are downward.

els) and recombinant skeletal muscle RyR from Sf9 cells (*right panels*) at high resolution (Fig. 5 *a*) in which Cs was used as the charge carrier. Both the native and cloned expressed channels responded to addition of ryanodine (0.5 μM, *n* = 4) by shifting to a characteristic subconductance state (Fig. 5 *b*), typical for the RyR/Ca release channel (Lai et al., 1988). The following Cs conductances were observed: 508 ± 35 ps for the native channel and 540 ± 48 ps for the expressed channel (Fig. 5 *c*; in this figure each current-voltage relationship was derived from 3 experiments), as reported for the native channel in multiple studies (Chu et al., 1990; Fill et al., 1991*a*, *b*; Smith et al., 1988). Expressed RyR exhibited a reversal potential of 32 mV, obtained with a CsCl gradient (250/50 mM), a result indicating that this channel was cation selective (11:1; Fig. 5 *c*), as previously reported for native skeletal muscle RyR channels (Coronado et al., 1992). All of the expressed channels that we studied (*n* > 100) exhibited conductances (including subconductance states) similar to those previously reported for the native skeletal muscle RyR.

With Cs as the charge carrier, caffeine (5 mM) consistently activated the recombinant RyR/Ca release channel (*n* = 27) (Fig. 6, *a* and *b*). Amplitude histograms revealed that a single type of channel was present (Fig. 6 *c*) with a mean amplitude of 14 ± 1.8 pA. The amplitude of the cloned expressed channel was not significantly altered by caffeine (Fig. 6 *c*, *right panel*). In six out of seven experiments, the cloned expressed RyR was activated by ATP (2 mM) increasing the Po by 360% on average.

With Ca as the charge carrier, the following conductances were observed: 103 for the native channel and for the expressed channels (Fig. 7). The amplitude of the Ca conductance was dependent on the concentration of Ca in the *trans* chamber (corresponding to the luminal side of the channel). Decreasing Ca from 53 mM to 10.6 mM in the *trans* chamber reduced the Ca conductance from 103 pS to 68 pS (Fig. 7). The Ca conductances for the cloned expressed RyR were indistinguishable from those of the native RyR at both 53 mM and 10.6 mM (Fig. 7). The Ca conductance of RyR was not altered by addition of FKBP12 (Fig. 7), which is not expressed in Sf9 cells. Ryanodine (500 nM) characteristically reduced the amplitude of the Ca-conducting RyR to 50% (Fig. 8) and at higher concentrations blocked the channel. No ryanodine-sensitive Ca channels were observed in microsomes or in sucrose density gradient fractions (comparable to those containing RyR in infected Sf9 cells) from uninfected Sf9 cells.

In the absence of FKBP12, the cloned expressed RyR exhibits multiple subconductance states when the charge carrier is Ca (Fig. 9) as observed previously when the charge carrier was Cs (Brillantes et al., 1994). The amplitude histogram of the expressed RyR with FKBP12 activated by caffeine (5 mM) and with Ca as the charge carrier revealed that a single type of channel was present (Fig. 10) with an amplitude of ~4 pA. Large conductance channels, which had been reported for skeletal RyR expressed in COS-1 cells (Chen et al., 1993) were not observed in these experiments with either Cs or Ca as the charge carrier.

Discussion

In this paper, functional expression of the RyR/Ca-release channel in insect cells was used to define the single channel properties of the cloned RyR with calcium as

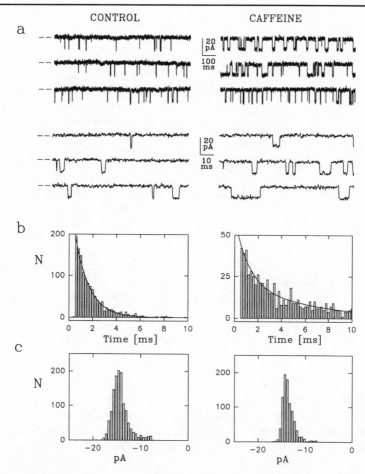

Figure 6. Single channel properties of the cloned expressed ryanodine receptor: activation by caffeine. (*a*) The effect of caffeine (5 mM) on single channel recording from purified recombinant RyR expressed in insect cells is shown. All of the traces shown in this figure are from the same experiment. The two tracings on the *left* show representative recordings before addition of caffeine. The two traces on the *right* show representative recordings after the addition of caffeine. (*b*) The mean open time before addition of caffeine was 1.2 ± 0.4 ms and after caffeine was 9.0 ± 1.2 ms. The histogram on the *left* represents data from 1278 channel openings recorded over 131 s, the histogram on the *right* represents data from 628 channel openings recorded over 60 s. The open probability increased after caffeine from 1.5% to 24%. (*c*) Addition of caffeine did not alter the amplitude of the single channel current. Data were fit with a Gaussian curve by use of pClamp. The mean amplitudes at 0 mV before and after caffeine were 14 ± 1.8 pA (1,280 openings) and 13.3 ± 1.3 (897 openings), respectively. Similar fits were made to the data obtained at each voltage tested.

the charge carrier. The same expression system was previously used to describe the cellular role of FKBP12, a channel accessory protein, or *CAP*, that stabilizes RyR function (Brillantes et al., 1994). The earlier studies used Cs as the charge carrier to assess channel function, however the physiologic charge carrier for RyR is Ca. This

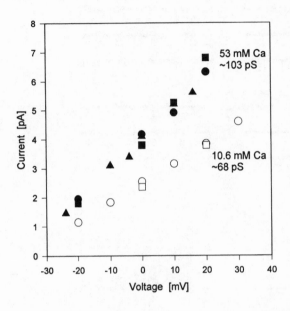

Figure 7. The amplitude of conductance of the ryanodine receptor/calcium-release channel depends on luminal calcium concentration. Calcium conductances of the cloned expressed ryanodine receptor (with and without FKBP12) and the native ryanodine receptor (with FKBP12) were compared. Increasing the luminal calcium concentration from 10.6 to 53 mM resulted in a 66% increase in conductance (from 68 to 103 pS). The amplitude of conductance was plotted versus voltage for three preparations of RyR at two different concentrations of calcium in the *trans* (luminal) chamber (*filled symbols*, 53 mM calcium; *open symbols*, 10.6 mM calcium). The three preparations of RyR included: 1. *circles*, native RyR; 2. *triangles*, expressed RyR plus FKBP12; 3. *squares*, expressed RyR without FKBP12.

paper provides analyses of the single channel properties of the cloned RyR compared with those of the native channel when Ca is the charge carrier.

An early step in the baculovirus/insect cell system requires homologous recombination between the baculovirus transfer vector and the viral genome that should result in incorporation of the heterologous cDNA into the viral genome. We found that this step was problematic, probably because of the large size of the RyR

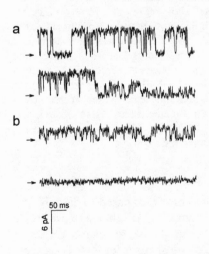

Figure 8. The effect of ryanodine on the cloned expressed ryanodine receptor (plus FKBP12) with calcium as the charge carrier. Cloned expressed RyR was incorporated into liposomes and fused to planar lipid bilayers, and FKBP12 (0.15 μM) was added to the bilayer chamber. In this experiment the holding potential across the bilayer membrane was +10 mV, therefore the conductance of the channels was increased by ~33%. (*a*) Channels with typically high conductances for calcium were observed, but the frequency of multiple subconductance states was markedly reduced and channels with full conductances (~6 pA) were primarily observed. (*b*) Ryanodine (500 nM) reduced the amplitude of the channel conductance by 50% and eventually blocked the channel. In all cases *arrows* on the left of each tracing represent the closed state, channel openings are upward.

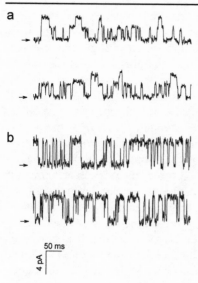

a

b

50 ms

4 pA

Figure 9. FKBP12 reduces subconductance states of the cloned expressed ryanodine receptor with calcium as the charge carrier. Cloned expressed RyR was isolated by sucrose gradient density purification, incorporated into liposomes, and fused to planar lipid bilayers in the absence of FKBP12. (*a*) Channels with typical conductances for calcium and multiple subconductance states. (*b*) Addition of FKBP12 to the cloned RyR in the bilayer chamber resulted in channels exhibiting full conductance and reduction of the frequency of subconductance states. In all cases *arrows* on the left of each tracing represent the closed state, channel openings are upward.

cDNA (15.2 kb) and resulted in truncation of the expressed mRNA and protein. We showed that by avoiding amplification of the virus immediately after the transfection, selection of smaller (truncated) clones could be avoided and expression of full-length mRNA and protein was optimized. This early clone selection procedure enabled us to express full length recombinant RyR mRNA (Fig. 2) and protein (Fig. 4) in insect cells.

Little is known regarding the assembly of the tetrameric Ca-release channel and its insertion into the SR. Our data indicate that the RyR expressed in insect cells forms a tetramer on the basis of its sedimentation on sucrose gradients (Fig. 4) and the integrity of the high affinity ryanodine binding site (Figs. 5 and 7). The fact

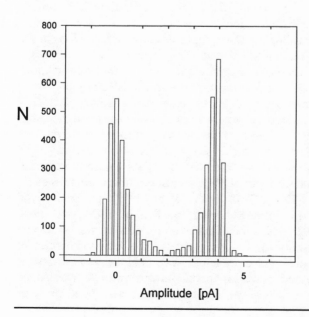

N

Amplitude [pA]

Figure 10. A single channel species is observed for the cloned expressed ryanodine receptor (plus FKBP12) with calcium as the charge carrier. Cloned expressed RyR was incorporated into liposomes and fused to planar lipid bilayers, and FKBP12 (0.15 μM) was added. An all-points histogram of the channel activated with 5 mM caffeine shows two states of the channel, fully closed (0 pA) and fully open (~4 pA).

that a tetrameric structure was expressed in insect cells demonstrates that the information required for association of four RyR molecules is encoded by the RyR cDNA. This finding also indicates that additional muscle-specific proteins or factors are not required for formation of the tetrameric structure of the SR Ca-release channel.

Comparison between the cloned expressed RyR and the native RyR showed that the cloned expressed RyR, with either Ca or Cs as the charge carrier, exhibits the single channel properties of the purified native channel. The RyR is the largest ion channel structure described to date. The functional importance of the large cytoplasmic portion of the molecule is not understood, although it is thought to contain the binding sites for channel modulators. This cytoplasmic portion accounts for as much as 90% of the linear sequence of the molecule, the remainder encoding the putative channel-forming region (four to ten transmembrane segments). It has recently been shown that the high- and low-affinity ryanodine binding sites are located near the carboxy terminus of the RyR (Callaway et al., 1994; Witcher et al., 1994). In these studies the localization of the ryanodine-binding site was achieved by use of purified and partially purified RyR that has been shown to contain associated proteins, therefore the possibility that modulation of channel function by ryanodine required associated protein(s) could not be excluded. In the present study, comparison of the cloned and native RyR shows that this high-affinity binding site is indeed encoded entirely by the RyR cDNA and does not require modulation by associated muscle-specific proteins.

The relationship between the SR luminal calcium concentration and the amplitude of conductance of the RyR shows that the conductance of the channel is reduced at lower luminal Ca concentrations (Fig. 7). This finding suggests that depletion of SR Ca stores could result in a decrease in the magnitude of Ca release even before the stores are fully depleted. This observation agrees with earlier studies in which sheep cardiac RyR was used (Tinker and Williams, 1992) and has implications for pathophysiologic conditions in which energy metabolism is reduced (i.e., during ischemia or prolonged exercise) and SR Ca reuptake via the Ca-ATPase is reduced, resulting in decreased SR Ca loading.

In addition to questions regarding the functional roles of various regions of the channel structure, multiple SR and non-SR proteins have been reported to be associated with the RyR. In most cases the functional significance of these associations has not been elucidated. We previously demonstrated that FKBP12 modulates the gating of RyR, with Cs as the charge carrier, by reducing the frequency of subconductance states, increasing the mean open time, and decreasing the open probability of the channel (Brillantes et al., 1994). In the present study we have demonstrated that with the physiologic charge carrier, Ca, FKBP12 also modulates RyR gating (Figs. 9 and 10). Other proteins associated with the RyR whose function remains less clear include: triadin (Brandt et al., 1992), calsequestrin (Ikemoto et al., 1991), annexin VI (Diaz et al., 1990), S-100 (Fano et al., 1989), glyceraldehyde 3-phosphate dehydrogenase and aldolase (Caswell and Brandt, 1989), and phosphoglucomutase (Lee et al., 1992). The availability of an expression system for the RyR now provides the opportunity for determination of the functional roles of these associated proteins. Moreover, one can exclude several of the important RyR channel properties from the list of potential functional attributes that could be modulated by associated proteins. Those properties in which associated proteins are now unlikely to play a role include: regulation by ryanodine, caffeine, ATP, and ruthenium red; tetrameric association; and membrane insertion.

The current study shows that when Ca is the charge carrier, the single channel properties of the cloned RyR are the same as those of the native channel as long as FKBP12 is present. We also describe a modification of the baculovirus/insect cell expression system that permits functional expression of extremely large proteins like the RyR. Establishment of a model for analyzing the function of the cloned expressed RyR in which the recombinant channel exhibits the properties of the native channel is a prerequisite to performing studies in which relationships between structure and function for intracellular Ca release channels can be characterized.

Acknowledgments

A.R. Marks is a Bristol-Meyers Squibb Established Investigator of the American Heart Association. This work was supported by grants from the National Institutes of Health (NS29814), the American Heart Association, the New York Affiliate of the American Heart Association, and the Louis B. Mayer Fund (to A.R. Marks), and the National Institutes of Health (HL33026) and the Connecticut Affiliate of the American Heart Association (to B.E. Ehrlich). K. Ondrias is on leave from the Institute of Experimental Pharmacology, Bratislava, Slovakia. A.-M.B. Brillantes is a Howard Hughes Medical Student Fellow.

References

Brandt, N., A. Caswell, J. Brunschwig, J. Kang, B. Antoniu, and N. Ikemoto. 1992. Effects of anti-triadin antibody on Ca^{2+} release from sarcoplasmic reticulum. *FEBS Lett.* 299:57–59.

Brillantes, A., P. Allen, T. Takahasi, S. Izumo, and A. Marks. 1992. Differences in cardiac calcium release channel (ryanodine receptor) expression in myocardium from patients with end-stage heart failure caused by ischemic versus dilated cardiomyopathy. *Circ. Res.* 71:18–26.

Brillantes, A.-M.B., K. Ondrias, A. Scott, E. Kobrinsky, E. Ondriasova, M.C. Moschella, T. Jayaraman, M. Landers, B.E. Ehrlich, and A.R. Marks. 1994. Stabilization of calcium release channel (ryanodine receptor) function by FK-506 binding protein. *Cell.* 77:513–523.

Callaway, C., A. Seryshev, J.-P. Wang, K. Slavik, D. Needleman, C. Cantu, Y. Wu, T. Jayaraman, A. Marks, and S. Hamilton. 1994. Localization of the high and low affinity [³H]ryanodine binding sites on the skeletal muscle Ca^{2+} release channel. *J. Biol. Chem.* 269:15876–15884.

Caswell, A., and N. Brandt. 1989. Triadic proteins of skeletal muscle. *J. Bioenerg. Biomembr.* 21:149–162.

Catterall, W.A. 1991. Excitation-contraction coupling in vertebrate skeletal muscle: A tale of two calcium channels. *Cell.* 64:871–874.

Chen, S.W., D.M. Vaughan, J.A. Airey, R. Coronado, and D.H. MacLennan. 1993. Functional expression of cDNA encoding the Ca^{2+} release channel (ryanodine receptor) of rabbit skeletal muscle sarcoplasmic reticulum in COS-1 cells. *Biochem. J.* 32:3743–3753.

Chu, A., M. Diaz-Munoz, M. Hawkes, K. Brush, and S. Hamilton. 1990. Ryanodine as a probe for the functional state of the skeletal muscle sarcoplasmic reticulum calcium release channel. *Mol. Pharmacol.* 37:735–741.

Chu, A., M. Fill, M.L. Entman, and E. Stefani. 1991. Different Ca^{2+} sensitivities of the ryano-dine-sensitive Ca^{2+} release channels of cardiac and skeletal muscle sarcoplasmic reticulum. *Biophysical. J.* 59:102a.

Coronado, R., S. Kawano, C. Lee, C. Valdivia, and H. Valdivia. 1992. Planar bilayer record-ing of ryanodine receptors of sarcoplasmic reticulum. *Methods Enzymol.* 207:699–707.

Diaz, M., M.S. Hamilton, M. Kaetzel, P. Hazarika, and J. Dedman. 1990. Modulation of Ca^{2+} release channel activity from sarcoplasmic reticulum by annexin V1 (67-kDa calcimedin). *J. Biol. Chem.* 265:15894–15899.

Fabiato, A. 1983. Calcium-induced release of calcium from the cardiac sarcoplasmic reticu-lum. *Am. J. Physiol.* 245:C1–C14.

Fabiato, A., and F. Fabiato. 1984. Calcium and cardiac excitation-contraction coupling. *Annu. Rev. Physiol.* 41:743.

Fano, G., P. Angelella, M. Aisa, I. Giambanco, and R. Donato. 1989. S-100 protein stimulates Ca^{2+}-induced Ca^{2+} release from isolated sarcoplasmic reticulum vesicles. *FEBS Lett.* 255:381–384.

Fill, M., R. Mejia-Alvarez, F. Zorzato, P. Volpe, and E. Stefani. 1991a. Antibodies as probes for ligand gating of single sarcoplasmic reticulum Ca^{2+}-release channels. *Biochem. J.* 273:449–457.

Fill, M., E. Stefani, and T. Nelson. 1991b. Abnormal human sarcoplasmic reticulum Ca^{2+} re-lease channels in malignant hyperthermic skeletal muscle. *Biophys. J.* 59.

Franzini-Armstrong, C., and G. Nunzi. 1983. Junctional feet and membrane particles in the triad of a fast twitch muscle fiber. *J. Muscle Res. and Cell. Motil.* 4:233–252.

Go, L.O., M.C. Moschella, J. Watras, K.K. Handa, B.S. Fyfe, and A.R. Marks. 1995. Differ-ential regulation of two types of intracellular calcium release channels during end-stage heart failure. *J. Clin. Invest.* 95:888–894.

Gwathmey, J.K., L. Copelas, R. Mackinnon, F. Schoen, M. Feldman, W. Grossman, and J. Morgan. 1987. Abnormal intracellular calcium handling in myocardium from patients with end-stage heart failure. *Circ. Res.* 61:70–76.

Ikemoto, N., B. Antoniu, J. Kang, L. Meszaros, and M. Ronjat. 1991. Intravesicular calcium transient during calcium release from the sarcoplasmic reticulum. *Biochemistry.* 30:5230–5237.

Jayaraman, T., A.-M.B. Brillantes, A.P. Timerman, H. Erdjument-Bromage, S. Fleischer, P. Tempst, and A.R. Marks. 1992. FK506 binding protein associated with the calcium release channel (ryanodine receptor). *J. Biol. Chem.* 267:9474–9477.

Lai, F.A., H.P. Erickson, E. Rousseau, Q.L. Liu, and G. Meissner. 1988. Purification and re-constitution of the calcium release channel from skeletal muscle. *Nature (Lond.).* 331:315–319.

Lee, Y.S., A. Marks, N. Gureckas, R. Lacro, B. Nadal-Ginard, and D.-H. Kim. 1992. Purifica-tion, characterization and molecular cloning of a 60-kDa phosphoprotein in rabbit skeletal muscle sarcoplasmic reticulum which is a novel isoform of phosphoglucomutase. *J. Biol. Chem.* 267:21080–21088.

Lindsay, A., and A. Williams. 1991. Functional characterization of the ryanodine receptor from sheep cardiac muscle sarcoplasmic reticulum. *Biochem. Biophys. Acta.* 1064:89–102.

Lu, X., L. Xu, and G. Meissner. 1994. Activation of the skeletal muscle calcium release chan-nel by a cytoplasmic loop of the dihydropyridine receptor. *J. Biol. Chem.* 269:6511–6516.

Marks, A.R., S. Fleischer, and P. Tempst. 1990. Surface topography analysis of the ryanodine receptor/junctional channel complex based on proteolysis sensitivity mapping. *J. Biol. Chem.* 265:13143–13149.

Marks, A.R., P. Tempst, K.S. Hwang, M.B. Taubman, M. Inui, C. Chadwick, S. Fleischer, and B. Nadal-Ginard. 1989. Molecular cloning and characterization of the ryanodine receptor/junctional channel complex cDNA from skeletal muscle sarcoplasmic reticulum. *Proc. Natl. Acad. Sci. USA.* 86:8683–8687.

Morgan, J., R. Erny, P. Allen, W. Grossman, and J. Gwathmey. 1990. Abnormal intracellular calcium handling: A major cause of systolic and diastolic dysfunction in ventricular myocardium from patients with end-stage heart failure. *Circulation.* 81(Suppl. III):21–32.

Sambrook, J., E.F. Fritsch, and T. Maniatis. 1989. Molecular Cloning: A Laboratory Manual. Cold Spring Harbor Laboratory Press, Cold Spring Harbor, N.Y.

Smith, J.S., R. Coronado, and G. Meissner. 1986. Single channel measurements of the calcium release channel from skeletal muscle sarcoplasmic reticulum. *J. Gen. Physiol.* 88:573–588.

Smith, J.S., T. Imagawa, J. Ma, M. Fill, K.P. Campbell, and R. Coronado. 1988. Purified ryanodine receptor from rabbit skeletal muscle is the calcium release channel of sarcoplasmic reticulum. *J. Gen. Physiol.* 2:1–26.

Takeshima, H., S. Nishimura, T. Matsumoto, H. Ishida, K. Kangawa, N. Minamino, H. Matsuo, M. Ueda, M. Hanaoka, T. Hirose, and S. Numa. 1989. Primary structure and expression from complementary DNA of skeletal muscle ryanodine receptor. *Nature (Lond.).* 339:439–445.

Tinker, A., and A.J. Williams. 1992. Divalent cation conduction in the ryanodine receptor channel of sheep cardiac muscle sarcoplasmic reticulum. *J. Gen. Physiol.* 100:479–493.

Witcher, D.R., P.S. McPherson, S.D. Kahl, T. Lewis, P. Bentley, M.J. Mullinnix, J.D. Windass, and K.P. Campbell. 1994. Photoaffinity labeling of the ryanodine receptor/Ca^{2+} release channel with an azido derivative of ryanodine. *J. Biol. Chem.* 269:13076–13079.

Zorzato, F., J. Fujii, K. Otso, M. Phillips, N.M. Green, F.A. Lai, G. Meissner, and D.H. MacLennan. 1990. Molecular cloning of cDNA encoding human and rabbit forms of the Ca^{2+} release channel (ryanodine receptor) of skeletal muscle sarcoplasmic reticulum. *J. Biol. Chem.* 265:2244–2256.

The Role of Ryanodine Receptor Isoforms in the Structure and Function of the Vertebrate Triad

Barbara A. Block,* John O'Brien,‡ and Jens Franck*

*Department of Biological Sciences, Hopkins Marine Station, Stanford University, Pacific Grove, California 93950; and ‡Department of Ophthalmology and Visual Sciences, University of Illinois, Chicago, Illinois 60612

Introduction

In skeletal muscles contraction and relaxation are regulated by the rapid release and reuptake of Ca^{2+} ions from an intracellular storage site, the sarcoplasmic reticulum (SR). Activation of Ca^{2+} release from the SR follows depolarization of the surface and transverse (T) tubular membranes. Communication between the T-tubular membranes and SR occurs at specialized junctional regions between the two membrane systems called *triads* (Franzini-Armstrong and Jorgensen, 1994). The triads contain the proteins involved in the voltage-sensitive step of excitation-contraction (EC) coupling, the process linking muscle depolarization to tension generation (Schneider and Chandler, 1973). Two key proteins, the T-tubule dihydropyridine receptor and the SR Ca^{2+} release channel/ryanodine receptor, span the gap between the two membranes and are proposed to mediate the signal transmission process across the triad. The dihydropyridine receptors (DHPRs), or voltage sensors, are located in the surface and T-tubular membranes (Rios and Brum, 1987; Tanabe et al., 1988). The ryanodine receptors (RyRs) are situated in the terminal cisternae portion of the SR membrane (Fleischer et al., 1985; Lai et al., 1988). Release of Ca^{2+} from the SR in vertebrate skeletal muscle is proposed to occur via direct mechanical linkage of the α1 subunit of the DHPR and the cytoplasmic domain of the RyR. Exactly how the depolarization of the surface membrane results in the release of Ca^{2+} ions from the Ca^{2+}-release channel remains the central question of EC-coupling studies. Direct evidence for the involvement of the DHPR in skeletal muscle EC coupling has been obtained via restoration of Ca^{2+} currents and charge movement in dysgenic muscle fibers by transfection with the DHPR cDNA (Adams et al., 1990). Experimental evidence indicates that the cytoplasmic loop between transmembrane repeats II and III of the α1 subunit of the DHPR in mammals is critical to the putative allosteric interaction that generates skeletal-specific EC coupling (Tanabe et al., 1988; Lu et al., 1994; El-Hayek et al., 1995).

Models of EC coupling in vertebrate skeletal muscles are based on structural and physiologic research from fish and amphibians as well as molecular, biochemical, and physiological results from mammals. The diversity of species employed for examining aspects of EC coupling has led to considerable progress in the field and the development of new hypotheses to describe the mechanistic interaction between the proteins located at the junction between SR and T-tubular membranes (Meissner, 1994; Rios and Pizarro, 1991). However, controversies persist and may

Organellar Ion Channels and Transporters © 1996 by The Rockefeller University Press

be associated with the synthesis of data from the diverse species being studied (Hollingworth et al., 1992; Jacquemond et al., 1991; Pape et al., 1993). The discovery of the coexpression of RyR isoforms (RyR1 and RyR3) in skeletal muscles of both non-mammals and mammals has further complicated current models of EC coupling. A major debate concerns whether or not there are dual pathways for Ca^{2+} release involving two types of activating mechanisms and separate RyR release channels (Rios and Pizzaro, 1991; O'Brien et al., 1995). This paper reexamines the structure and function of the vertebrate skeletal muscle triad in light of new data on the isoform distribution of the SR Ca^{2+}-release channel isoforms in non-mammalian vertebrates.

Architecture of the Junctional Proteins at the Triad

Electron microscopy studies utilizing the fast-contracting swimbladder muscles of the oyster toadfish (*Opsanus tau*) have been critical for the establishment of the morphology of the SR and T-tubule membrane systems as well as the disposition and detailed structure of the junctional proteins associated with the process of Ca^{2+} release (Fawcett and Revel, 1961; Franzini-Armstrong, 1975; Franzini-Armstrong and Nunzi, 1983; Ferguson et al., 1984; Block et al., 1988; Franzini-Armstrong and Jorgensen, 1994). In toadfishes, two external bands of fast-twitch skeletal muscle are wrapped around the gas-filled swimbladder, the buoyancy organ of fishes. Physiological studies have demonstrated that the swimbladder muscles are capable of superfast contractions, resulting in vibrations that generate sound. Electrically stimulated fibers achieve peak tension in 3 ms and have a fusion frequency in excess of 100 Hz (Skoglund, 1961). The high contraction speeds are functionally related to the hypertrophy of the volume of the muscle fiber occupied by the SR and T-tubule membranes, and the corresponding reduction in the myofibrillar volume (Appelt et al., 1991). The toadfish swimbladder preparation is ideal for freeze-fracture studies aimed at examination of the disposition of the integral membrane proteins because of the extensive straight regions of junctional SR and T-tubular membranes (Fig. 1). Freeze-fracture techniques remain among the only experimental avenues for investigation in situ of the architecture of the SR and T-tubule junctional proteins at the triad.

Freeze-fracture of the junctional SR and T-tubule membranes in toadfish swimbladder muscles revealed the spatial relationships between the RyRs and orderly clusters of four proteins in the T-tubular membrane called the *junctional T-tubular* (jT) *tetrads* (Franzini-Armstrong and Nunzi, 1983; Block et al., 1988). The direct alignment of the jT tetrads and foot proteins led to the hypothesis that the structures together form a protein complex that has molecular continuity across both membranes (Block et al., 1988) and provides evidence for a possible direct interaction between DHPRs and RyRs across the triad. This structural complex has become an integral part of the current models of vertebrate EC coupling (e.g., Rios and Pizarro, 1991; Rios et al., 1993). However, certain points concerning the structural model remain to be clarified. The disposition of jT tetrads in toadfish swimbladder muscle revealed an anomaly: only every other foot protein could form a complex with a jT tetrad. That is, the distance between jT tetrads was twice the distance between adjacent RyRs in a row (60 nm apart rather than 30 nm). The distri-

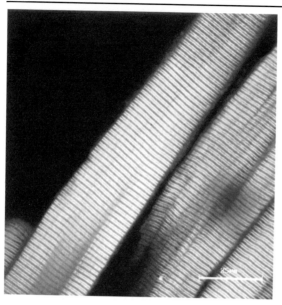

Figure 1. Confocal micrograph of swimbladder muscle fibers of toadfish labeled with an RyR1 polyclonal antibody. In toadfish, the RyR label has a junctional pattern of labeling (A/I band) and is punctate at higher magnification. The intense labeling with the RyR antibody is indicative of the remarkable stretches of junctional SR in this fiber type.

bution of the jT tetrads in the junctional T-tubular membrane has suggested that the clusters are the DHPRs or voltage sensors involved in EC coupling (Block et al., 1988; Franzini-Armstrong and Jorgensen, 1994), although no studies have actually demonstrated the triad localization of the DHPR in this specialized skeletal muscle. The identity of the jT tetrads has not been firmly established, although several lines of indirect evidence favor identification of the tetrads as DHPRs. This is based primarily on the junctional location and size of the jT tetrads. Stronger evidence of this correlation comes from the observation that tetrads are absent in dysgenic mouse muscle (Franzini-Armstrong et al., 1991) which does not express the α1 subunit of the DHPR, but are evident in rescued dysgenic myotubes transfected with the cDNA for the missing DHPRs (Flucher, 1991; Franzini-Armstrong et al., 1991; Takekura et al., 1994).

The freeze-fracture results from toadfish swimbladder muscles led to a model for direct interaction across the triad with an unusual feature: alternate couplings of RyRs and the DHPRs (the jT tetrads). The jT tetrads are proposed to be aligned alternately with the array of foot proteins so that every other foot protein remains unpaired. The inability to correlate the 1:1 stoichiometry between jT tetrads and RyRs remains a puzzle. Block et al. (1988) and Franzini-Armstrong and Jorgensen (1994) proposed several explanations for the unusual structural model: (*1*) Neighbor RyRs, situated side by side in the junctional SR membrane, may be activated by different mechanisms or in a cooperative fashion; (*2*) every other foot was not contributing to the Ca^{2+}-release process, i.e., it was silent; and (*3*) steric hindrance within the tight limits of the junctional membranes prevents interaction of all tetrads and feet. Questions remaining about the toadfish structural results include establishment of the identity of the jT tetrads and the ubiquity of the pattern of alternate couplings in vertebrate triads. The structural model has been extremely difficult to confirm in other vertebrates because of the challenge of obtaining skeletal muscle fibers with linear arrays of junctional SR and T-tubule membranes that lend themselves well to freeze-fracture experiments. It is not clear if the structural conformation of an alternating complex of junctional proteins is unique to the toad-fish swimbladder muscle or a common structural motif in all vertebrate triads.

Non-Mammalian Triads Express Two Distinct RyR Isoforms

The skeletal muscles of all vertebrates, with the exception of mammals, lizards and snakes, co-express two RyRs (Airey et al., 1990; Olivares et al., 1991; Lai et al., 1992; Murayama and Ogawa, 1992; O'Brien et al., 1993). The isoforms, initially termed RyRs α and β because of their unknown homologies to mammalian RyR isoforms, were identified by their different mobilities on SDS gels, immunological reactivity, and peptide maps (Airey et al., 1990; Olivares et al., 1991). The two iso-forms are expressed in the same muscle fibers and have been localized in the same triad junctions (Airey et al., 1990; Olivares et al., 1991; Lai et al., 1992; Murayama and Ogawa, 1992; O'Brien et al., 1993). The stoichiometric relationship between the two isoforms and whether or not they are situated exactly side by side remains unclear. Recent studies using imperatoxin A (IpTx$_A$), a peptide component of *P. imperator* scorpion venom that selectively activates the RyR1 isoform of mammalian skeletal muscle, support stoichiometries of approximately 1:1 for the two RyR iso-forms (Valdivia et al., 1994). Dose-response curves for IpTx$_A$-activation of [^{3}H]ry-anodine binding reveals the percentage of receptors in each preparation activated by IpTx$_A$. The binding analyses indicate that almost half of the RyRs from skeletal muscles of fish, frog, turtle (immunologically both α and β are present), and the majority of the RyRs from skeletal muscles of rabbit, lizard, and toadfish swimblad-der muscle (α only) are sensitive to IpTx$_A$ (Valdivia et al., 1994).

Physiological studies of the two RyR isoforms in non-mammalian vertebrate muscles reveal the distinct ion-channel properties of the RyRs in heavy SR prepa-rations (Bull and Marengo, 1993; Percival et al., 1994; O'Brien et al., 1995). SR preparations were isolated from fish muscles that solely express the RyR1 isoform (extraocular muscle) as well as SR preparations from muscles that co-express RyR1 and RyR3 (body-wall skeletal muscles). Single-channel recordings from heavy SR preparations from fish swimming muscle revealed two distinct high-conductance Ca^{2+} channels that were identified on the basis of unitary channel conductance in response to ryanodine, ATP, and Ca^{2+}. In extraocular muscle SR, which expresses the α or RyR1 isoform only, a 530-ps channel was identified that had maximal open probability when cytosolic Ca^{2+} is between 10 μm and 100 μm and is completely in-activated by 1 mM Ca^{2+} (O'Brien et al., 1995) (Fig. 2). In swimming muscles, in ad-dition to the 530-ps channel, a 380-pS channel was also identified. In contrast to the 530-ps channel, the 380-pS channel displayed little inactivation at 1 mM Ca^{2+}. [^{3}H]ryanodine binding studies corroborate the single-channel conductance studies of the α isoform revealing a biphasic response to free Ca^{2+}. The α isoform (530-ps channel) from fish extraocular and epaxial muscles displays similar properties of Ca^{2+} activation and inactivation of [^{3}H]ryanodine binding, nearly identical single-channel conductance, and similar Ca^{2+} activation and inactivation of channel P_o to the rabbit skeletal muscle RyR1 (mammalian data from Pessah et al., 1987; Smith et al., 1988; Chu et al., 1990). In addition to these physiological similarities, the α isoform of fish and other vertebrates is the specific target of IpTx$_A$, and channel activity of the RyR in the swimbladder muscles (RyR1/α) increases with applica-

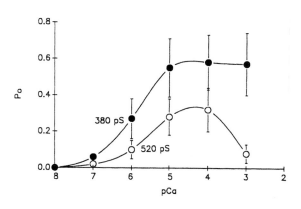

Figure 2. The Ca^{2+} dependence of open probability of the two types of RyR channels from toadfish white swimming muscle heavy SR incorporated into planar lipid bilayers. Two types of channels with different conductances (520-ps channel/α; 380 ps channel/β) were identified in this SR preparation, which contains both α and β RyR isoforms (See O'Brien et al., 1995 for information on preparation and techniques.) Data are means±SD from a total of 14 channels.

tion of the toxin (Valdivia et al., 1994). The results are consistent with the identification of the non-mammalian α isoform as a functional homologue of mammalian skeletal muscle RyR1 (Percival et al., 1994; O'Brien et al., 1995).

The single-channel conductance of the fish β RyR isoform is similar to that of the bovine cardiac RyR2 (O'Brien et al., 1995; Valdivia et al., 1994). Both the fish β isoform and the mammalian RyR2 and RyR3 are insensitive to IpTx$_A$ (Valdivia et al., 1994). There are distinct differences that suggest that the fish cardiac muscle SR (RyR2) and β isoforms are not functionally homologous. In the presence of AMP-PCP and Mg^{2+} the fish cardiac RyR2 is more sensitive to activation by Ca^{2+} than is the fish β isoform. The insensitivity to inactivation by millimolar concentrations of Ca^{2+} is similar for the RyR2 and fish skeletal muscle β RyR isoform; however, the two are not functionally identical. This result is in agreement with biochemical studies that distinguish between these two isoforms in chickens (Airey et al., 1991) and the recent molecular studies on frog RyR isoforms that suggest homology of the β isoform with the mammalian RyR3 (Oyamada et al., 1994). The physiological studies on the fish RyR ion channels are in agreement with other physiological studies on non-mammalian skeletal muscles (Bull and Marengo, 1993; Percival et al., 1994), an observation indicating there are two populations of functionally distinct RyRs in piscine, amphibian, and avian muscles. Single-channel studies of α and β RyRs from fish muscle SR, in which we have unambiguously (because of sole expression of α only in certain muscles) identified the α isoform from the β RyR isoforms, is corroborated by the general conclusions of the chicken and frog studies, which assign α as being functionally homologous with mammalian RyR1. Thus, similar physiological behavior of the α and β isoforms in fish, frog, and chick demonstrates that the fundamental properties of the two isoforms are likely conserved among the vertebrates that express both RyRs. The studies on non-mammals reveal that a major difference between the two types of non-mammalian RyRs co-expressed within the same muscles is in the nature of their activation and inactivation by Ca^{2+}.

Sequence Identity of Non-Mammalian RyRs

Cloning and sequencing has established the homology of the non-mammalian α and β isoforms in frogs and fish with mammalian RyR1 and RyR3 isoforms, respectively (Oyamada et al., 1994; Franck et al., 1994, 1995). Total RNA isolated from the fish extraocular muscle (α only expression) was used to construct a representative cDNA library (Franck et al., 1994). A PCR product generated with conserved primers from the channel region of the RyR was initially used to screen the library. Immunoscreening of the expression library with RyR-specific antibodies, in addition to the PCR-based strategies, has resulted in characterization of 90% of the predicted 16-kb message. As for all RyR isoforms characterized to date, the RyR isoform of the fish superior rectus is highly conserved at the COOH-terminal channel region (Fig. 3). Analysis of homologous amino acid substitutions across all RyRs reveals numerous synapamorphies that define the RyR1 gene family among fish, frog, and mammals. Phylogenetic analyses of the deduced amino acid sequence clusters the fish eye muscle RyR with the rabbit and human RyR1 sequences (Zorzato et al., 1990; Takeshima et al., 1989) isoforms and with the frog α isoform (Oyamada et al., 1994). The RyR isoform of the fish eye muscle and the α isoform of frogs therefore appear to be the homologues of the mammalian RyR1 isoform. This result strongly supports the biochemical and physiological results which suggest that the fish α isoform is functionally homologous to the mammalian RyR1 isoform.

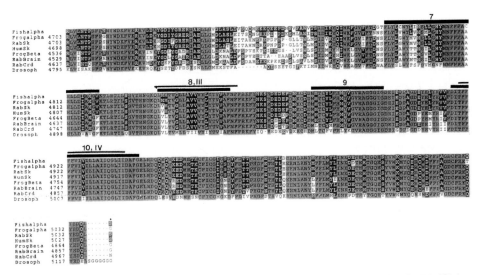

Figure 3. Multiple alignment of the deduced amino acid sequence of the fish RyR1 (Fish α; Franck et al., 1994) sequence to published RyR isoform sequences. The partial sequence represents the highly conserved COOH-terminal channel region of the RyR. The fish RyR1 sequence is aligned to frog RyR1 (Frog α; Oyamada et al., 1995), rabbit RyR1 (RabSk, Takeshima et al., 1989; Zorzato et al., 1990), human RyR1 (HumSk, Zorzato et al., 1990), frog RyR3 (FrogBeta, Oyamada et al., 1994), rabbit RyR3 (RabBrain, Hakamata et al., 1992), rabbit RyR2 (RabCrd, Otsu et al., 1990) and *Drosophila* RyR (Drosoph, Takeshima et al., 1994). Thick bars with Arabic numerals and thin black bars with Roman numerals overhead of the alignment indicate putative transmembrane spanning domains proposed by Zorzato et al. (1990) and Takeshima et al. (1989), respectively. Black shaded residues in the alignment indicate those conserved with the fish RyR1 sequence, and gray shaded residues indicate those conserved throughout all isoforms represented in the figure.

Structure and Functional Implication of Coexpression of RyRs in Skeletal Muscles

The discovery of the coexpression of two distinct RyR isoforms in non-mammals and the earlier finding of the freeze-fracture work with the toadfish swimbladder muscles has led several authors (Airey et al., 1990; Lai et al., 1992; Olivares et al., 1991) to suggest that the alternating conformation of the molecular coupling across the triad was related to the presence of two RyR isoforms. This intriguing interpretation provided an explanation for the unusual structural result of the toadfish triad (Block et al., 1988) and strengthened the hypothesis that dual regulation of Ca^{2+} release may be occurring in non-mammalian skeletal muscles (Rios et al., 1993). Localization studies with both light and electron microscopy indicated that the two RyR isoforms co-localize in the same triad junctions (Airey et al., 1990; Lai et al., 1992). However, a positional relationship with electron microscopy techniques aimed at discerning whether or not the two isoforms are situated side by side could not be established, due to the lack of resolution with immunofluorescence techniques (30-nm resolution is required). The presence of two RyR isoforms in non-mammals, a published report indicating that toadfish swimbladder expressed two isoforms (Olivares et al., 1991), and the apparent fit with the toadfish structural model (which suggested two forms of EC coupling) led to the suggestion that the structural result from the freeze-fracture studies on toadfish swimbladder muscle was congruent with the non-mammalian two-isoform arrangement (Lai et al., 1992; Olivares et al., 1991). Such agreement between the toadfish structural model and the emerging data based on non-mammalian RyR isoforms provided an attractive explanation for the distinct differences between adjacent RyRs in the freeze-fracture study. However, O'Brien et al. (1993) reported exceptions to the two-RyR–isoform expression pattern that have significant implications for vertebrate EC coupling.

O'Brien et al. (1993) discovered a functional exception to the two-RyR–isoform expression pattern in non-mammalian triads that may offer a clue to the evolution of the vertebrate triad. RyR1 and RyR3 isoforms are differentially expressed in certain non-mammalian skeletal muscles with functional specializations for superfast contraction. Avian and piscine muscle tissues that have high frequency contraction speeds (extraocular and fish swimbladder muscles) express only the RyR1 isoform. A possible linkage between gating properties of the RyR1 isoform and the expression of all RyR1 receptors in the triads of certain vertebrates implies that there may be a selective advantage of RyR1, such as increased sensitivity to opening in response to Ca^{2+} or rapid inactivation of Ca^{2+} release (O'Brien et al., 1993). Rapid contraction-relaxation cycles depend on the mechanisms that ensure a fast decay of the rise in Ca^{2+}. Vertebrate triads composed of only RyR1 may inactivate more rapidly because of the rapid kinetics of Ca^{2+}-dependent inactivation unique to the RyR1 isoform (O'Brien et al., 1995).

Only RyR1 Is Expressed in Toadfish Swimbladder Muscle

The toadfish swimbladder muscle, like mammalian skeletal muscle, is a one-RyR isoform (RyR1) muscle. The protein profile of the heavy SR vesicle fraction of toadfish swimbladder muscle (Fig. 4 *A*) reveals enrichment in the Ca^{2+} ATPase and the presence of only one high molecular weight polypeptide in this skeletal muscle.

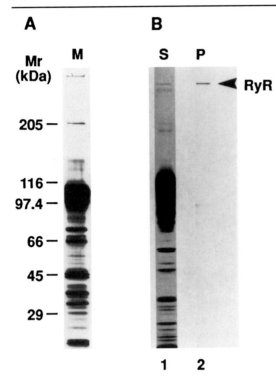

Figure 4. (*A*) SR profile of crude toadfish swimbladder muscle. Crude SR fractions were separated on 3%–15% gradient SDS-PAGE gels and stained with Coomassie brilliant blue. The high molecular weight band in toadfish crude microsomal fractions (*M*) co-migrated with a single polypeptide in heavy SR fractions of mouse skeletal muscle. (*B*) Purification of the ryanodine receptor from a solubilized fraction (*S*) of toadfish skeletal muscle heavy SR. Purification of the RyR from swimbladder muscle by CHAPS solubilization and sucrose gradient centrifugation reveals a single protein band. A single high-molecular weight polypeptide is isolated from the heavy SR fraction in toadfish.

The high molecular weight protein band co-migrated with the purified mammalian skeletal RyR (M_r 565,000), which was used as a high molecular weight marker, and ran slightly higher than purified fibronectin (M_r 510,000). CHAPS solubilization of the heavy SR fraction (Fig. 4 *B, lane 1*) followed by centrifugation through two sucrose gradients, yielded a purified fraction with only one high molecular weight polypeptide (Fig. 4 *B, lane 2*). The presence of only one high M_r protein band in the toadfish swimbladder muscle is in contrast to the swimming or body wall muscles of toadfish and other teleost fishes, which express two high M_r bands identified as the two non-mammalian RyR isoforms (Olivares et al., 1991; O'Brien et al., 1993). To discern which form of the non-mammalian RyR (α or β) was expressed in the toadfish swimbladder muscle, the heavy SR proteins were separated on a 3–12% SDS polyacrylamide gradient. Proteins were electrophoretically transferred to Immobilon P membranes and probed with an antibody that recognized both forms of the non-mammalian RyRs in fish (O'Brien et al., 1993). The immunoblot (Fig. 5) revealed a pattern of recognition consistent with the finding on the SDS-PAGE gel. As in most non-mammalian skeletal muscles, two RyR isoforms were found in toadfish white swimming muscle, a fast-twitch muscle (Fig. 5, *lane 2*), whereas only one isoform is present in the toadfish swimbladder muscle (*lane 3*). The mobility of the swimbladder RyR isoform was closest to that of the mammalian skeletal muscle RyR (*lane 1*) and was the same as that of the upper band in swimming muscle. This corresponds to the α RyR isoform in fish skeletal muscle SR fractions.

[³H]Ryanodine binding has been used to characterize the activation properties of the SR Ca^{2+}-release channel and can be used, in the presence of ligands that acti-

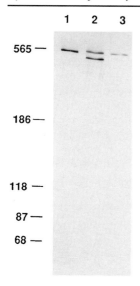

Figure 5. Immunoblot with a canine anti-cardiac RyR mono-clonal antibody RyR CO10. Two isoforms of the RyR are recognized in the toadfish swimming muscle (*lane 2*) while only one is recognized in swimbladder muscle (*lane 3*). The rabbit skeletal muscle RyR (*lane 1*) is also recognized and has a similar mobility to the RyR isoform present in swimbladder muscle.

vate and close the SR Ca^{2+}-release channel, as a means of distinguishing between mammalian isoforms of the RyR. Recent studies have established that [³H]ryanodine binding can also be used to characterize differences between non-mammalian α and β RyR isoforms (O'Brien, et al., 1995). The Ca^{2+} dependency of [³H]ryanodine binding to toadfish swimbladder muscle heavy SR was examined in the absence of other ligands that open and close the channel. Under these conditions, [³H]ryanodine binding to the SR Ca^{2+}-release channels of toadfish swimbladder muscle displays a bell-shaped dependency on free Ca^{2+} (O'Brien et al., 1995). Ryanodine binding is activated with a threshold of approximately 0.1 μM Ca^{2+} and is maximal at 3.3 μM free Ca^{2+}. Higher concentrations of Ca^{2+} inhibit [³H]ryanodine binding with essentially complete inactivation at 1 mM. The Ca^{2+} dependency of the [³H]ryanodine binding curve is similar to that of other fish skeletal muscles (e.g., extraocular) that express only the α isoform (O'Brien et al., 1995). In particular the Ca^{2+}-dependent inactivation of [³H]ryanodine binding distinguishes this isoform from the fish β isoform, which does not show inactivation in the presence of high Ca^{2+}. The modulation of the [³H]ryanodine binding curve by Ca^{2+} is also similar to that seen with rabbit skeletal muscle SR in which the single mammalian skeletal muscle RyR (Type 1) is present (O'Brien et al., 1995; Michalak et al., 1988). This differs substantially from the Ca^{2+} activation and inactivation profile observed with toadfish white muscle heavy SR, which contains both α and β RyR. The most significant difference when the RyR3/β isoform is present is that [³H]ryanodine binding in white muscle is only partially inactivated by free Ca^{2+} as high as 3.3 mM (O'Brien et al., 1995).

Models of the Triads of Toadfish Swimbladder Muscle

The recent discovery of two distinct isoforms of the RyRs in non-mammalian vertebrates provides suggestive evidence indicating that alternate coupling may represent dual pathways for Ca^{2+} release (Airey et al., 1990; Lai et al., 1992). In Fig. 6 we present a model for the structure of the triad junction in swimbladder muscle (after

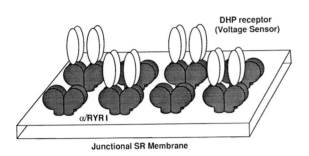

Figure 6. The toadfish swimbladder triad junction following the model of Block et al. (1988). All ryanodine receptors in this tissue are the α isoform (RyR1), though alternating contacts with the jT tetrads are evident. Schematic representation of a skeletal muscle triad junction showing the ryanodine receptor tetramers interacting with the jT tetrads (dihydropyridine receptors).

Block et al., 1988) in light of the biochemical and immunological data indicating expression of the α/RyR1 alone in this specialized skeletal muscle. In toadfish swimbladder muscle there. is only one possible structural configuration for a junctional complex that contains the α isoform only. This conformation, placing an α/RyR1 across from a jT tetrad, indicates that the RyR1/α isoform must have the capacity for direct coupling and should contain the primary sequence differences that facilitate interaction with the II-III loop of the α1 subunit of the DHPR.

The purification of only a single high molecular weight RyR isoform, its electrophoretic mobility, and the [³H]ryanodine binding data all indicate that the α RyR isoform is predominantly expressed in the toadfish swimbladder muscle. This is in contrast to the epaxial and hypaxial swimming muscles of the toadfish, where both α and β RyR isoforms are expressed. The α RyR isoform in toadfish swimbladder muscle has a number of properties that relate it to the mammalian skeletal muscle RyR. [³H]Ryanodine binding has a bell-shaped Ca^{2+} dependency in the toadfish swimbladder muscle unfractionated SR preparation, with prominent inactivation of [³H]ryanodine binding at millimolar free concentrations of Ca^{2+}. Similar results were obtained in marlin extraocular muscle, another α–only muscle, and rabbit skeletal muscle (O'Brien et al., 1995). Single channel recordings from the toadfish α RyR isoform confirm that at high Ca^{2+} concentrations the open probability of the toadfish α RyR is decreased. β, unlike α, does not show Ca^{2+}-dependent inactivation and instead appears insensitive to channel closure with high Ca^{2+} (O'Brien et al., 1995). A number of other results indicate that the fish α RyR isoform is a functional homologue of the mammalian skeletal RyR. It is affected by compounds that activate (IpTx$_A$) and inhibit (100 μM-tetracaine) the channel in a similar fashion to the mammalian skeletal RyR (Valdivia et al., 1994; O'Brien et al., 1995).

The presence of only the α isoform in the toadfish swimbladder muscle, when combined with the structural model of Block et al. (1988) from the same muscle preparation, indicates that both paired (RyR/jT tetrad) and unpaired RyRs in the triads of swimbladder muscle are composed of the same RyR1 isoform (Fig. 6). This important observation indicates that the structural organization of alternate couplings in the toadfish swimbladder muscle is not a function of the presence of two isoforms in the triad junction, but is instead the basic architecture of a triad junction. It also implies that jT tetrads are forming direct connections with only one-half of the α/RyR1 isoforms. Thus, the toadfish swimbladder muscle triad serves as an excellent model for all triads (mammals, reptiles) that have a single RyR isoform junction. This has most recently been confirmed in mammalian muscle, where peripheral couplings with an alternate spacing similar to that in the toadfish swimbladder muscle junctions has been identified (Franzini-Armstrong and Jorgensen, 1994).

The above results and discussion indicate that alternate groups of tetrads are the rule in RyR1-only junctions and are not directly associated with a two-RyR-isoform arrangement. Triad junctions that have only one RyR isoform (mammals, lizard, snakes, extraocular muscles of fish and birds) should appear similar to the toadfish swimbladder muscle. The body wall musculature or fast-twitch muscle of toadfish has two RyR isoform junctions. Two-isoform junctions, which are present in the majority of vertebrates, have several possible coupling conformations, one of which is depicted in Fig. 7. Non-mammalian junctions built on the two-isoform plan would, in this model, appear structurally similar to the one-isoform junctions, with every other RyR isoform (presumably α) forming a direct coupling with the DHPR. The obtaining of structural evidence for the alternate disposition of jT tetrads in a two-RyR isoform junction has been difficult. This is because freeze-fracture images as consistent as those from the toadfish swimbladder skeletal muscle are difficult to obtain because of the less-orderly arrangement of SR and T junctional membranes in other muscle types.

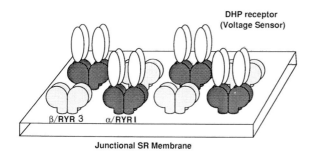

Figure 7. Schematic representation of a non-mammalian triad junction with two isoforms present. The CICR isoform would be the β RyR, which would amplify the voltage-dependent Ca^{2+} release from the direct-coupled α/RyR1.

A Two-Component Model for Calcium Release in Non-Mammals

The presence of two RyR isoforms (RyR1/α and RyR3/β) with different physiologies in most non-mammalian vertebrate skeletal muscles has important implications for the mechanism of Ca^{2+} release. Current models of skeletal muscle EC coupling invoke a direct mechanical coupling between the voltage-dependent, T-tubule DHPR or voltage sensor and the RyR1 as the mechanism for triggering SR Ca^{2+} release (Rios and Pizzaro 1991; Rios et al., 1993). However, the structural model of the triad junction implies that only half of the RyRs (all RyR1) in the triad may be mechanically coupled to DHPRs. The remaining RyRs were presumed either to couple cooperatively with the mechanically linked RyRs or to be silent. A model in which a portion of the RyRs are mechanically coupled while others are activated secondarily by Ca^{2+} released by the directly coupled channels agrees with the physiological properties of the two RyR isoforms identified in non-mammalian muscles. In Fig. 8, a two-component model for a two isoform junction is based upon the results of our lab and the physiological models of Rios and colleagues (Rios and Piz-

Two-component model of calcium release

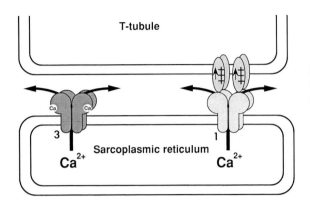

Figure 8. Two-component model for Ca^{2+} release after O'Brien et al. (1995).

zaro, 1991; Rios et al., 1993; O'Brien et al., 1995). The model accommodates data suggesting functionally separate SR Ca^{2+}-release channels in non-mammalian vertebrates as well as the alternating junctional complex (Block et al., 1988). Voltage-sensitive DHPRs are activated by depolarization, which in turn elicits Ca^{2+} release from the direct-coupled RyR, while adjacent SR Ca^{2+}-release channels are presumed to operate by calcium-induced Ca^{2+} release (CICR). Activation of one channel by voltage would result in the release of Ca^{2+} and thereby activate a neighboring "slave" channel. The approximately 30-nm distances between neighboring RyRs in a triad (Block et al., 1988) would allow for tight physiological coupling of the two types of channels. Our structural results indicate that in a two-component model the α RyR isoform of fish, which is homologous to the RyR1 of mammals, must be the RyR isoform directly coupled to the DHPR. The β isoform is a logical candidate to be the Ca^{2+}-coupled RyR isoform since it is a homologue of RyR3 and recent results of Takeshima et al. (1995) suggest it is a CICR type of RyR.

If one-half of the RyRs in all vertebrate triad junctions are cooperatively coupled to each other, the question arises: Why have two different RyR isoforms? The answer to this question is not clear, but there is evidence of evolutionary selection in the expression patterns of non-mammalian skeletal muscles that may offer a clue. The most prominent differences between the RyR1/α and RyR3/β isoforms is the sensitivity to both activation and inactivation by Ca^{2+}. It is possible in an all-RyR1 triad, neigboring RyR1s that are uncoupled to DHPRs open quicker (than RyR3 would in the same position) in response to trigger Ca^{2+} and close quicker in response to high Ca^{2+}. Both of these properties would create a shorter-duration Ca^{2+}-release event, which would enable the fiber to activate more quickly to a subsequent stimulation. An important point to resolve in this interpretation of the vertebrate triad is the role of alternate coupling in all-RyR1 triads. The model proposes that even in an all-RyR1 triad CICR is occurring.

How To Explain Alternate Couplings: Evolutionary Considerations

When one is synthesizing data from diverse species into models of skeletal muscle EC coupling, comparative data must be considered carefully both in a phylogenetic

and evolutionary perspective. Below we attempt to synthesize the available physiological, structural, and biochemical data from non-mammals and mammals. Our
goal is to provide a hypothesis that can explain the alternate coupling of the toadfish swimbladder muscle triad architecture, a one-RyR isoform junction, in light of
results indicating the presence of two isoforms in most non-mammalian muscle triads.

A major interest of the current EC coupling literature is the resolution of
whether or not all vertebrate skeletal muscles utilize the same mechanism for Ca^{2+}
release. That is, are all triad junctions built and functioning the same from fish to
mammals? Whole-fiber studies in amphibians as well as mammals have suggested
that dual regulation of Ca^{2+}-release pathways exists (Jacquemond et al., 1991; Csernoch et al., 1993). Results to date indicate that the majority of vertebrates construct
the triad junction of skeletal muscles with two physiologically distinct RyR isoforms, α and β, rather than one (O'Brien et al., 1993; O'Brien et al., 1995). Exceptions to the two-isoform condition include mammals, lizards, snakes, and the specialized fast-contracting muscles, all of which are built with one RyR isoform (α or
skeletal). How exactly the physiology of activation and inactivation of Ca^{2+} release
differs between a two-isoform junction and a one-isoform junction has not been established; however several results indicate there may be significant physiological
differences associated with the variation in RyR isoforms expressed in vertebrate
muscle (O'Brien et al., 1995). One problem in reconciling all the available data may
be related to this RyR isoform expression problem, and thus adoption of one paradigm for all vertebrate skeletal muscles may be incorrect. The mechanisms of signal
transduction at the triad junction have evolved over a long period of time, and to
understand fully how the mammalian coupling at SR/T junctions works we must
consider that evolutionary progression in signal transduction in the myofibril has
occurred. Our view is that an evolutionary perspective will offer insight into the
mechanisms of vertebrate EC coupling.

EC coupling is considered to be essentially the same in all vertebrates despite
the fact that non-mammalian vetebrates have two distinct populations of RyRs
(Airey et al., 1990; Olivares et al., 1991; Lai et al., 1992; Murayama and Ogawa,
1992; O'Brien et al., 1993; Bull and Marengo, 1993; Percival et al., 1994; O'Brien et
al., 1995). More recently, the expression of a single RyR isoform in mammalian
skeletal muscles is being called into question; while western blots with RyR-specific
antibodies indicate that mammals predominantly express a single RyR isoform,
molecular results as well as in situ hybridization studies suggest that mammalian
muscles transcribe small quantities of RyR3 (Gianinni et al., 1995). The selective
advantage provided by a skeletal muscle triad built with two isoforms, RyR1 and
RyR3 (non-mammals), versus a triad with reduced expression of RyR3 (mammalian) are not clear. Given that vertebrate skeletal muscle triads co-expressed two
RyR isoforms (1 and 3) for millions of years, it is important to discern how or if
RyR3 is down-regulated in mammals and certain reptiles.

How Did Primitive Vertebrate Muscles Release Calcium?

Invertebrates may offer some clues to the transitions that have taken place in the
evolution of signal transduction in primitive vertebrate skeletal muscles. Several
studies indicate that crustacean muscle contains the same molecular machinery for

EC coupling as vertebrate striated muscle. Most significant is that contraction in crustacean muscles requires depolarization-induced Ca^{2+} entry (reviewed by Palade and Gyorke, 1993). Only one isoform of the RyR has been isolated from invertebrate muscle (Seok et al., 1992), and its exact relationship to mammalian isoforms is unknown. Recent sequence data from the *Drosophila* RyR (Takeshima et al., 1994) has not clarified the homology of the invertebrate RyR. A key to understanding the evolution of the vertebrate triad is to establish whether the α (RyR1) or β (RyR3) isoform of non-mammals is more closely related to the invertebrate isoform sequenced from *Drosophila* muscle. The acquisition of more sequence data from primitive vertebrates is required to polarize the RyR gene family relationships between the mammalian isoforms of the RyR and the invertebrate RyR. However, the identification thus far of only one RyR isoform in invertebrate tissues and the numerous results indicating a requirement for external calcium for initiation of Ca^{2+} release from the SR in invertebrate muscles would indicate that the single invertebrate RyR isoform operates by CICR. Important clues to the transition in the signal transduction process from invertebrate to vertebrate muscles are revealed in the studies on early chordates (Benterbusch et al., 1992) such as amphioxus (*Branchiostoma lanceolatum*). The skeletal muscles of amphioxus exhibit voltage-sensitive Ca^{2+} release and are not dependent on influx of external Ca^{2+} for maintaining twitch kinetics (Melzer, 1982). In this way, the EC-coupling process in this early chordate does not differ greatly from that in vertebrate muscle preparations. However, several studies provide evidence that external Ca^{2+} fluxes modulate the release of intracellular Ca^{2+} from amphioxus muscle as if there has been retention of some aspects of a cardiac-like EC coupling apparatus (Hagiwara et al., 1971; Benterbusch, et al., 1992). The acquisition of some Ca^{2+} independency in EC coupling in the *Branchiostoma* twitch muscles indicates that at, or close to, this deep branch of the evolutionary tree giving rise to vertebrates, the molecules involved in direct coupling of surface membrane depolarization to Ca^{2+} release in skeletal muscle had evolved. We have amplified by PCR a 500-bp product from amphioxus using fish RyR1-specific primers (Keen et al., 1996). The deduced amino acid sequence corresponds to amino acid residues 4743–4898 in the rabbit RyR1 sequence and phylogenetic analyses cluster the amphioxus sequence with all published RyR1 sequences to date. Parsimony analysis indicates that the region sequenced is homologous with the RyR1 protein family, an observation supporting the physiological results and suggestive of a RyR isoform with the properties of the RyR1. The acquisition of the voltage-dependent mode of EC coupling in amphioxus does not imply the immediate loss of the CICR mode of EC coupling exhibited by invertebrates. The presence of two isoforms of the RyR in early vertebrates (sharks) suggests that both types of RyRs (CICR and voltage-dependent activation) were present in the SR during the evolutionary transition from CICR to voltage-activated Ca^{2+} release.

One possible selective reason for the switch from an invertebrate mode of Ca^{2+} influx-based activation to a voltage-gated Ca^{2+} release in muscle is a requirement for faster activation and precision control of muscle tension in vertebrates. Early triads of pre-chordates may have been composed of an invertebrate-like RyR isoform (perhaps like β). If β is more primitive, as the functional physiological studies would imply (i.e., β appears more similar to a CICR type of RyR than to a direct-coupled type), it would suggest that α evolved early on in vertebrate evolution, possibly from a gene duplication of β. This scenario implies that α might retain some properties of β, such as CICR, while acquiring new capabilities such as direct coupling and Ca^{2+}-dependent inactivation.

O'Brien et al. (1993) surveyed the non-mammalian vertebrates and established via western blotting techniques that the primitive or ancestral character state in vertebrates is to have both α and β RyR isoforms in skeletal muscles. These two RyR isoforms thus represent a period of vertebrate evolution in which dual regulation of Ca^{2+} release persisted for millions of years (CICR and voltage gated). Recognition that two forms of Ca^{2+} release persisted together in vertebrate triads, side by side, provides an intriguing way of fitting together several results that until now seemed contradictory.

The α and β RyR isoforms are present in the majority of vertebrates. The stable presence of two isoforms for an extended period of time in vertebrate history indicates that there is a selective advantage to the presence of both. That is, the fact that β was not eliminated at an early stage of vertebrate evolution would imply that the two isoforms together met the contractile needs of most vertebrate skeletal muscles. The only exceptions thus far identified are the super-fast contracting muscles of non-mammals and the skeletal muscles of lizards, snakes, and mammals (O'Brien, et al., 1993). The functional specialization of the super-fast contracting muscles leads to selection for expression of only the α isoform, presumably because there is some physiological characteristic of this isoform that is preferable for continuous, high-frequency contraction. We hypothesize that it is the sensitivity to Ca^{2+}-dependent activation and inactivation of the α or skeletal RyR isoform that may be the key selective advantage of this RyR isoform over β. The presence of an all α triad may be required to shut down Ca^{2+} release rapidly.

The structural arrangement of the triad junction is most easily explained in the context of dual regulation of Ca^{2+} release. Figs. 6 and 7 provide one model of a non-mammalian junction in which the α non-mammalian RyR is the isoform that forms a junctional complex with the T-tubular voltage sensors. The model of the two-isoform junction indicates that the α isoform requires contact with the T-tubular voltage sensors, while the β isoform does not (see also O'Brien et al., 1995). Activation of the β isoform in this model relies on its CICR properties, with Ca^{2+} released from the directly coupled α RyRs triggering Ca^{2+} release. In a two-isoform junction in which only the α RyR isoform is coupled to the T-tubule membrane DHPR, such as fast-twitch skeletal muscle of a frog, the positioning of the RyR isoforms as in Fig. 7 would result in an alternate pattern of coupling between the T-tubular voltage sensor and the α RyR.

When only the α isoform is expressed, as in toadfish swimbladder muscle or mammalian skeletal muscle, why would the alternate coupling pattern persist? That is, why are not all the α RyRs coupled to the T-tubule membrane? One hypothesis is that it is a vestige of the two-isoform state from which the vertebrate triad has evolved. The alternate coupling is a direct result of the evolution via a two-isoform stage where dual regulation of Ca^{2+} release persisted for hundreds of millions of years. It remains plausible that the α isoform, because of its possible evolution from the common ancestor of all RyRs (presumably a CICR type of RyR), may be able to couple physiologically both ways and thus it is not necessary that every α RyR interact directly with the DHPR. Activation of the α isoform via a voltage sensor would allow for rapid Ca^{2+}-channel opening directly controlled by the T-tubular membrane depolarization. Ca^{2+} release from the voltage-controlled channels would then trigger Ca^{2+} release from the neighbor RyR (30 nm apart) and would amplify the voltage-dependent Ca^{2+}-release event. Thus, voltage-dependent activation of one-half of the RyRs via direct coupling would immediately open all neighbor RyRs. This hypothesis suggests that the addition of more jT tetrads would not be necessary. The quick rise in the concentration of junctional cytoplasmic Ca^{2+} would also turn on the Ca^{2+}-dependent inactivation mechanism characteristic of the α isoform, shutting down Ca^{2+} release until the next depolarization event. The conservation of the stoichiometry of alternate coupling (which requires more proof) in a two-isoform junction (frog, bird, fish, or turtle) as well as a one-isoform junction, such as toadfish swimbladder and mammals, would imply that the presence of alternately coupled RyRs is suffcient to activate opening of all RyRs in a time course necessary for muscle contraction.

References

Adams, B.A., T. Tanabe, A. Mikami, S. Numa, and K.G. Beam. 1990. Intramembrane charge movement restored in dysgenic skeletal muscle by injection of dihydropyridine receptor cDNAs. *Nature (Lond.).* 346:569–572.

Airey, J.A., C.F. Beck, K. Murakami, S.J. Tanksley, T.J. Deerinck, M.H. Ellisman, and J.L. Sutko. 1990. Identification and localization of two triad junctional foot protein isoforms in mature avian fast twitch skeletal muscle. *J. Biol. Chem.* 265:14187–14194.

Airey, J.A., M.J. Rogers, and J.L. Sutko. 1991. Use of a reversible polyacrylamide gel cross-linker in western blotting for rapid transfer of a wide size range of polypeptides. *Biotechniques.* 10:605–608.

Appelt, D., V. Shen, and C. Franzini-Armstrong. 1991. Quantitation of Ca^{2+} ATPase, feet and mitochondria in superfast muscle fibres from the toadfish, *Opsanus tau. J. Muscle Res. Cell Motil.* 12:543–552.

Benterbusch, R., F.W. Herberg, W. Melzer, and R. Thieleczek. 1992. Excitation-contraction coupling in a pre-vertebrate twitch muscle: The myotomes of *Branchiostoma lanceolatum. J. Membr. Biol.* 129:237–252.

Block, B.A., T. Imagawa, K.P. Campbell, and C. Franzini-Armstrong. 1988. Structural evidence for direct interaction between the molecular components of the transverse tubule/sarcoplasmic reticulum junction in skeletal muscle. *J. Cell Biol.* 107:2587–2600.

Bull, R., and J.J. Marengo. 1993. Sarcoplasmic reticulum release channels from frog skeletal muscle display two types of calcium dependence. *FEBS Lett.* 331:223–227.

Chu, A., M. Diaz-Munoz, M.J. Hawkes, K. Brush, and S. L. Hamilton. 1990. Ryanodine as a probe of the functional state of the skeletal muscle sarcoplasmic reticulum calcium release channel. *Mol. Pharmacol.* 337:735–741.

Csernoch, L., V. Jacquemond, and M.F. Schneider. 1993. Microinjection of strong calcium buffers suppresses the peak of calcium release during depolarization in frog skeletal muscle fibers. *J. Gen. Physiol.* 101:297–333.

El-Hayek, R., B. Antoniu, J. Wang, S. Hamilton, and N. Ikemoto. 1995. *J. Biol. Chem.* 270:22116–22118.

Fawcett, D.W., and J.P. Revel. 1961. The sarcoplasmic reticulum of a fast-acting fish muscle. *J. Cell Biol.* 10:89–105.

Ferguson, D.G., H.W. Schwartz, and C. Franzini-Armstrong. 1984. Subunit structure of junctional feet in triads of skeletal muscle: A freeze-drying rotary-shadowing study. *J. Cell Biol.* 99:1735–1742.

Fleischer, S., E.M. Ogunbunmi, M.C. Dixon, and E.A.M. Fleer. 1985. Localization of Ca^{2+} release channels with ryanodine in junctional terminal cisternae of sarcoplasmic reticulum of fast skeletal muscle. *Proc. Natl. Acad. Sci. USA.* 82:7256–7259.

Flucher, B.E., J.L. Phillips, and J.A. Powell. 1991. Dihydropyridine receptor alpha subunits in normal and dysgenic muscle in vitro: Expression of alpha1 is required for proper targeting and distribution of alpha2. *J. Cell Biol.* 115:1345–1356.

Franck, J.P.C., J.E. Keen, R.L. Londraville, M.B. Beamsley, and B.A. Block. 1995. Evidence for the presence of a novel skeletal-like ryanodine receptor (RyR) isoform in striated muscle of fish. *Biophys. J.* 68:A50.

Franck, J.P.C., M. Beamsley, J.E. Keen, R.L. Londraville, and B.A. Block. 1994. Cloning and characterization of the ryanodine receptor α isoform from fish. *The Physiologist.* 37:A83.

Franzini-Armstrong, C. 1975. Membrane particles and transmission at the triad. *Fed. Proc.* 34:1382–1387.

Franzini-Armstrong, C., and A.O. Jorgensen. 1994. Structure and development of E-C coupling units in skeletal muscle. *Annu. Rev. Physiol.* 56:509–534.

Franzini-Armstrong, C., and G. Nunzi. 1983. Junctional feet and particles in the triads of a fast-twitch muscle fibre. *J. Muscle Res. Cell Motil.* 4:233–252.

Franzini-Armstrong, C., M. Pincon-Raymond, and F. Rieger. 1991. Muscle fibers from dysgenic mouse in vivo lack a surface component of peripheral couplings. *Dev. Biol.* 146:364–376.

Giannini, G., A. Conti, S. Mammarella, M. Scrobogna, and V. Sorrentino. 1995. The ryanodine receptor/calcium channel genes are widely and differentially expressed in murine brain and peripheral tissues. *J. Cell Biol.* 128:893–904.

Hagiwara, S., M.P. Henkart, and Y. Kidokoro. 1971. Na^{2+} and Ca^{2+} components of action potential in amphioxus muscle cells. *J. Physiol. (Lond.).* 219:217–232.

Hakamata, Y., J. Nakai, H. Takeshima, and K. Imoto. 1992. Primary structure and distribution of a novel ryanodine receptor/calcium release channel from rabbit brain. *FEBS Lett.* 312:229–235.

Hollingworth, S., A.B. Harkins, N. Kurebayashi, M. Konishi, and S.M. Baylor. 1992. Excitation-contraction coupling in intact frog skeletal muscle fibers injected with millimolar concentrations of fura-2. *Biophys. J.* 63:224–234.

Jacquemond, V., L. Csernoch, M.G. Klein, and M.F. Schneider. 1991. Voltage-gated and calcium-gated calcium release during depolarization of skeletal muscle fibers. *Biophys. J.* 60:867–873.

Keen, J.E., J.P.C. Franck, R.L. Londraville, S. Polgar, and B.A. Block 1996. Partial characterization of the channel region of ryanodine receptor isoforms: An evolutionary perspective. *Biophys. J.* 70:A165.

Lai, F.A., H.P. Erickson, E. Rousseau, Q.Y. Liu, and G. Meissner. 1988. Purification and reconstitution of the calcium release channel from skeletal muscle. *Nature (Lond.).* 331:315–319.

Lai, F.A., Q.-Y Liu, L. Xu, A. El-Hashem, N.R. Kramarcy, R. Sealock, and G. Meissner. 1992. Amphibian ryanodine receptor isoforms are related to those of mammalian skeletal and cardiac muscle. *Am. J. Physiol.* 263:C365–C372.

Lu, X., L. Xu, and G. Meissner. 1994. *J. Biol. Chem.* 269:6511–6516.

Meissner, G. 1994. Ryanodine receptor/Ca^{2+} release channels and their regulation by endogenous effectors. *Annu. Rev. Physiol.* 56:485–508.

Melzer, W. 1982. Twitch activation in Ca^{2+}-free solutions in the myotomes of the lancelet (*Branchiostoma lanceolatum*). *Eur. J. Cell Biol.* 28:219–225.

Michalak, M., P. Dupraz, and V. Shoshan-Barmatz. 1988. Ryanodine binding to sarcoplasmic reticulum membrane; comparison between cardiac and skeletal muscle. *Biochem. Biophys. Acta.* 939:587–594.

Murayama, T., and Y. Ogawa. 1992. Purification and characterization of two ryanodine-binding protein isoforms from sarcoplasmic reticulum of bullfrog skeletal muscle. *J. Biochem. (Tokyo).* 112:514–522.

O'Brien, J., G. Meissner, and B.A. Block. 1993. The fastest contracting skeletal muscles of non-mammalian vertebrates express only one isoform of the ryanodine receptor. *Biophys. J.* 65:2418–2427.

O'Brien, J., H.H. Valdivia, and B.A. Block. 1995. Physiological differences between the α and β ryanodine receptors of fish skeletal muscle. *Biophys. J.* 68:471–482.

Olivares, E.B., S.J. Tanksley, J.A. Airey, C. Beck, Y. Ouyang, T.J. Deerinck, M.H. Ellisman, and J.L. Sutko. 1991. Nonmammalian vertebrate skeletal muscles express two triad junctional foot protein isoforms. *Biophys. J.* 59:1153–1163.

Otsu, K., H.F. Willard, V.K. Khanna, F. Zorzato, N.M. Green, and D.H. MacLennan. 1990. Molecular cloning of cDNA encoding the Ca^{2+} release channel (ryanodine receptor) of rabbit cardiac muscle sarcoplasmic reticulum. *J. Biol. Chem.* 265:13472–13483.

Oyamada, H., T. Murayama, T. Takai, M. Iino, N. Iwabe, T. Miyata, Y. Ogawa, and M. Endo. 1994. Primary structure and distribution of ryanodine-binding protein isoforms of the bullfrog skeletal muscle. *J. Biol. Chem.* 269:17206–17214.

Palade, P., and S. Gyorke. 1993. Excitation-contraction coupling in crustacea: Do studies of these primitive creatures offer insights about EC coupling more generally? *J. Muscle Res. Cell Motil.* 14:283–287.

Pape, P.C., D.S. Jong, W.K. Chandler, and S.M. Baylor. 1993. Effect of fura-2 on action potential-stimulated calcium release in cut twitch fibers from frog muscle. *J. Gen. Physiol.* 102:295–332.

Percival, A.L., A.J. Williams, J.L. Kenyon, M.M. Grinsell, J.A. Airey, and J.L. Sutko. 1994. Chicken skeletal muscle ryanodine receptors isoforms: Ion channel properties. *Biophys. J.* 67:1834–1850.

Pessah, I.N., R.A. Stambuk, and J.E. Casida. 1987. Ca^{2+}-activated ryanodine binding: Mechanisms of sensitivity and intensity modulation by Mg^{2+}, caffeine, and adenine nucleotides. *Mol. Pharmacol.* 31:232–238.

Rios, E., and G. Brum. 1987. Involvement of dihydropyridine receptors in excitation-contraction coupling in skeletal muscle. *Nature (Lond.).* 325:717–720.

Rios, E., and G. Pizarro. 1991. Voltage sensor of excitation-contraction coupling in skeletal muscle. *Physiol. Rev.* 71:849–908.

Rios, E., M. Karhanek, J. Ma, and A. Gonzalez. 1993. An allosteric model of the molecular interactions of excitation-contraction coupling in skeletal muscle. *J. Gen. Physiol.* 102:449–481.

Schneider, M.F., and W.K. Chandler. 1973. Voltage dependent charge movement in skeletal muscle: A possible step in excitation-contraction coupling. *Nature (Lond.)*. 242:244–246.

Seok, J.-H., L. Xu, N.R. Kramarcy, R. Sealock, and G. Meissner. 1992. The 30S lobster skeletal muscle Ca^{2+} release channel (ryanodine receptor) has functional properties distinct from the mammalian channel proteins. *J. Biol. Chem.* 267:15893–15901.

Skoglund, C.R. 1961. Functional analysis of swim-bladder muscles engaged in sound production of the toadfish. *J. Biophys. Biochem. Cytol.* 10:187–200.

Smith, J.S., T. Imagawa, J. Ma, M. Fill, K.P. Campbell, and R. Coronado. 1988. Purified ryanodine receptor from rabbit skeletal muscle is the calcium-release channel of sarcoplasmic reticulum. *J. Gen. Physiol.* 92:1–26.

Takekura, H., L. Bennett, T. Tanabe, K.G. Beam, and C. Franzini-Armstrong. 1994. Restoration of junctional tetrads in dysgenic myotubes by dihydropyridine receptor cDNA. *Biophys. J.* 67:793–804.

Takeshima, H., S. Nishimura, T. Matsumoto, H. Ishida, K. Kangawa, N. Minamino et al. 1989. Primary structure and expression from complementary DNA of skeletal muscle ryanodine receptor. *Nature (Lond.)*. 339:439–445.

Takeshima, H., M. Nishi, N. Iwabe, T. Miyata, T. Hosoya, I. Masai, and Y. Hotta. 1994. Isolation and characterization of a gene for a ryanodine receptor/calcium release channel in Drosphila melanogaster. *FEBS Lett.* 337:81–87.

Takeshima, H., T. Yamazawa, T. Ikemoto, H. Takekura, M. Nishi, T. Noda, and I. Masamitsu. 1995. Ca^{2+}-induced Ca^{2+} release in myocytes from dyspedic mice lacking the type-1 ryanodine receptor. *EMBO (Eur. Mol. Biol. Organ.) J.* 14:2999–3006.

Tanabe, T., K.G. Beam, J.A. Powell, and S. Numa. 1988. Restoration of excitation-contraction coupling and slow calcium current in dysgenic muscle by dihydropyridine receptor complementary DNA. *Nature (Lond.)*. 336:134–139.

Valdivia, H.H., O. Fuentes, and B.A. Block. 1994. Imperatoxin A, a selective activator of skeletal ryanodine receptors RyR, distinguishes between α and β RyR isoforms in non-mammalian muscle. *Biophys. J.* 66:A418.

Zorzato, F., O. Fujii, K. Otsu, M. Phillips, N. Green, F.A. Lai, G. Meissner, and D. MacLennan. 1990. *J. Biol. Chem.* 265:2244–2256.

Functional Properties of Inositol 1,4,5-Trisphosphate Receptor and Ca^{2+} Signaling

Masamitsu Iino

Department of Pharmacology, Faculty of Medicine, The University of Tokyo, Bunkyo-ku, Tokyo 113, Japan

Introduction

Many types of agonist receptors, such as α-adrenergic and muscarinic receptors, transmit signals with inositol 1,4,5-trisphosphate (InsP$_3$) as the intracellular messenger (Berridge, 1993). InsP$_3$ is produced by the hydrolysis of phosphatidyl inositol 1,4-bisphosphate by a family of enzymes, phospholipase C (PLC). Upon binding of agonists, G-protein–coupled receptors and tyrosine-kinase receptors activate PLC-β and PLC-γ, respectively. InsP$_3$ is a hydrophilic product of the reaction and diffuses freely inside the cell without permeation through lipid membranes. InsP$_3$ then binds to the InsP$_3$ receptor (InsP$_3$R) on the endoplasmic reticulum, which is the major intracellular Ca^{2+} storage site. The InsP$_3$R functions as a Ca^{2+} channel, and the binding of InsP$_3$ induces the opening of the channel and the release of Ca^{2+} from the store (but see below).

The advent of fluorescent Ca^{2+} indicators and digital imaging techniques has enabled visualization of [Ca^{2+}]$_i$ change within a cell with subsecond time resolution. Recent studies have demonstrated complex spatio-temporal patterns of the InsP$_3$-induced Ca^{2+} release (Berridge and Irvine, 1989; Lechleiter and Clapham, 1992; Kasai and Petersen, 1994), which cannot be explained by the simple scheme that InsP$_3$ induces Ca^{2+} release as outlined in the previous paragraph. I would like to review our recent studies on the mechanism of complex kinetics of InsP$_3$-induced Ca^{2+} release and its physiologic significance.

Ca^{2+} Dependence of InsP$_3$R and Structural and Functional Similarities between InsP$_3$R and Ryanodine Receptor

In addition to the InsP$_3$R, there is another type of Ca^{2+}-release channel called the ryanodine receptor (RyR), which functions without InsP$_3$ and is explained fully in other sections of this book. Not only do both InsP$_3$R and RyR function as the Ca^{2+}-release channels on the ER, but they also show structural similarity. There are patches of homologous amino acid sequences in both Ca^{2+}-release channels (Furuichi et al., 1989; Mignery et al., 1989). Phylogenetic analysis indicates that these channels have derived from a prototype intracellular Ca^{2+}-release channel of eukaryotic cells (Takeshima et al., 1994). Furthermore, both form individual channel complexes as tetramers.

Long before structural kinship between the two Ca^{2+}-release channels was recognized, similarities between their functional properties had been discovered. The

Organellar Ion Channels and Transporters © 1996 by The Rockefeller University Press

most important property for both types of channels is their Ca^{2+} sensitivity. The RyR is known to function as a Ca^{2+}-induced Ca^{2+}-release (CICR) channel (Endo, 1977; Fleischer and Inui, 1989); i.e., an increase in cytoplasmic Ca^{2+} concentration at micromolar levels activates the channel activity of the RyR. In 1987, InsP$_3$-induced Ca^{2+} release in smooth muscle also was discovered to be enhanced by sub-micromolar concentrations of cytoplasmic Ca^{2+} (Iino, 1987). Later, the activity of the InsP$_3$R was found to depend on the cytoplasmic Ca^{2+} concentration in a biphasic manner with a peak near 300 nM (Iino, 1990). This property was then demonstrated in a wide variety of cells by use of different methods (Bezprozvanny et al., 1991; Finch et al., 1991; Parys et al., 1992; Tshipamba et al., 1993; Marshall and Taylor, 1993; Stehno-Bittel et al., 1995). Therefore, the Ca^{2+} dependence of the InsP$_3$R seems to be common to the various types of InsP$_3$ receptors. Ca^{2+} was found to have immediate effects on the rate of InsP$_3$-induced Ca^{2+} release in experiments in which caged InsP$_3$ and caged Ca^{2+} were used (Iino and Endo, 1992). Thus, the Ca^{2+} dependence of the InsP$_3$R is an important mechanism for the spatio-temporal regulation of Ca^{2+} release as discussed later.

We have recently developed a method to measure real-time change in the Ca^{2+} concentration in the lumen of the Ca^{2+} store by use of a low-affinity fluorescent Ca^{2+} indicator, Furaptra (Hirose and Iino, 1994). We re-examined the Ca^{2+} and InsP$_3$ concentration dependence of InsP$_3$-induced Ca^{2+} release rate. Our recent results indicate that InsP$_3$, even at very high concentrations, is not sufficient to activate the InsP$_3$R and that InsP$_3$ and Ca^{2+} are required concomitantly to activate the InsP$_3$R. In other words, the InsP$_3$R is a coincidence detector of InsP$_3$ and Ca^{2+}.

Another important modulator of the InsP$_3$R is ATP. It potentiates the activity of the InsP$_3$R (Ferris et al., 1990; Iino, 1991; Bezprozvanny and Ehrlich, 1993), while it seems to inhibit the InsP$_3$ binding at higher (millimolar) concentrations (Iino, 1991; Bezprozvanny and Ehrlich, 1993). It is also known that ATP enhances CICR from the RyR without changing the Ca^{2+} sensitivity (Endo, 1985). It has also been shown that the activity of both Ca^{2+}-release channels is inhibited at low pH (Endo, 1985; Tsukioka et al., 1994). Comparison of these functional properties clearly indicates that there are both structural and functional kinships between the two Ca^{2+}-release channels.

Role of Ca^{2+} Stores in Agonist-Induced Smooth Muscle Contraction

We addressed the question of the roles of the InsP$_3$R in physiologic functions. To examine the functional significance of the Ca^{2+}-release mechanism in smooth muscle contraction, we measured Ca^{2+}-concentration changes during carbachol (CCh)-induced contractions in enzymatically isolated intestinal smooth muscle cells (Fig. 1) (Iino et al., 1993). Almost no increase in the $[Ca^{2+}]_i$ (lag phase) was observed for a few seconds after the application of CCh in the absence of extracellular Ca^{2+}. This was followed by a slow rise in $[Ca^{2+}]_i$ (foot), then an abrupt increase in the rate of $[Ca^{2+}]_i$ rise (upstroke). A transition level of Ca^{2+} separated the foot and upstroke phases, and we termed it the critical concentration (CC). These $[Ca^{2+}]_i$ changes up to the peak of the Ca^{2+} transients were essentially the same with or without extracellular Ca^{2+}. Therefore, Ca^{2+} derived from internal stores can contribute significantly to the $[Ca^{2+}]_i$ rise during agonist activation and has a complex time course of change.

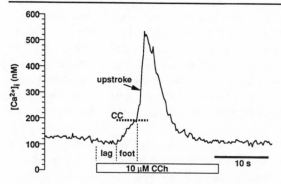

Figure 1. $[Ca^{2+}]_i$ response in an agonist-stimulated single smooth muscle cell in the absence of extracellular Ca^{2+}. Carbachol (*CCh*, 10 μM) was applied to a single cell obtained from guinea pig taenia caeci. A slow rise in $[Ca^{2+}]_i$ (foot) was observed up to the critical concentration (*CC*), after which a rapid upstroke of $[Ca^{2+}]_i$ was observed.

Ca²⁺ Waves in Single Smooth Muscle Cells

In an attempt to clarify the intracellular events underlying the complex kinetics of $[Ca^{2+}]_i$ change during agonist activation, we used a digital imaging technique to visualize spatio-temporal aspects of the Ca^{2+} transient. We found that $[Ca^{2+}]_i$ change propagated within the cell in a wave-like fashion. $[Ca^{2+}]_i$ in small areas within the cell also had the lag, foot, and upstroke phases similar to those measured in the entire cell region (Iino et al., 1993). These results suggest that the local Ca^{2+} concentration is important for the regulation of Ca^{2+} release and that there seems to be a Ca^{2+}-mediated regenerative mechanism.

These results can now be explained by the Ca^{2+} sensitivity of the $InsP_3R$. As the $InsP_3R$ functions as a coincidence detector, increase in the $InsP_3$ concentration alone is not sufficient for full activation of the $InsP_3$ receptor. However, if Ca^{2+} is released at a small local area, possibly via a stochastic process called a Ca^{2+} puff (Yao et al., 1995), then the Ca^{2+} release is expected to propagate, inducing a Ca^{2+}-mediated feedback process. Other Ca^{2+}-dependent mechanisms, such as RyR or PLC, have been proposed to underlie the Ca^{2+} waves. However, we have shown that the involvement of the RyR or the PLC in the feedback loop is unlikely, at least in smooth muscle cells (Iino et al., 1993). The same conclusion has been obtained for Ca^{2+} waves in vertebrate oocytes (Lechleiter and Clapham, 1992; Miyazaki et al., 1992; Galione et al., 1993).

As a consequence of the regenerative Ca^{2+} release, the peak height of the agonist-induced responses is rather constant even at different levels of agonist concentrations (Iino et al., 1993). In other words, agonist-induced Ca^{2+} release is an all-or-none phenomenon. This has led us to suspect that under certain conditions the contractile response of smooth muscle might be regulated by the number of responding cells rather than the degree of activation in each cell. To explore this possibility, we measured the $[Ca^{2+}]_i$ in individual cells within an intact tissue by use of a digital imaging technique.

Ca²⁺ Measurement in Vascular Wall

We isolated a rat tail artery with an outer diameter of ~300 μm. The artery was cleaned, and Fluo-3AM was loaded to the tissue. Then a rectangular glass capillary was inserted into the lumen of the artery to make the artery flat so that the layer of cells within the vascular wall could be examined by a confocal microscope (Fig. 2 *A*) (Iino et al., 1994). We were able to clearly discern three layers of cells. The innermost layer was composed of a monolayer of endothelial cells, which were surrounded by a single layer of circular smooth muscle cells. The connective tissue cells constituted the outermost layer. Staining of the tissue with 4-(4-diethylaminostyryl)-*N*-methylpyridium iodide, a fluorescent probe for nerve fibers (Magrassi et al., 1987), revealed a perivascular sympathetic nerve network within the connective tissue layer.

We observed fluorescence intensity changes within individual smooth muscle cells during electrical stimulation of the perivascular sympathetic nerve. As shown in Fig. 2 *B*, the $[Ca^{2+}]_i$ in the smooth muscle cells showed intermittent increases (Ca^{2+} oscillations) during the train of nerve stimulation. These Ca^{2+} transients were induced as the result of activation of the sympathetic nerve rather than direct activation of the smooth muscle cells because all the responses were blocked by 1 μM tetrodotoxin. With the addition of α or $α_1$ blockers (phentolamine or prazocin), all but the initial Ca^{2+} oscillations were abolished. The initial transient, which was in-

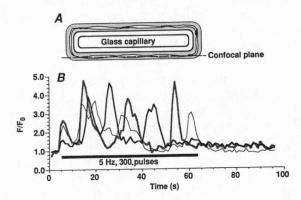

Figure 2. $[Ca^{2+}]_i$ measurement in individual vascular smooth muscle cells in situ. (*A*) Schematic drawing of the cross-sectional view of rat tail artery mounted over a glass capillary. (*B*) Changes in $[Ca^{2+}]_i$ in three different smooth muscle cells in response to electrical stimulation of the perivascular sympathetic nerve at 5 Hz (*horizontal line*).

sensitive to α blockers, was inhibited by 500 μM suramine, a P_{2X} receptor antagonist (Bao and Stjärne, 1993). We therefore think that the initial transient was induced by ATP, which was released as a co-transmitter from the sympathetic nerve endings, and that the following oscillations were due to norepinephrine. In accordance with this notion, we were able to observe similar Ca^{2+} oscillations upon application of 0.1–1 μM norepinephrine to the bath (Iino et al., 1994).

Interestingly, during each norepinephrine-induced oscillation, the $[Ca^{2+}]_i$ rise propagated within the cell in a wave-like manner. The velocity of the wave was typically ~20 μm/s, which was too low when compared with the propagation velocity of action potentials. The Ca^{2+} oscillations were abolished after depletion of the intracellular Ca^{2+} store by ryanodine (Iino et al., 1994). We were able to observe Ca^{2+} oscillations upon application of norepinephrine even in the absence of extracellular Ca^{2+}. However, in the absence of extracellular Ca^{2+}, Ca^{2+} oscillations took place only a few times and then completely disappeared. From these results, we conclude that Ca^{2+} release from intracellular Ca^{2+} stores is of fundamental importance to the Ca^{2+} oscillation. Ca^{2+} in the extracellular space is required for the maintenance of the Ca^{2+} oscillations, but Ca^{2+} influx through the plasma membrane is not the main pathway involved in each Ca^{2+} oscillation in smooth muscle cells.

General Discussion

From the first discovery of Ca^{2+} waves in medaka eggs (Gilkey et al., 1978) and Ca^{2+} oscillation in hepatocytes (Woods et al., 1986), the complex spatio-temporal patterns of Ca^{2+} rises stimulated a wide range of research. One of the important roles of Ca^{2+} waves/oscillation in eggs is to cause cortical granule exocytosis. However, the physiologic significance of Ca^{2+} waves/oscillation within tissues and organs has been rather obscure because these phenomena have been observed in isolated or cultured cells. We have shown in intact vascular wall that the Ca^{2+} response in smooth muscle cells during a physiologic stimulus by the innervating sympathetic nerve network takes place in the form of Ca^{2+} waves and oscillations (Iino et al., 1994). Smooth muscle contraction is mainly regulated by the level of myosin light chain phosphorylation, which is catalyzed by the Ca^{2+}-calmodulin–dependent myosin light chain kinase (for review see Somlyo and Somlyo, 1994). As dephosphorylation of myosin light chain takes time after a decrease in the $[Ca^{2+}]_i$, tension will not immediately follow the decrease in $[Ca^{2+}]_i$ and may decay with a considerable delay after the fall of $[Ca^{2+}]_i$. Therefore, the physiologic significance of the Ca^{2+} oscillation in smooth muscle cells may be to maintain force without a sustained increase in $[Ca^{2+}]_i$, which would have adverse effects on other cell functions.

Demonstration of Ca^{2+} waves and oscillation in physiologic responses indicates the importance of studying the mechanism of these processes. We believe that the Ca^{2+} requirement of the $InsP_3R$ is the most plausible candidate that accounts for the regenerative mechanism during the propagation of Ca^{2+} waves. The mechanism of Ca^{2+} oscillation, on the other hand, seems more complex. There must be a "delay line" within the system to explain intermittent release of Ca^{2+} from the internal stores. In some cells Ca^{2+} oscillation is dependent on the presence of extracellular Ca^{2+}. In those cell types Ca^{2+} extrusion from the cell and subsequent reuptake into the store may give rise to the delay line. However, in other cell types Ca^{2+} oscillation persists in the absence of extracellular Ca^{2+}, although extracellular Ca^{2+} is required for the maintenance of prolonged Ca^{2+} oscillation. Therefore, an intracellular delay line must exist.

Many mathematical models postulate time-dependent inactivation and repriming of the $InsP_3R$ to play the role of the delay process. Although several works have suggested the presence of time-dependent inactivation and recovery processes of the $InsP_3R$, we still do not have concrete evidence that the time-dependent inactivation mechanism of the $InsP_3R$ is present under physiologic conditions (Iino and Tsukioka, 1994; Hirose and Iino, 1994). We have shown that density of the $InsP_3R$ can be heterogeneous among different compartments of Ca^{2+} stores (Hirose and Iino, 1994). The heterogeneity in the channel density together with the cytoplasmic Ca^{2+} dependence of the $InsP_3R$ can bring about an apparently complex time course of $InsP_3$-induced Ca^{2+} release without inactivation mechanisms (Hirose and Iino, 1994).

Our next goal, therefore, would be to clarify the Ca^{2+} oscillation mechanism. This would contribute to our understanding of many physiologic processes. It will also help us understand pathophysiologic or pharmacologic aspects of important biologic functions.

Acknowledgments

This work was supported by a Grant-in-Aid for Scientific Research from the Ministry of Education, Science and Culture, Japan and a research grant from the Mitsubishi Foundation.

References

Bao, J.-X., and L. Stjärne. 1993. Dual contractile effects of ATP released by field stimulation revealed by effects of α,β-methylene ATP and suramine in rat tail artery. *Br. J. Pharmacol.* 110:1421–1428.

Berridge, M.J. 1993. Inositol trisphosphate and calcium signalling. *Nature (Lond.).* 361:315–325.

Berridge, M.J., and R.F. Irvine. 1989. Inositol phosphates and cell signalling. *Nature (Lond.).* 341:197–205.

Bezprozvanny, I., and B. Ehrlich. 1993. ATP modulates the function of inositol 1,4,5-trisphosphate-gated channels at two sites. *Neuron.* 10:1175–1184.

Bezprozvanny, I., J. Watras, and B.E. Ehrlich. 1991. Bell-shaped calcium-response curve of $Ins(1,4,5)P_3$- and calcium-gated channels from endoplasmic reticulum of cerebellum. *Nature (Lond.).* 351:751–754.

Endo, M. 1977. Calcium release from the sarcoplasmic reticulum. *Physiol. Rev.* 57:71–108.

Endo, M. 1985. Calcium release from sarcoplasmic reticulum. *Curr. Top. Membr. Trans.* 25:181–230.

Ferris, C., R. Huganir, and S. Snyder. 1990. Calcium flux mediated by purified inositol 1,4,5-trisphosphate receptor in reconstituted lipid vesicles is allosterically regulated by adenine nucleotides. *Proc. Natl. Acad. Sci. USA.* 87:2147–2151.

Finch, E.A., T.J. Turner, and S.M. Goldin. 1991. Calcium as a coagonist of inositol 1,4,5-trisphosphate-induced calcium release. *Science (Wash. DC).* 252:443–252.

Fleischer, S., and M. Inui. 1989. Biochemistry and biophysics of excitation-contraction coupling. *Ann. Rev. Biophys. Biophys. Chem.* 18:333–364.

Furuichi, T., S. Yoshikawa, A. Miyawaki, K. Wada, N. Maeda, and K. Mikoshiba. 1989. Primary structure and functional expression of the inositol 1,4,5-trisphosphate-binding protein P_{400}. *Nature (Lond.).* 342:32–38.

Galione, A., A. McDougall, W. Busa, N. Willmott, I. Gillot, and M. Whitaker. 1993. Redundant mechanisms of calcium-induced calcium release underlying calcium waves during fertilization of sea urchin eggs. *Science (Wash. DC).* 261:348–352.

Gilkey, J., L. Jaffe, E. Ridgway, and G. Reynolds. 1978. A free calcium wave traverses the activating egg of the medaka, *Orizias laptis. J. Cell Biol.* 76:448–466.

Hirose, K., and M. Iino. 1994. Heterogeneity of channel density in inositol 1,4,5-trisphosphate-sensitive Ca^{2+} stores. *Nature (Lond.).* 372:791–794.

Iino, M. 1987. Calcium dependent inositol trisphosphate-induced calcium release in the guinea-pig taenia caeci. *Biochem. Biophys. Res. Commun..* 142:47–52.

Iino, M. 1990. Biphasic Ca^{2+} dependence of inositol 1,4,5-trisphosphate-induced Ca release in smooth muscle cells of the guinea pig taenia caeci. *J. Gen. Physiol.* 95:1103–1122.

Iino, M. 1991. Effects of adenine nucleotides on inositol 1,4,5-trisphosphate–induced calcium release in vascular smooth muscle cells. *J. Gen. Physiol.* 98:681–698.

Iino, M., and M. Endo. 1992. Calcium-dependent immediate feedback control of inositol 1,4,5-trisphosphate-induced Ca²⁺ release. *Nature (Lond.).* 360:76–78.

Iino, M., T. Yamazawa, Y. Miyashita, M. Endo, and H. Kasai. 1993. Critical intracellular Ca²⁺ concentration for all-or-none Ca²⁺ spiking in single smooth muscle cells. *EMBO J.* 12:5287–5291.

Iino, M., and M. Tsukioka. 1994. Feedback control of inositol trisphosphate signalling by calcium. *Mol. Cell. Endocrinol.* 98:141–146.

Iino, M., H. Kasai, and T. Yamazawa. 1994. Visualization of neural control of intracellular Ca²⁺ concentration in single vascular smooth muscle cells in situ. *EMBO J.* 13:5026–5031.

Kasai, H., and O. Petersen. 1994. Spatial dynamics of second messengers: IP₃ and cAMP as long-range and associative messengers. *Trends Neurosci.* 17:95–101.

Lechleiter, J.D., and D.E. Clapham. 1992. Molecular mechanisms of intracellular calcium excitability in *X. laevis* oocytes. *Cell.* 69:283–294.

Magrassi, L., D. Purves, and J.W. Lichman. 1987. Fluorescent probes that stain living nerve terminals. *J. Neurosci.* 7:1207–1214.

Marshall, I.C.B., and C.W. Taylor. 1993. Biphasic effects of cytosolic Ca²⁺ on Ins(1,4,5)P₃-stimulated Ca²⁺ mobilization in hepatocytes. *J. Biol. Chem.* 268:13214–13220.

Mignery, G.A., T.C. Südhof, K. Takei, and P. De Camilli. 1989. Putative receptor for inositol 1,4,5-trisphosphate similar to ryanodine receptor. *Nature (Lond.).* 342:192–195.

Miyazaki, S., M. Yuzaki, K. Nakada, H. Shirakawa, S. Nakanishi, S. Nakade, and K. Mikoshiba. 1992. Block of Ca²⁺ wave and Ca²⁺ oscillation by antibody to the inositol 1,4,5-trisphosphate receptor in fertilized hamster eggs. *Science (Wash. DC).* 257:251–255.

Parys, J.B., S.W. Sernett, S. DeLisle, P.M. Snyder, M.J. Welsh, and K.P. Campbell. 1992. Isolation, characterization, and localization of the inositol 1,4,5-trisphosphate receptor protein in *Xenopus laevis* oocytes. *J. Biol. Chem.* 267:18776–18782.

Somlyo, A., and A. Somlyo. 1994. Signal transduction and regulation in smooth muscle. *Nature (Lond.).* 372:231–236.

Stehno-Bittel, L., A. Lückhoff, and D. Clapham. 1995. Calcium release from the nucleus by InsP₃ receptor channels. *Neuron.* 14:163–167.

Takeshima, H., M. Nishi, N. Iwabe, T. Miyata, T. Hosoya, I. Masai, and Y. Hotta. 1994. Isolation and characterization of a gene for a ryanodine receptor/calcium release channel in *Drosophila melanogaster.* *FEBS Lett.* 337:81–87.

Tshipamba, M., H. DeSmedt, L. Missiaen, B. Himpens, L. Van den Bosch, and R. Borghgraef. 1993. Ca²⁺ dependence of inositol 1,4,5-trisphosphate-induced Ca²⁺ release in renal epithelial LLC-PK₁ cells. *J. Cell. Physiol.* 155:96–103.

Tsukioka, M., M. Iino, and M. Endo. 1994. pH dependence of inositol 1,4,5-trisphosphate-induced Ca²⁺ release in permeabilized smooth muscle cells of the guinea-pig. *J. Physiol.* 485:369–375.

Woods, N.M., K.S.R. Cuthbertson, and P.H. Cobbold. 1986. Repetitive transient rises in cytoplasmic free calcium in hormone-stimulated hepatocytes. *Nature (Lond.).* 319:600–602.

Yao, Y., J. Choi, and I. Parker. 1995. Quantal puffs of intracellular Ca²⁺ evoked by inositol trisphosphate in *Xenopus* oocytes. *J. Physiol.* 482:533–553.

Inositol (1,4,5)-Trisphosphate Receptors: Functional Properties, Modulation, and Role in Calcium Wave Propagation

Ilya Bezprozvanny

Department of Molecular and Cellular Physiology, Beckman Center, Stanford University Medical Center, Stanford, California 94305

Introduction

Inositol (1,4,5)-trisphosphate receptors ($InsP_3R$) play a major role in intracellular Ca^{2+} signaling in many cell types (Berridge, 1993) and have been a subject of intense investigation using a variety of biochemical, molecular biological, and biophysical techniques (for recent reviews see Taylor and Richardson, 1991; Ferris and Snyder, 1992; Furuichi et al., 1994; Bezprozvanny and Ehrlich, 1995). Extensive characterization of $InsP_3R$ functional properties at the single-channel level was obtained when cerebellar $InsP_3R$ was reconstituted into planar lipid bilayers (Bezprozvanny et al., 1991; Watras et al., 1991; Bezprozvanny and Ehrlich, 1993; Bezprozvanny and Ehrlich, 1994; reviewed in Bezprozvanny and Ehrlich, 1995). In the first part of this chapter, recently characterized conduction properties of $InsP_3R$ (Bezprozvanny and Ehrlich, 1994) are compared with the conduction properties of other calcium channels.

$InsP_3R$ displays a bell-shaped dependence on the cytosolic free Ca^{2+} level (Iino, 1990; Bezprozvanny et al., 1991; Finch et al., 1991). This property of the $InsP_3R$ is of fundamental importance for understanding of complex spatiotemporal characteristics of intracellular Ca^{2+} signaling, such as Ca^{2+} waves and oscillations (De Young and Keizer, 1992; Lechleiter and Clapham, 1992; Berridge, 1993). In this analysis regulation of $InsP_3R$ by Ca^{2+} may be accounted for by use of a simplified four-state gating model of $InsP_3R$ (Bezprozvanny, 1994). When this model was used in the analysis of Ca^{2+} wave properties in *Xenopus* oocytes, analytical expressions for the amplitude of Ca^{2+} wave and the Ca^{2+}-wave propagation velocity were obtained (Bezprozvanny, 1994). The second part of this chapter is devoted to discussion of these results and their potential implications for Ca^{2+} signaling in various cell types on the basis of recent estimations of $InsP_3R$ density (Parys and Bezprozvanny, 1995).

$InsP_3R$ Conduction Properties

The conduction properties of $InsP_3R$ for divalent cations were studied in detail in channels reconstituted into planar lipid bilayers (Bezprozvanny and Ehrlich, 1994). All four alkaline earth cations tested were able to pass through the $InsP_3R$ (Fig. 1) with a current amplitude and single-channel conductance that ranged from 2.2 pA and 85 pS (with Ba^{2+} as a charge carrier) to 1.1 pA and 42 pS (with Mg^{2+} as a

Organellar Ion Channels and Transporters © 1996 by The Rockefeller University Press

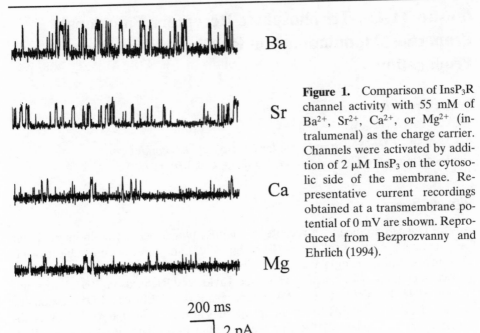

Figure 1. Comparison of InsP$_3$R channel activity with 55 mM of Ba^{2+}, Sr^{2+}, Ca^{2+}, or Mg^{2+} (intralumenal) as the charge carrier. Channels were activated by addition of 2 μM InsP$_3$ on the cytosolic side of the membrane. Representative current recordings obtained at a transmembrane potential of 0 mV are shown. Reproduced from Bezprozvanny and Ehrlich (1994).

charge carrier). The permeability sequence was Ba^{2+} > Sr^{2+} > Ca^{2+} > Mg^{2+}. When InsP$_3$R activity was recorded with a mixture of Ba^{2+} and Mg^{2+}, the size of the single-channel current was a monotonic function of Mg^{2+}/Ba^{2+} molar ratios without evidence of the anomalous mole-fraction effect. From a recording of InsP$_3$R activity in the presence of cytosolic K$^+$, a $P_{Ba/K}$ permeability ratio of 6.3 was estimated by use of the Goldman-Hodgkin-Katz equation. It is concluded from these results that InsP$_3$R is a relatively nonselective cationic, single-ion pore channel.

InsP$_3$R conduction properties are compared with properties of other known Ca^{2+} channels in Table I. It is striking that InsP$_3$R is very similar in selectivity and permeation properties to the ryanodine receptor (RyanR), another intracellular Ca^{2+}-release channel. In contrast, the rank order of conductances for divalent cations, selectivity against monovalent cations, and the mechanism of ion permeation for InsP$_3$R and RyanR differ dramatically from plasma membrane voltage-gated

TABLE I
Comparison of Permeation and Selectivity Properties of Ca^{2+} Channels

Channel	Conductance	AMFE	$P_{Div/Mon}$
RyanR*	Ba > Sr > Ca > Mg	no	6.0
InsP$_3$R‡	Ba > Sr > Ca > Mg	no	6.3
L-type§	Ba > Sr = Ca >> Mg	yes	> 1,200
I$_{CRAC}$	Ca > Ba = Sr >> Mg‖	yes¶	> 2,000‖¶

*Tinker and Williams, 1992.
‡Bezprozvanny and Ehrlich, 1994.
§Hess et al., 1986.
‖Premack et al., 1994.
¶Hoth, 1995.

Ca^{2+} channels, exemplified by L-type channels, and depletion-activated Ca^{2+} channels (I_{CRAC}).

One noticeable difference between intracellular and plasma membrane Ca^{2+} channels is the ability of Mg^{2+} to carry substantial currents through intracellular Ca^{2+}-release channels (Tinker and Williams, 1992; Bezprozvanny and Ehrlich, 1994). This fact is especially striking given the very high hydration energy and extremely slow substitution rate of water molecules in the inner hydration shell of Mg^{2+} ions. One possible explanation of this observation is that when Mg^{2+} ions pass through the selectivity filters of both intracellular Ca^{2+} channels, they are able to maintain an inner shell of water molecules; this implies a fairly wide permeation pore for both the InsP₃R and RyanR.

The anomalous mole fraction effect is observed in the presence of a mixture of divalent cations for both the L-type Ca^{2+} channel (Almers and McClesky, 1984; Hess and Tsien, 1984; Tsien et al., 1987) and I_{CRAC} (Hoth, 1995). The anomalous mole fraction effect is indicative of a multi-ion mechanism of permeation in these channels. Indeed, a two-site model proposed for voltage-gated channels (Almers and McClesky, 1984; Hess and Tsien, 1984; Tsien et al., 1987) described Ca^{2+} permeation as a result of electrical repulsion between Ca^{2+} ions bound within the pore. The fact that both InsP₃R and RyanR lack the anomalous mole fraction effect suggests that the mechanism of ion selectivity of these channels does not require the simultaneous presence of two ions in the pore.

It is tempting to speculate that the underlying reason for differences in conduction properties between intracellular Ca^{2+} channels and Ca^{2+} channels in the plasma membrane relate to differences in the ionic compositions of intraluminal, cytosolic, and extracellular media. Indeed, under physiological conditions there is no gradient for K^+ and Na^+ across the intracellular Ca^{2+}-store membrane (Somlyo et al., 1977). The current through RyanR and InsP₃R is carried largely by Ca^{2+} because of the large electrochemical gradient for Ca^{2+} across sarcoplasmic reticulum or endoplasmic reticulum membrane. Thus, in vivo InsP₃R and RyanR are able to function as Ca^{2+} channels despite a relatively low selectivity for divalent over monovalent cations ($P_{Div/Mon} < 10$) (Smith et al., 1988; Liu et al., 1989; Tinker and Williams, 1992; Bezprozvanny and Ehrlich, 1994; Mak and Foskett, 1994; Stehno-Bittel et al., 1995). Voltage-gated Ca^{2+} channels open in response to depolarizing action potentials when the electrical potential across the plasma membrane is close to zero. However, there is a very significant chemical gradient for Na^+ ions to enter the cell and for K^+ ions to leave the cell. Thus, the voltage-gated Ca^{2+} channels must discriminate against Na^+ and K^+ ions to avoid large fluxes of monovalent cations at every opening of a channel. Indeed, for voltage-gated Ca^{2+} channels $P_{Div/Mon} > 1200$ (Lee and Tsien, 1984; Hess et al., 1986). Whereas voltage-gated Ca^{2+} channels open only during a brief action potential, depletion-activated Ca^{2+} channels (I_{CRAC}) remain active for extended periods of time in order to replenish intracellular Ca^{2+} stores. These channels normally function at resting membrane potentials, close to the equilibrium potential for K^+. At these potentials Na^+ ions are driven into the cell by a combination of electrical and chemical gradients and the task of discriminating against Na^+ ions is even more important for I_{CRAC} than for voltage-gated Ca^{2+} channels. Indeed, I_{CRAC} channels appear to be very selective for divalent versus monovalent cations ($P_{Ca/Na} > 2000$) (Hoth and Penner, 1992; Hoth and Penner, 1993; Premack et al., 1994). It is also not surprising that the single-channel conductance of these channels is very small (less than 1 pS; Zweifach and Lewis, 1993) since Ca^{2+} must bind very tightly in the channel pore (Hoth and Penner, 1993; Premack et al., 1994).

The main physiological function of Ca^{2+} channels is to conduct Ca^{2+} ions into the cytosol. It is of interest to compare the ability of different Ca^{2+} channel types to perform this function. No consensus has been reached so far regarding the value of the free Ca^{2+} concentration in the lumen of intracellular Ca^{2+} stores, but for the sake of comparison, let us assume that the intraluminal free Ca^{2+} concentration is equal to 2.5 mM. If this value is taken, then the estimated amplitude for the single-channel current is 0.5 pA for the $InsP_3R$ (Bezprozvanny and Ehrlich, 1994) and 2.0 pA for the cardiac RyanR (Tinker et al., 1993). For L-type channels the estimated amplitude of the single-channel current at 2.5 mM extracellular free Ca^{2+} is 0.09 pA (Hess et al., 1986). The mean open time is ~4 ms for the $InsP_3R$ (Bezprozvanny and Ehrlich, 1994), ~ 20 ms for the RyanR (Smith et al., 1986), and ~1 ms for the L-type Ca^{2+} channels in the absence of DHP agonists (Hess et al., 1986). It follows from these values (Table II) that at every opening of RyanR, over 100,000 Ca^{2+} ions enter the cytosol, ~ 20-fold more than for each opening of the $InsP_3R$. Although the absolute numbers of Ca^{2+} ions in these estimates depend on the assumed level of intralumenal free Ca^{2+} concentration, the relative difference between RyanR and $InsP_3R$ does not. One can speculate that the coexistence of two intracellular Ca^{2+} channel types activated via different mechanisms allows the cell to choose between two modes of Ca^{2+} release—rapid dumping of accumulated Ca^{2+} through the RyanR channel (as in skeletal or cardiac muscle) or slow leakage through the $InsP_3R$ (as in smooth muscle). It also follows from Table II that only 260 Ca^{2+} ions enter the cell with each opening of L-type channel. Perhaps intracellular Ca^{2+} channels are important for global Ca^{2+} signaling, often in the form of Ca^{2+} waves and oscillations, whereas voltage-gated Ca^{2+} channels are better suited for local and rapid change in Ca^{2+} as, for example, during synaptic transmission and cardiac excitation-contraction coupling.

Regulation of the $InsP_3R$ by Ca^{2+} and Ca^{2+} Waves

The $InsP_3R$ is regulated by pH (Worley et al., 1987; Tsukioka et al., 1994), ATP (Ferris et al., 1990; Iino, 1991; Bezprozvanny and Ehrlich, 1993), and phosphoryla-

TABLE II
Comparison of the Ability of Three Types of Ca^{2+} Channels to Deliver Ca^{2+} into the Cytoplasm

Channel	I (pA)	τ (ms)	Ca^{2+}/Single opening
RyanR	2.0*	~ 20[‡]	117,000
$InsP_3R$[§]	0.5	~4	5,400
L-type[‖]	0.09	~1	260

*Tinker et al., 1993.
[‡]Smith et al., 1986.
[§]Bezprozvanny and Ehrlich, 1994.
[‖]Hess et al., 1986.

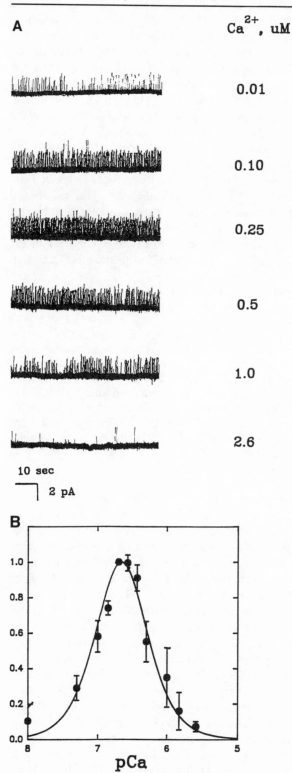

A

Ca^{2+}, uM

0.01

0.10

0.25

0.5

1.0

2.6

10 sec

2 pA

B

pCa

Figure 2. Bell-shaped Ca^{2+} dependence of the InsP₃R in planar lipid bilayers. (*A*) Channels were activated by addition of 2 μM InsP₃ and 330 μM AMP-PCP. Free Ca^{2+} on the cytosolic side of the membrane was clamped by the mixture of 1 mM EGTA and 1 mM HEEDTA. Free cytosolic Ca^{2+} concentration (indicated in μM Ca^{2+} at the right of each record) was calculated according to Fabiato (1988). Data are shown on a compressed time scale. (*B*) Open channel probability of the InsP₃R is plotted versus the free cytosolic Ca^{2+}. In each experiment, the open channel probability was normalized to the maximum open probability (less than 15%) and the data from four independent experiments were pooled. Modified from Bezprozvanny et al., 1991.

tion (Supattapone et al., 1988; Ferris et al., 1991). Notably, InsP$_3$R is also modulated by cytosolic Ca^{2+} in a biphasic manner (Iino, 1990; Parker and Ivorra, 1990; Bezprozvanny et al., 1991; Finch et al., 1991; Yao and Parker, 1992). When the effects of cytoplasmic Ca^{2+} on InsP$_3$R activity were monitored in planar lipid bilayers (Bezprozvanny et al., 1991), a bell-shaped Ca^{2+}-dependence curve was obtained with maximum open probability at 200–300 nM free Ca^{2+} (Fig. 2). The single-channel open probability of InsP$_3$R decreased sharply on both sides of the maximum with the entire curve falling within physiologic range of cytosolic Ca^{2+}.

Although the bell-shaped dependence of InsP$_3$R on cytosolic Ca^{2+} is likely to be important for its physiologic function, it should be realized that the curve was obtained as the result of measurements of channel activity at fixed cytosolic Ca^{2+} levels. In vivo InsP$_3$R responds to rapid changes in cytosolic Ca^{2+}. The response of single InsP$_3$R to rapid changes in cytosolic Ca^{2+} has not been measured in bilayer experiments. However, a simplified four-state model of InsP$_3$R gating by Ca^{2+} (Bezprozvanny, 1994) may be used for prediction of the InsP$_3$R behavior in the course of rapid changes in cytosolic Ca^{2+}. It is postulated in this model (Fig. 3) that

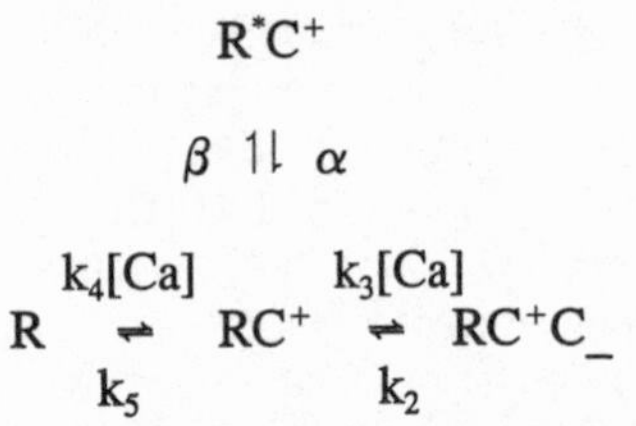

$$R^*C^+$$

$$\beta \updownarrow \alpha$$

$$R \underset{k_5}{\overset{k_4[Ca]}{\rightleftharpoons}} RC^+ \underset{k_2}{\overset{k_3[Ca]}{\rightleftharpoons}} RC^+C_-$$

Figure 3. Simplified four-state model of InsP$_3$R regulation by cytosolic Ca^{2+} (Bezprozvanny, 1994). State R is the InsP$_3$R without Ca^{2+} bound, state RC^+ is the InsP$_3$R with Ca^{2+} bound to the activating site, state RC^+C_- is the InsP$_3$R with Ca^{2+} bound to both activating and inhibitory sites and R^*C^+ is the open state of the channel. It is postulated that the channel can open only when Ca^{2+} is bound to the activating site and cannot open when Ca^{2+} is bound to the inhibitory site. InsP$_3$ is bound to the InsP$_3$R in all four states of the model. The model is based on the bell-shaped Ca^{2+} dependence of InsP$_3$R (Iino, 1990; Parker and Ivorra, 1990; Bezprozvanny et al., 1991; Finch et al., 1991; Yao and Parker, 1992), but it is simplified since several activating and inhibitory sites are present in the InsP$_3$R complex (Bezprozvanny et al., 1991).

there are two Ca^{2+}-binding sites on the InsP$_3$R: one activating site ($+$) and one inhibitory site ($-$). InsP$_3$R can open only when Ca^{2+} is bound to the activating site but not to the inhibitory site. It is also postulated that Ca^{2+} first binds to the activating site and then it can bind to the inhibitory site. It is assumed that InsP$_3$ is bound to InsP$_3$R in all four states of the model, so channel gating is determined completely by changes in cytosolic Ca^{2+}. This model will adequately predict the bell-shaped Ca^{2+} dependence of InsP$_3$R under steady-state conditions (Fig. 2), and it can be used for the analysis of complex spatiotemporal patterns in Ca^{2+} signaling.

Ca^{2+}-imaging techniques revealed that, in many instances, stimulation of the InsP$_3$-signaling pathway caused repetitive Ca^{2+} waves propagating through the cytoplasm of the cell or periodic oscillations in the cytosolic Ca^{2+} level (for reviews see Tsien and Tsien, 1990; Meyer, 1991; Meyer and Stryer, 1991; Rooney and Thomas, 1993; Clapham and Sneyd, 1995). *Xenopus* oocytes are used extensively for the studies of Ca^{2+} waves (Parker and Ivorra, 1990; Lechleiter et al., 1991; Parker and Yao, 1991; DeLisle and Welsh, 1992; Lechleiter and Clapham, 1992; Parker and Ivorra, 1993). As *Xenopus* oocytes have only InsP$_3$-sensitive Ca^{2+} stores (Parys et al., 1992), the properties of Ca^{2+} waves in oocytes are determined by the functional properties of InsP$_3$R. It is generally accepted that the bell-shaped Ca^{2+} dependence of the InsP$_3$R (Fig. 2) is critical for Ca^{2+}-wave propagation in *Xenopus* oocytes (De Young and Keizer, 1992; Lechleiter and Clapham, 1992; Atri et al., 1993; Othmer and Tang, 1993; Clapham and Sneyd, 1995).

Several simplifying assumptions are useful in modeling Ca^{2+}-wave propagation in *Xenopus* oocytes. Let us assume that InsP$_3$Rs are distributed homogeneously in the oocyte cytoplasm with a density γ, expressed as the number of InsP$_3$Rs per unitary volume of cytoplasm. Let us also assume that each individual receptor behaves according to the four-state gating model (Fig. 3) and InsP$_3$ concentration is high, such that all InsP$_3$ binding sites are saturated. Theoretical analysis of Ca^{2+}-wave propagation process based on these assumptions (Bezprozvanny, 1994) leads to the derivation of an analytical expression for the unique value of Ca^{2+}-wave amplitude possible in this system:

$$Ca^{2+} \text{ wave amplitude} = c = [i \times \beta \times \gamma \times B / 2\alpha \times k_3 \times F]^{1/2} \qquad (1)$$

where i is the single channel current amplitude for the InsP$_3$R, β and α are the rate constants of the InsP$_3$R opening and closing (Fig. 3), k_3 is the on-rate of Ca^{2+} binding to the inhibitory site of the InsP$_3$R, γ is the InsP$_3$R density, B is the buffering capacity of the cytosol determined as the ratio of d[Ca^{2+}]/d[Ca$_{total}$] and F is the Faraday constant. Thus, the amplitude of the Ca^{2+} wave is determined by the combination of cell-specific characteristics (γ and B) and the functional properties of single InsP$_3$R (i, β, α, k_3).

It is more difficult to derive an analytical equation for the velocity of Ca^{2+}-wave propagation. However, the semi-empirical Luther equation, useful in the analysis of diffusion-driven autocatalytic reactions (Jaffe, 1991), allows an approximate estimation for the Ca^{2+}-wave velocity in this model (Bezprozvanny, 1994):

$$\text{Velocity} = v \simeq [D \times c \times k_3 / (1 + \beta/\alpha)]^{1/2} \qquad (2)$$

where D is the diffusion coefficient for Ca^{2+} in the oocyte cytosol, and c is the Ca^{2+} wave amplitude. It follows from equation (2) that the Ca^{2+} wave amplitude determines the velocity of the wave propagation, but because the Ca^{2+} diffusion coefficient depends on cytosolic free Ca^{2+} (Allbritton et al., 1992), it is not a simple square-root dependence.

Single-channel properties of *Xenopus* oocyte InsP$_3$R (Mak and Foskett, 1994; Stehno-Bittel et al., 1995) are remarkably similar to the properties of cerebellar InsP$_3$R (Bezprozvanny and Ehrlich, 1995; Parys and Bezprozvanny, 1995). Thus, the values of the rate constants and the size of the single-channel current determined in planar lipid bilayer experiments with cerebellar InsP$_3$R (Bezprozvanny and Ehrlich, 1994) can be used in numerical calculations of Ca^{2+} wave amplitude and velocity in *Xenopus* oocytes. Ca^{2+} buffering of *Xenopus* oocyte cytoplasm has been characterized (Allbritton et al., 1992). The density of InsP$_3$Rs in *Xenopus* oocytes was estimated to be in the range 1.1–4.1 × 10^{14} InsP$_3$Rs/liter on the basis of radiolabeled InsP$_3$ binding measurements (Parys et al., 1992; Parys and Bezprozvanny, 1995). If numerical values of parameters are used, then the Ca^{2+} wave amplitude (equation 1) is predicted to fall in the range between 0.8 μM and 1.5 μM Ca^{2+}, and the velocity of the wave propagation (equation 2) is between 12 μm/s and 24 μm/s. The predicted characteristics of Ca^{2+} waves are in a good agreement with the data reported for Ca^{2+} waves in *Xenopus* oocytes (Lechleiter et al., 1991; Parker and Yao, 1991; Lechleiter and Clapham, 1992).

Although theoretical analysis of Ca^{2+} wave propagation was performed with the *Xenopus* oocyte model system in mind (Bezprozvanny, 1994), it is also of interest to determine the predictions of the model for Ca^{2+} waves in other cell types. Endogenous Ca^{2+} buffering capacity of neuronal cells was determined in experiments with bovine chromaffin cells (Neher and Augustine, 1992). An exceptionally high density of $InsP_3Rs$ in Purkinje cells of cerebellum ($\sim 9 \times 10^{18}$ $InsP_3Rs$/liter; Parys and Bezprozvanny, 1995) results in a very high value for the predicted Ca^{2+} wave amplitude (82 μM Ca^{2+}) and velocity of Ca^{2+} wave propagation (250 μm/sec). Indeed, flash photolysis of caged $InsP_3$ in a single Purkinje cell evoked extremely fast and massive Ca^{2+} release from intracellular stores with an amplitude > 30 μM Ca^{2+} (Khodakhah and Ogden, 1993). The physiologic significance of very high $InsP_3Rs$ density and the amplitude of Ca^{2+} spike in Purkinje cells remains a fascinating mystery. In other neuronal cells the $InsP_3R$ density is ~ 1000-fold less than in Purkinje cells (Parys and Bezprozvanny, 1995). For these cells the model predicts a Ca^{2+} wave amplitude of 2.6 μM Ca^{2+} and a velocity of wave propagation of ~ 40 μm/s—in reasonable agreement with experimental observations (Jaffe and Brown, 1994; Yagodin et al., 1994).

Conclusions

1. $InsP_3R$ is a relatively nonselective cation channel. The conduction properties of the $InsP_3R$ are very similar to the properties of the RyanR and in dramatic contrast with the properties of plasma membrane Ca^{2+} channels (voltage-gated or I_{CRAC}). Differences in conduction properties between intracellular Ca^{2+} release channels and plasma membrane Ca^{2+} channels could be understood on the basis of differences in the ionic composition of extracellular, cytosolic, and intraluminal compartments.

2. The number of Ca^{2+} ions released into the cytosol with every channel opening is ~ 20-fold less for the $InsP_3R$ than for the RyanR. Therefore, coexistence of two intracellular Ca^{2+} channels enables the cell to exploit two modes of Ca^{2+} release—very rapid release through RyanR (as in skeletal and cardiac muscle) and a much slower and more tightly regulated release through $InsP_3R$ (as in smooth muscle). Both intracellular Ca^{2+} channels are estimated to be much more potent in their ability to increase cytosolic Ca^{2+} than voltage-gated Ca^{2+} channels. Thus, one can imagine that intracellular Ca^{2+} channels are important for a global Ca^{2+} signaling by a massive increase in cytosolic Ca^{2+} and/or Ca^{2+} waves and oscillations mechanisms, whereas voltage-gated Ca^{2+} channels are better suited for local and rapid changes in Ca^{2+} concentration as, for example, during synaptic transmission or cardiac excitation-contraction coupling.

3. Under steady-state conditions the $InsP_3R$ displays a bell-shaped Ca^{2+} dependence within the physiologic range of cytosolic Ca^{2+} concentrations with a maximum at 200–300 nM Ca^{2+}. A simplified four-state model of $InsP_3R$ gating is postulated to account for $InsP_3R$ modulation by Ca^{2+}. This model is able to predict the behavior of $InsP_3R$ in response to rapid changes in cytosolic free Ca^{2+} and is useful in the analysis of complex spatiotemporal patterns in Ca^{2+} signaling.

4. Analytical equations for the amplitude and velocity of Ca^{2+} waves in *Xenopus* oocytes are derived with the use of the four-state model of $InsP_3R$ gating by

Ca²⁺. These equations result in reasonable estimations of Ca^{2+} wave amplitude (0.8–1.5 μM Ca^{2+}) and velocity (12–24 μm/s) for *Xenopus* oocytes. These results can be extrapolated to other cell types, such as, for example, Purkinje cells of cerebellum and other neuronal cells.

Acknowledgments

I am thankful to Dr. Barbara Ehrlich for support, helpful discussions, and permission to use the results from Bezprozvanny et al. (1991) and Bezprozvanny and Ehrlich (1994). I am grateful to Svetlana Bezprozvannaya for her continuous support of my work.

This work was supported by National Institutes of Health (NIH) grants HL 33026 and GM 39029 (Dr. Barbara Ehrlich), NIH training grant HL 07740 (Dr. Ilya Bezprozvanny), and by the Russian Academy of Sciences (Dr. Ilya Bezprozvanny).

References

Allbritton, N.L., T. Meyer, and L. Stryer. 1992. Range of messenger action of calcium ion and inositol 1,4,5-trisphosphate. *Science (Wash. DC)*. 258:1812–1815.

Almers, W., and E.W. McCleskey. 1984. Non-selective conductance in calcium channels in frog muscle: calcium selectivity in a single-file pore. *J. Physiol.* 353:585–608.

Atri, A., J. Amundson, D. Clapham, and J. Sneyd. 1993. A single-pool model for intracellular calcium oscillations and waves in the *Xenopus laevis* oocyte. *Biophys. J.* 65:1727–1739.

Berridge, M.J. 1993. Inositol trisphosphate and calcium signalling. *Nature (Lond.)*. 361:315–325.

Bezprozvanny, I. 1994. Theoretical analysis of calcium wave propagation based on inositol (1,4,5)-trisphosphate (InsP₃) receptor functional properties. *Cell Calcium.* 16:151–166.

Bezprozvanny, I., and B.E. Ehrlich. 1993. ATP modulates the function of inositol 1,4,5-trisphosphate-gated channels at two sites. *Neuron.* 10:1175–1184.

Bezprozvanny, I., and B.E. Ehrlich. 1994. Inositol (1,4,5)-trisphosphate (InsP₃)-gated Ca channels from cerebellum: conduction properties for divalent cations and regulation by intraluminal calcium. *J. Gen. Physiol.* 104:821–856.

Bezprozvanny, I., and B.E. Ehrlich. 1995. The inositol 1,4,5-trisphosphate (InsP₃) receptor. *J. Membr. Biol.* 145:205–216.

Bezprozvanny, I., J. Watras, and B.E. Ehrlich. 1991. Bell-shaped calcium-response curves of Ins(1,4,5)P₃- and calcium-gated channels from endoplasmic reticulum of cerebellum. *Nature.* 351:751–754.

Clapham, D.E., and J. Sneyd. 1995. Intracellular calcium waves. *Adv. Second Messenger Phosphoprotein Res.* 30:1–24.

De Young, G.W., and J. Keizer. 1992. A single pool IP₃-receptor-based model for agonist stimulated Ca^{2+} oscillations. *Proc. Natl. Acad. Sci. USA.* 89:9895–9899.

DeLisle, S., and M.J. Welsh. 1992. Inositol trisphosphate is required for the poropagation of calcium waves in *Xenopus* oocytes. *J. Biol. Chem.* 267:7963–7966.

Fabiato, A. 1988. Computer programs for calculating total from specified free or free from specified total ionic concentrations in aqueous solutions containing multiple metals and ligands. *Meth. Enzymol.* 157:378–417.

Ferris, C.D., R.L. Huganir, D.S. Bredt, A.M. Cameron, and S.H. Snyder. 1991. Inositol tris-phosphate receptor—phosphorylation by protein kinase-C and calcium calmodulin-dependent protein kinases in reconstituted lipid vesicles. *Proc. Natl. Acad. Sci. USA.* 88:2232–2235.

Ferris, C.D., R.L. Huganir, and S.H. Snyder. 1990. Calcium flux mediated by purified inositol 1,4,5-trisphosphate receptor in reconstituted lipid vesicles is allosterically regulated by adenine nucleotides. *Proc. Natl. Acad. Sci. USA.* 87:2147–2151.

Ferris, C.D., and S.H. Snyder. 1992. Inositol phosphate receptors and calcium disposition in the brain. *J. Neurosci.* 12:1567–1574.

Finch, E.A., T.J. Turner, and S.M. Goldin. 1991. Calcium as a coagonist of inositol 1,4,5-trisphosphate-induced calcium release. *Science.* 252:443–446.

Furuichi, T., K. Kohda, A. Miyawaki, and K. Mikoshiba. 1994. Intracellular channels. *Curr. Opin. Neurobiol.* 4:294–303.

Hess, P., J.B. Lansman, and R.W. Tsien. 1986. Calcium channel selectivity for divalent and monovalent cations. *J. Gen. Physiol.* 88:293–319.

Hess, P., and R.W. Tsien. 1984. Mechanism of ion permeation through calcium channels. *Nature.* 309:453–456.

Hoth, M. 1995. Calcium and barium permeation through calcium release-activated calcium (CRAC) channels. *Pflügers Arch.* 430:315–322.

Hoth, M., and R. Penner. 1992. Depletion of intracellular calcium stores activates a calcium current in mast cells. *Nature.* 355:353–356.

Hoth, M., and R. Penner. 1993. Calcium release-activated calcium current in rat mast cells. *J. Physiol.* 465:359–386.

Iino, M. 1990. Biphasic Ca^{2+} dependence of inositol 1,4,5-trisphosphate-induced Ca release in smooth muscle cells of the guinea pig *Taenia caeci. J. Gen. Physiol.* 95:1103–1122.

Iino, M. 1991. Effects of adenine nucleotides on inositol 1,4,5-trisphosphate-induced calcium release in vascular smooth muscle cells. *J. Gen. Physiol.* 98:681–698.

Jaffe, D., and T. Brown. 1994. Metabotropic glutamate receptor activation induces calcium waves within hippocampal dendrites. *J. Neurophysiol.* 72:471–474.

Jaffe, L.F. 1991. The path of calcium in cytosolic calcium oscillations—a unifying hypothesis. *Proc. Natl. Acad. Sci. USA.* 88:9883–9887.

Khodakhah, K., and D. Ogden. 1993. Functional heterogeneity of calcium release by inositol trisphosphate in single Purkinje neurones, cultured cerebellar astrocytes, and peripheral tissues. *Proc. Natl. Acad. Sci. USA.* 90:4976–4980.

Lechleiter, J., S. Girard, E. Peralta, and D. Clapham. 1991. Spiral calcium wave propagation and annihilation in *Xenopus laevis* oocytes. *Science.* 252:123–126.

Lechleiter, J.D., and D.E. Clapham. 1992. Molecular mechanisms of intracellular calcium excitability in *X. laevis* oocytes. *Cell.* 69:283–294.

Lee, K.S., and R.W. Tsien. 1984. High selectivity of calcium channels in single dialyzed heart cells of the guinea-pig. *J. Physiol.* 354:253–272.

Liu, Q.-Y., F.A. Lai, E. Rousseau, R.V. Jones, and G. Meissner. 1989. Multiple conductance states of the purified calcium release channel complex from skeletal sarcoplasmic reticulum. *Biophys. J.* 55:415–424.

Mak, D.D., and J.K. Foskett. 1994. Single-channel inositol 1,4,5-trisphosphate receptor currents revealed by patch clamp of isolated *Xenopus* oocyte nuclei. *J. Biol. Chem.* 269:29375–29378.

Meyer, T. 1991. Cell signalling by second messenger waves. *Cell.* 64:675–678.

Meyer, T., and L. Stryer. 1991. Calcium spiking. *Annu. Rev. Biophys. Biophys. Chem.* 20:153–174.

Neher, E., and G.J. Augustine. 1992. Calcium gradients and buffers in bovine chromaffin cells. *J. Physiol.* 450:273–301.

Othmer, H.G., and Y. Tang. 1993. Oscillations and waves in a model of InsP₃-controlled calcium dynamics. *In* Experimental and Theoretical Advances in Biological Pattern Formation. H.G. Othmer, editor. Plenum Press, New York. 277–299.

Parker, I., and I. Ivorra. 1990. Inhibition by Ca^{2+} of inositol trisphosphate-mediated Ca^{2+} liberation: A possible mechanism for oscillatory release of Ca^{2+}. *Proc. Natl. Acad. Sci. USA.* 87:260–264.

Parker, I., and I. Ivorra. 1993. Confocal microfluorimetry of Ca signals evoked in *Xenopus* oocytes by photoreleased inositol trisphosphate. *J. Physiol.* 461:133–165.

Parker, I., and Y. Yao. 1991. Regenerative release of calcium from functionally discrete subcellular stores by inositol trisphosphate. *Proc. Royal Soc. B (Lond.).* 246:269–274.

Parys, J.B., and I. Bezprozvanny. 1995. The inositol trisphosphate receptor of *Xenopus* oocytes. *Cell Calcium.* 18:353–363.

Parys, J.B., S.W. Sernett, S. DeLisle, P.M. Snyder, M.J. Welsh, and K.P. Campbell. 1992. Isolation, characterization and localization of the inositol 1,4,5-trisphosphate receptor protein in *Xenopus laevis* oocytes. *J. Biol. Chem.* 267:18776–18782.

Premack, B.A., T.V. McDonald, and P. Gardner. 1994. Activation of Ca^{2+} current in Jurkat T cells following the depletion of Ca^{2+} stores by microsomal Ca^{2+}-ATPase inhibitors. *J. Immunol.* 152:5226–5240.

Rooney, T.A., and A.P. Thomas. 1993. Intracellular calcium waves generated by Ins(1,4,5)P₃-dependent mechanisms. *Cell Calcium.* 14:674–690.

Smith, J., R. Coronado, and G. Meissner. 1986. Single channel measurements of the calcium release channel from skeletal muscle sarcoplasmic reticulum. Activation by Ca^{2+} and ATP and modulation by Mg^{2+}. *J. Gen. Physiol.* 88:573–588.

Smith, J.S., T. Imagawa, J. Ma, M. Fill, K.P. Campbell, and R. Coronado. 1988. Rurified ryanodine receptor from rabbit skeletal muscle is the calcium release-channel of sarcoplasmic reticulum. *J. Gen. Physiol.* 92:1–26.

Somlyo, A.V., H. Shuman, and A.P. Somlyo. 1977. Elemental distribution in striated muscle and effects of hypertonicity: electron probe analysis of cryosections. *J. Cell Biol.* 74:828–857.

Stehno-Bittel, L., A. Luckhoff, and D.E. Clapham. 1995. Calcium release from the nucleus by InsP₃ receptor channels. *Neuron.* 14:163–167.

Supattapone, S., S.K. Danoff, A. Theibert, S.K. Joseph, J. Steiner, and S.H. Snyder. 1988. Cyclic AMP-dependent phosphorylation of a brain inositol trisphosphate receptor decreases its release of calcium. *Proc. Natl. Acad. Sci. USA.* 85:8747–8750.

Taylor, C.W., and A. Richardson. 1991. Structure and function of inositol trisphosphate receptors. *Pharmacol. Therapeut.* 51:97–137.

Tinker, A., A.R.G. Lindsay, and A.J. Williams. 1993. Cation conduction in the calcium release channel of the cardiac sarcoplasmic reticulum under physiological and pathophysiological conditions. *Cardiovascular Res.* 27:1820–1825.

Tinker, A., and A.J. Williams. 1992. Divalent cation conduction in the ryanodine receptor of sheep cardiac muscle sarcoplasmic reticulum. *J. Gen. Physiol.* 100:479–493.

Tsien, R.W., P. Hess, E.W. McCleskey, and R.L. Rosenberg. 1987. Calcium channels: mechanisms of selectivity, permeation, and block. *Ann. Rev. Biophys. Biophys. Chem.* 16:265–290.

Tsien, R.W., and R.Y. Tsien. 1990. Calcium channels, stores and oscillations. *Annu. Rev. Cell. Biol.* 6:715–760.

Tsukioka, M., M. Iino, and M. Endo. 1994. pH Dependence of inositol 1,4,5-trisphosphate-induced Ca^{2+} release in permeabilized smooth muscle cells of the guinea-pig. *J. Physiol.* 475:369–375.

Watras, J., I. Bezprozvanny, and B.E. Ehrlich. 1991. Inositol 1,4,5-trisphosphate-gated channels in cerebellum—presence of multiple conductance states. *J. Neurosci.* 11:3239–3245.

Worley, P.F., J.M. Baraban, S. Supattapone, V. Wilson, and S.H. Snyder. 1987. Characterization of inositol trisphosphate receptor binding in brain. *J. Biol. Chem.* 262:12132–12136.

Yagodin, S.V., L. Holtzclaw, C.A. Sheppard, and J. Russell. 1994. Nonlinear propagation of agonist-induced cytoplasmic calcium waves in single astrocytes. *J. Neurobiol.* 25:265–280.

Yao, Y., and I. Parker. 1992. Potentiation of inositol trisphosphate-induced Ca^{2+} mobilization in *Xenopus* oocytes by cytosolic Ca^{2+}. *J. Physiol.* 458:319–338.

Zweifach, A., and R.S. Lewis. 1993. The mitogen-regulated calcium current of T lymphocytes is activated by depletion of intracellular calcium stores. *Proc. Natl. Acad. Sci. USA.* 90:6295–6299.

Chapter 2

Intracellular Pumps and Channels in the Endoplasmic Reticulum

Regulatory Interactions between Calcium ATPases and Phospholamban

David H. MacLennan and Toshihiko Toyofuku

Banting and Best Department of Medical Research, University of Toronto, Charles H. Best Institute, Toronto, Ontario, Canada M5G1L6

Ca^{2+} Regulation

Ca^{2+} release into muscle cells is responsible for the activation of muscle contraction, while its removal results in muscle relaxation (Ebashi et al., 1969; Zot and Potter, 1987). In heart, Ca^{2+} enters through a slow Ca^{2+} channel in the plasma membrane (the dihydropyridine receptor), triggering Ca^{2+}-induced Ca^{2+} release through the Ca^{2+}-release channel of the sarcoplasmic reticulum (the ryanodine receptor) (Fabiato, 1983). In skeletal muscle, Ca^{2+} is recycled within the muscle cells and Ca^{2+} entry from external sources is not important (Fleischer and Inui, 1989; Catterall, 1991). Ca^{2+} is removed from cardiac muscle cells through the combined actions of sarcoplasmic or endoplasmic reticulum Ca^{2+} ATPases (SERCA-type pumps), calmodulin-activated plasma membrane Ca^{2+} ATPases (PMCA-type pumps), plasma membrane Na^{+}/Ca^{2+} exchangers, and, potentially, through the Ca^{2+}-uptake system of the mitochondria (Carafoli, 1987). In skeletal muscle, Ca^{2+} is sequestered by the action of the SERCA pumps, with very little loss of sarcoplasmic Ca^{2+} to the exterior of the cell. Of the systems for Ca^{2+} removal from the sarcoplasm, the SERCA and PMCA pumps have the highest affinity for Ca^{2+} and ultimately set the resting Ca^{2+} level in the cell.

Function of SERCA Pumps

SERCA pumps are asymmetrically oriented, transmembrane proteins of about 1,000 amino acids, with a mass of about 110 kD. They form a phosphoprotein intermediate during the course of ATP hydrolysis and alternate among a series of conformations (de Meis and Vianna, 1979; Inesi and Kirtley, 1990). By definition, E$_1$ conformations have high affinity for Ca^{2+} and can be phosphorylated by ATP to form a high energy phosphorylated intermediate, E$_1$P. E$_2$ conformations have a low affinity for Ca^{2+} and can be phosphorylated by inorganic phosphate (Pi), in the absence of Ca^{2+}, to form a low-energy phosphorylated intermediate, E$_2$P. The proteins bind 2 moles of Ca^{2+} with high affinity and 1 mole of ATP per mole of protein. Binding of the two Ca^{2+} ions is cooperative, and the two Ca^{2+} binding steps can be resolved (Inesi, 1987). The two Ca^{2+} ions, bound from the cytoplasmic surface, are stacked and are released to the lumenal surface through the same narrow channel (Forge et al., 1995; Inesi, 1987). Phosphoenzyme formation from ATP is dependent on the occupation of these two Ca^{2+} binding sites (de Meis and Vianna, 1979; Petithory and Jencks, 1988). E$_1$P is initially of high energy and capable of catalyzing

Organellar Ion Channels and Transporters © 1996 by The Rockefeller University Press

ATP/ADP exchange. Ca^{2+}, which is bound initially with high affinity and is readily exchangeable, is rapidly occluded, probably through conformational changes surrounding the Ca^{2+} binding sites (Takisawa and Makinose, 1981). As the phosphoenzyme decays to the low-energy E_2P form, the tightly occluded state relaxes so that the affinity of the Ca^{2+}-binding site is reduced by 3 orders of magnitude and Ca^{2+} is released to the lumenal surface. H^+ ions have been shown to be counter-transported by the Ca^{2+} ATPase (Yu et al., 1993). Presumably, H^+ ions replace Ca^{2+} ions in the amino acids to which Ca^{2+} is bound. The final steps in the Ca^{2+} translocation process consist of hydrolytic cleavage of the phosphoenzyme and reformation of its high-affinity Ca^{2+} binding sites. The entire process is reversible (Makinose and Hasselbach, 1971). Rate constants for measurable steps in the translocation of Ca^{2+} from the cytoplasmic to the lumenal surface have been calculated (Inesi, 1985; Cantilina et al., 1993).

Structure and Function of SERCA Pumps

As a result of our cloning and sequencing of cDNAs encoding Ca^{2+} ATPases (MacLennan et al., 1985; Brandl et al., 1986), we proposed the existence in SERCA molecules of 10 transmembrane sequences, 4 in the NH_2-terminal quarter and 6 in the COOH-terminal quarter. These transmembrane sequences, M1 to M10, would comprise 5 transmembrane hairpin loops making up the transmembrane sector, with NH_2 and COOH-termini in the cytoplasm (Reithmeier and MacLennan, 1981; Matthews et al., 1989). M1, M3, and M5 are contiguous with long-predicted α-helices at their NH_2-terminal ends, while M2 and M4 are contiguous with similar α-helices at their COOH-termini. These five amphipathic, cytoplasmic, α-helices were predicted to make up a stalk sector. A headpiece sector was proposed to be made up from 4 domains, a β-strand domain, lying between stalk sequences S2 and S3, and a kinase-like domain lying between stalk sequences S4 and S5 and consisting approximately of residues Asn^{330} to Asp^{738}. This cytoplasmic domain could be further resolved into a phosphorylation domain, linked directly to a nucleotide-binding domain by a short loop and indirectly by a COOH-terminal "hinge" domain, which would extend from the nucleotide-binding domain back into the phosphorylation domain. The structure of the Ca^{2+} pump at 14-Å resolution (Toyoshima et al., 1993) is fully consistent with our model.

We have used site-directed mutagenesis to confirm the assignment of the phosphorylation domain (Maruyama and MacLennan, 1988; Maruyama et al., 1989). Mutation of residues proposed by Taylor and Green (1989) to lie in loops involved in ATP binding has supported the essentiality of these specific residues for Ca^{2+} transport (Clarke et al., 1990b). We have also shown that Ca^{2+}-binding and transport sites are composed of six acidic or polar residues located near the centers of transmembrane sequences M4, M5, M6, and M8 (Clarke et al., 1989; Clarke et al., 1990a; Clarke et al., 1993; Andersen et al., 1992). Helices M4, M5, M6, and M8 must lie adjacent to each other to form the transmembrane channel through which Ca^{2+} is pumped. Glu^{309}, Asn^{796}, and Asp^{800} contribute to the more cytoplasmic Ca^{2+}-binding site, while Glu^{771}, Thr^{799}, Asp^{800}, and Glu^{908} contribute to the second Ca^{2+}-binding site (Andersen and Vilsen, 1992; Vilsen and Andersen, 1992a; Vilsen and Andersen, 1992b; Skerjanc et al., 1993; Andersen and Vilsen, 1994).

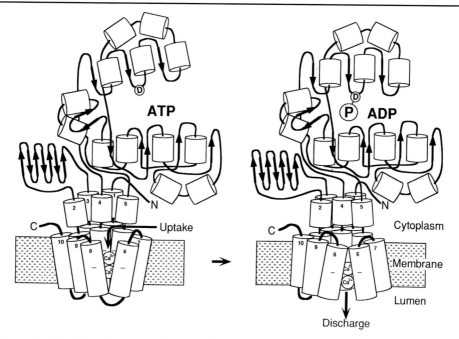

Figure 1. Model for the mechanism of Ca^{2+} transport by the Ca^{2+}-ATPase. In the E_1 conformation, high affinity Ca^{2+} binding sites located near the center of the transmembrane domain are accessible to cytoplasmic Ca^{2+}, but not to luminal Ca^{2+}. The sites are made up from amino acid residues located in proposed transmembrane sequences M4, M5, M6, and M8. Conformational changes induced by Ca^{2+}-dependent phosphorylation of Asp^{351} by ATP in the cytoplasmic domain lead to the E_2 conformation in which the high-affinity Ca^{2+} binding sites are disrupted, access to the sites by cytoplasmic Ca^{2+} is closed off, and access to the sites by luminal Ca^{2+} is gained. The Ca^{2+} transport cycle thus involves binding of cytoplasmic Ca^{2+} to high-affinity sites in one conformation and release of the same Ca^{2+} to the lumen when the high affinity sites are disrupted in the transition to the second conformation. (Reprinted from MacLennan et al., 1992a, with permission from *Acta Physiologica Scandinavica*).

Structural and functional studies are consistent with a mechanism (MacLennan, 1990) in which long-range interactions between the ATP hydrolytic (catalytic) site in the headpiece and the Ca^{2+}-binding and transport site in the transmembrane sequence are an integral feature of Ca^{2+} transport (Fig. 1). In the E_1 conformation, the Ca^{2+}-binding sites are accessible from the cytoplasm, they are inaccessible to the lumen, and they have very high affinity. When the protein is phosphorylated from ATP, a series of conformational changes (Bigelow and Inesi, 1992) must begin in the headpiece sector and be transmitted over a very long distance to the Ca^{2+}-transport site. Conformational changes in the Ca^{2+}-transport site result in the occlusion of Ca^{2+} so that Ca^{2+} becomes inaccessible to either the cytoplasm or the lumen. As the conformational changes progress, energy in the high-energy phosphoryl bond, which is initially capable of phosphorylating ADP, is used up in conformational movement and the enzyme moves into a series of lower-energy E_2 conformations. In the E_2 form, the Ca^{2+}-binding sites are altered. They now have

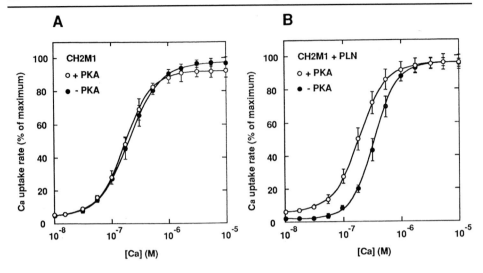

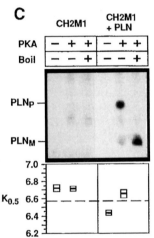

Figure 2. Effects of cAMP-dependent protein kinase on phospholamban-dependent alterations in Ca^{2+} dependence of Ca^{2+} transport by chimeric Ca^{2+}-ATPase molecule. The chimeric molecule CH2M1 was constructed in two steps. It was a SERCA2 molecule substituted with residues 336–412 of SERCA3. The sequence QGEQL[401] was further substituted with the corresponding SERCA2 sequence, KDDKP[401]. Ca^{2+} dependence of Ca^{2+} uptake rate was measured in microsomes from cDNA-transfected HEK-293 cells. Microsomes were preincubated with (*open circles*) and without (*closed circles*) 25 units of the catalytic subunit of cAMP-dependent protein kinase (PKA). *A* and *B* show the effects of PKA on Ca^{2+} dependence of Ca^{2+} uptake rates for CH2M1. Each point with a bar represents the mean ± S.D. obtained from three experiments. In *C*, microsomes prepared from HEK-293 cells were preincubated with [γ-^{32}P]ATP in the absence and presence of PKA. Phosphorylated microsomes were subjected to SDS-polyacrylamide gel electrophoresis in 13.5% polyacrylamide, with or without boiling. The effects of PKA on $K_{0.5}$ for Ca^{2+} dependence of Ca^{2+} transport are summarized. *Boxes* represent the mean (*central vertical line*) and S.D. (*right and left edges of box*). (Reprinted from Toyofuku et al., 1994*a*, with permission from the *Journal of Biological Chemistry*).

access to the lumen, they are inaccessible from the cytoplasm, and Ca^{2+} binding affinity is lowered by several orders of magnitude. In our model (MacLennan, 1990; MacLennan et al., 1992*a*) the structural basis for the transport of Ca^{2+} lies in a change in orientation of peptide strands constituting the Ca^{2+} binding sites; this results in disruption of the Ca^{2+}-binding sites so that their affinity for Ca^{2+} is lowered at the same time that they become exposed to the lumen.

Phospholamban

In the mid 1970s, Tada et al. (1975) found that Ca^{2+} transport by cardiac sarcoplasmic reticulum was stimulated about 3-fold when protein kinase A catalyzed the phosphorylation of a 22,000-D membrane protein, which they named phospholamban (PLN). The full curves plotting Ca^{2+} transport against free Ca^{2+} in the uptake medium (Ca^{2+} dependency of Ca^{2+} transport; see Fig. 2) for SERCA2 were shifted to lower apparent Ca^{2+} affinity in the presence of PLN and to higher apparent affinity in the presence of phospho PLN (pPLN) (Tada and Katz, 1982). Although K_{Ca} shifts approaching 1 pCa unit have been reported in cardiac sarcoplasmic reticulum, shifts of about 0.3 pCa units are more common, both in vivo and in reconstituted systems.

Phospholamban Function at the Physiological Level

β-adrenergic stimulation of the heart, mediated by cAMP and cAMP-dependent protein kinase (PKA), is associated with an increase in the force of contraction and in the rate of rise and fall of force. Phosphorylation of PLN correlates with these changes; this supports the hypothesis that stimulation of SERCA2 by release of PLN inhibition of the Ca^{2+} pump underlies the effects of β-adrenergic stimulation of the heart (Lindemann et al., 1983). Since phosphorylation of PLN leads to activation of SERCA2, the positive inotropy induced by β-adrenergic stimulation may result from increased Ca^{2+} accumulation into the sarcoplasmic reticulum. Greater Ca^{2+} release from a larger store can result in a stronger contraction of the myofilaments. Positive lusitropy, the increased rate and extent of relaxation of cardiac muscle, could be due to an increased rate of Ca^{2+} uptake. These proposed effects of PLN phosphorylation on inotropy and lusitropy were proven in analysis of the PLN-ablated mouse (Luo et al., 1994). These animals exhibited enhanced myocardial performance without any change in heart rate. The time to peak pressure and the time to half relaxation were significantly shorter in PLN deficient mice, as assessed in work-performing mouse heart preparations under identical venous returns, afterloads and heart rates. The first derivatives of intraventricular pressure ($\pm dP/dt$) were also significantly elevated and this was associated with an increase in the apparent affinity of SERCA2 for Ca^{2+} in the PLN-deficient hearts. Baseline levels of these parameters in PLN-deficient hearts were equal to those observed in hearts of wild type littermates normally stimulated with isoproterenol.

Phospholamban Structure

Phospholamban is a 6,000-D protein located in the sarcoplasmic reticulum of cardiac, slow-twitch, and smooth muscles. It contains 52 amino acids, which are organized into 3 physical and functional domains (Fujii et al., 1986; Fujii et al., 1987; Simmerman et al., 1986). Domain Ia, consisting of residues 1-20, and domain Ib, consisting of residues 21-30, constitute the cytoplasmic sector. Domain Ia is highly charged, with acidic residues at positions 2 and 19 and basic residues at positions 3, 9, 13, and 14. Ser^{16} is phosphorylated by protein kinase A, and Thr^{17} is phosphorylated by calmodulin (CaM) kinase (Simmerman et al., 1986). Domain Ib is polar and positively charged, with Gln at positions 22, 23, 26, and 29, Asn at positions 27 and 30, and Arg at position 25. Domain II is the transmembrane domain, made up solely of uncharged residues, Asn, Met, Val, Phe, Cys, Ile, and Leu.

Since PLN is an insoluble, amphipathic membrane protein, it has been difficult to determine its 3-dimensional structure. Circular dichroism (CD), Fourier transform infrared (FTIR) spectroscopy, and nuclear magnetic resonance (NMR) spectroscopy measurements show that the cytoplasmic domains of PLN are about 70% α-helical and that the transmembrane domain is up to 82% α-helical (Mortishire-Smith et al., 1995; Tatulian et al., 1995). The NMR studies of Mortishire-Smith et al. (1995) showed that residues 1-16 are α-helical in PLN and residues 1-11 are α-helical in pPLN. FTIR results, however, led Tatulian et al. (1995) to propose a novel structure for PLN in which residues 1-7 are random coil and residues 22-32 form an antiparallel β-sheet located at the membrane-water interface.

The overall structure of the transmembrane domain is complicated because PLN is pentameric, moving with a mobility equivalent to about 25,000 D in SDS polyacrylamide gel electrophoresis. Upon boiling in SDS, the protein is fully or partially dissociated into bands representing tetramers, trimers, dimers, and monomers (Wegener and Jones, 1984). Mutation of Cys^{41} to Phe destabilizes the pentamer so that it appears monomeric in SDS gels without boiling (Fujii et al., 1989). The monomeric protein can be phosphorylated and it is functional in altering Ca^{2+} dependence of Ca^{2+} transport when coexpressed with SERCA2 (Toyofuku et al., 1993).

Pentameric PLN forms Ca^{2+} channels when inserted into planar bilayers in the presence of an electrical field (Kovacs et al., 1988). Adams and colleagues (Adams et al., 1995; Arkin et al., 1994) used an experimental mutagenesis approach, combined with modelling, to develop a 3-dimensional structural prediction for the pentameric PLN channel. Mutagenesis of all of the 22 amino acids making up the transmembrane sequence of PLN showed three classes of residues: those in which pentamer formation was disrupted by all mutations; those in which some mutations disrupted pentamer formation; and those in which mutations had little effect on pentamer formation. Mutations to Leu^{37}, Ile^{40}, Leu^{44}, and Ile^{47} invariably led to monomerization, an observation suggesting that these were the most critical residues in pentamer formation.

Modelling showed that Leu^{37}, Ile^{40}, Leu^{44}, and Ile^{47} would be located on one face of an α helix with 3.5 residues per turn. Further modelling predicted that, in the most likely pentameric structure, these helices would be left-handed and slightly tilted from perpendicular. In this model, the pore formed by the pentamer would be lined by Leu^{37}, Ile^{40}, Leu^{44}, and Ile^{47} and would have an internal diameter of 2–3Å, about the same size as an unhydrated Ca^{2+} ion. The large side chains of Leu^{37}, Ile^{40}, Leu^{44}, and Ile^{47} would form inter monomeric contacts among adjacent helices. Cys^{36} would lie at the cytoplasmic entrance to the channel, while both Cys^{41} and Cys^{46} would be located partially on the external (lipid facing) face of the pentamer. Cys^{41} would pack against Leu^{39} on the neighboring helix while Cys^{46} would interact with neighboring Ile^{47} and Ile^{48}. The channel would be unusual in that the pore would be very narrow and would have a very hydrophobic lining. Only Cys^{36}, near the channel mouth, would be polar. Since Cys^{36} is the likely site of Cd^{2+}-inactivation of the channel, it might also be involved in selection of Ca^{2+} ions for transport.

Phospholamban Interaction with SERCA2 at the Kinetic Level

Cantilina et al. (1993) investigated the influence of PLN on SERCA2 function under conditions where phosphorylation to dissociate the two proteins was supplanted by the use of a monoclonal antibody against an epitope surrounding the phosphorylation site of PLN (Suzuki and Wang, 1986). Various partial reactions of Ca^{2+} transport were measured in the presence and absence of the activating antibody. Even though PLN lowers the apparent affinity of SERCA2 for Ca^{2+}, the true measured Ca^{2+} affinity was unaffected. The major kinetic effect of PLN on SERCA2 was a reduction in the activation energy for a slow transition triggered by Ca^{2+} binding, with consequent enhancement of overall kinetics under conditions enhancing the rate-limiting contribution of this transition. If this different rate of conformational transition were factored into equations defining the overall function of Ca^{2+} transport, then the reduction in apparent Ca^{2+} affinity was predictable.

Sites of Interaction Between Phospholamban and SERCA2

James et al. (1989) were able to crosslink Lys^3 of PLN to Lys^{397} or Lys^{400} of SERCA2 under conditions where SERCA2 was inhibited. Crosslinking did not occur in the presence of saturating levels of Ca^{2+} or when PLN was phosphorylated. These results suggest that there is a physical interaction between PLN and SERCA2 to inhibit the rate of Ca^{2+} transport and that this physical interaction is broken up by phosphorylation of PLN or by the availability to SERCA2 of higher levels of Ca^{2+}. The addition of other highly charged molecules can also disrupt the interaction between PLN and SERCA2 (Chiesi and Schwaller, 1989; Xu and Kirchberger, 1989); this suggests that electrostatic interactions are important in functional association between PLN and SERCA2. Mild proteolysis of the sarcoplasmic reticulum, which should cleave PLN at Arg^{14}, activates the Ca^{2+} ATPase by alteration of its Ca^{2+} affinity (Kirchberger et al., 1986). An antibody against residues 7–16 of PLN mimics phosphorylation of PLN in its activation of the Ca^{2+} ATPase (Morris et al., 1991; Briggs et al., 1992). Thus residues in PLN domain Ia are critical to interaction between SERCA2 and PLN.

Several investigators have attempted to reconstitute purified PLN (Jones et al., 1985) with purified SERCA2 (Inui et al., 1986; Kim et al., 1990; Reddy et al., 1995; Sasaki et al., 1992; Szymanska et al., 1992). Reconstitution has also been used to study the interaction of PLN domains with SERCA2 (Hughes et al., 1994; Reddy et al., 1995; Sasaki et al., 1992). In general, high concentrations of PLN have been required to achieve functional interaction. Reddy et al. (1995) reported reconstitution with 8-fold excess of PLN. Sasaki et al. (1992) reported that reconstitution of SERCA2 with a synthetic hydrophilic domain peptide (PLN_{1-31} at 400 mg/ml) lowered V_{max}. The addition of a synthetic transmembrane domain peptide (PLN_{28-47}) altered K_{Ca} from 0.52 to 1.33 mM, without affecting V_{max}, when applied in 100-fold molar excess. Hughes et al. (1994) have reproduced the V_{max} inhibition with PLN_{1-25}, while Reddy et al. (1995) used reconstitution with an 8-fold excess of PLN_{26-52} to decrease Ca^{2+} uptake at both pCa 5.4 and 6.8 without lowering Ca^{2+} ATPase activity. They proposed that PLN_{26-52} uncoupled Ca^{2+} uptake from Ca^{2+} ATPase. Because reconstitution experiments are difficult to perform and reproduce and because the ratio between the interacting proteins is so far from physiologic, we have chosen to use coexpression as a means of reconstitution between PLN and SERCA2 (Fujii et al., 1990; MacLennan et al., 1992*b*; Toyofuku et al., 1993; Toyofuku et al., 1994*a*; Toyofuku et al., 1994*b*).

Phospholamban-Ca^{2+} ATPase Interactions in Proteins Expressed in Heterologous Cell Culture

A major research goal in our laboratory is to define the sites of molecular interaction between phospholamban (PLN) and the cardiac Ca^{2+}-ATPase (SERCA2). When we initiated our studies of interactions between PLN and SERCA2, we recognized that reconstitution of the interactions with purified proteins would be difficult because the interaction does not survive solubilization in detergent. Moreover, reconstitution is limited to either purified native proteins or synthetic peptides, which are very expensive. Accordingly, it was important to explore the possibility that we could achieve reconstitution by coexpressing PLN and SERCA2 in a heterologous cell culture system. In our first experiments, we demonstrated that we could express PLN cDNA in COS-1 cells (Fujii et al., 1989). The expressed protein was phosphorylated by cAMP and calmodulin-dependent protein kinases. We used site-directed mutagenesis to show that Ser^{16} and Thr^{17} were phosphorylated by cAMP-dependent protein kinase (PKA) and calmodulin-dependent kinase (CaM kinase), respectively, that Arg^{13} and Arg^{14} were essential for both types of phosphorylation and that Arg^9 was essential for CaM kinase-dependent phosphorylation.

The expressed protein formed pentamers, which could be disaggregated to a monomer by boiling in SDS. We showed that mutation of many amino acids between Met^1 and Asn^{30} in the cytoplasmic domain of PLN did not affect the thermal stability of the pentamers, but that mutation of Cys^{36}, Cys^{41}, and Cys^{46} in the transmembrane domains did affect thermal stability. The protein containing the Cys^{41} Phe mutation was monomeric in SDS at ambient temperature.

In our next series of experiments, we coexpressed PLN with SERCA2 (Fujii et al., 1990). When we measured the Ca^{2+} dependence of Ca^{2+} uptake by SERCA2 in the presence and absence of PLN, we found that PLN shifted the full curve of Ca^{2+} dependence so that the apparent Ca^{2+} affinity was lowered by about 0.3 pCa units. In later experiments (Toyofuku et al., 1993), we demonstrated that this effect of PLN on apparent Ca^{2+} affinity was reversible. If we phosphorylated PLN with added PKA, the full curve of Ca^{2+} dependence was shifted about 0.3 pCa units to a higher affinity. Thus we could reproduce the essential measures of SERCA2-PLN interaction using microsomes from a transfected, heterologous cell culture system. This system provides an excellent alternative to in vitro reconstitution systems.

The Use of Chimeric SERCA Proteins to Define Regions of PLN Interaction

In early studies, we cloned cDNAs encoding three isoforms of the Ca^{2+} ATPase: SERCA1, the fast twitch isoform (Brandl et al., 1986); SERCA2, the cardiac/slow twitch isoform (MacLennan et al., 1985), which, in an alternatively spliced form, is ubiquitously expressed in non-muscle tissues (Lytton and Maclennan, 1988); and

SERCA3, a widely expressed isoform with specialized function (Burk et al., 1989). In more recent studies (Lytton et al., 1992; Toyofuku et al., 1992), we expressed SERCA1, SERCA2a, SERCA2b, and SERCA3 and found that SERCA3 had an apparent Ca^{2+} affinity, as measured by Ca^{2+} dependence of Ca^{2+} transport, about 0.6 pCa units lower than the apparent Ca^{2+} affinity of SERCA1 or SERCA2. When we coexpressed PLN with SERCA1 or SERCA2, we found that apparent Ca^{2+} affinity was lowered. When we coexpressed SERCA3 and PLN, we saw no effect on apparent Ca^{2+} affinity of SERCA3 (Toyofuku et al., 1993).

These observations led us to try to localize the regions in the different ATPases responsible for the differences in apparent Ca^{2+} affinity (Toyofuku et al., 1992). We made chimeras between SERCA2 and SERCA3 by inserting the same restriction endonuclease sites into corresponding sequences of the two DNA molecules and swapping 4 domains; the NH_2-terminal transmembrane and β-strand domain; the phosphorylation domain; the nucleotide binding/hinge domain; and the COOH-terminal transmembrane domain. We found high apparent Ca^{2+} affinity to be linked to the inclusion of the nucleotide binding/hinge domain of SERCA2 in the chimeras. Attempts to subdivide this region in chimeras were unsuccessful.

We then coexpressed each of the 14 SERCA2/SERCA3 chimeras with PLN (Toyofuku et al., 1993). We found that PLN would interact functionally only with those chimeras that had both the nucleotide binding/hinge domain of SERCA2 (which conferred high Ca^{2+} affinity to the chimera) and the phosphorylation domain of SERCA2 (which apparently contained the PLN interaction site). The phosphorylation domains of SERCA2 and SERCA3 were subdivided, and two new chimeras were formed. We then found that a SERCA3 chimera containing residues 336–412 and 467–762 of SERCA2 would interact functionally with PLN, thereby defining the regions in SERCA2 essential for PLN interaction.

Identification of Amino Acids in SERCA2 Essential for PLN Interaction

In our experiments with chimeras, function would only be affected if the amino acids involved in the interaction between the ATPase and PLN differed between the two proteins contributing to the chimera. Thus, we were confident of the existence of an essential site of interaction between ATPase residues 370 and 400, but we wanted to determine whether other residues essential to the interaction, but invisible because of their identity between SERCA2 and SERCA3, existed in this region. Accordingly, we made mutations of all of the charged residues and some of the uncharged residues in SERCA2 between Arg^{365} and Asp^{408}. Mutation affected functional interaction only for residues Lys^{397}, Asp^{398}, Asp^{399}, Lys^{400}, Pro^{401}, and Val^{402} (Toyofuku et al., 1994*b*). To prove that these were the essential interacting residues, we made a SERCA2 chimera containing the SERCA3 phosphorylation domain. This chimera did not interact functionally with PLN. If the SERCA3 sequence Gln-Gly-Glu-Gln-Leu-Val^{402} were substituted with the SERCA2 sequence Lys-Asp-Asp-Lys-Pro-Val^{402} or with the sequence Lys-Gly-Glu-Tyr-Pro-Val^{402}, function was restored (Fig. 2). These and other experiments demonstrated that the SERCA2 residues essential for PLN interaction are: at least one basic residue at positions 397 or 400; at least one acidic residue at positions 398 or 399; a Pro at position 401 and a long chain hydrophic residue at position 402 (Toyofuku et al., 1994*b*).

Cytoplasmic PLN Residues Essential for Interaction with SERCA2

Phospholamban is made up of three domains. Domain Ia, residues 1–20, probably largely in α-helical conformation, is the functional cytoplasmic domain containing sites of phosphorylation (Fujii et al., 1986). Domain Ib, residues 21–30, probably existing as a random coil, is a linker domain between domain Ia and domain II. Domain II, residues 31–52, probably in an α-helical conformation, traverses the membrane. We have used our coexpression and mutagenesis system to evaluate the roles of amino acids 1 to 30 in domains Ia and Ib of PLN in the SERCA2/PLN interaction (Toyofuku et al., 1994*a*). Our results were more complex than those with SERCA2. We found that the following mutations in domain Ia of PLN affected functional interaction with SERLA2: positively charged residues Lys[3], Arg[9], Arg[13], and Arg[14]; negatively charged residue Glu[2]; hydrophobic residues Val[4], Leu[7], Ala[11], Ile[12], Ala[15], and Ile[18]; and phosphorylation residues Ser[16] and Ser[17]. Charge appears to be an important element in the interaction. If residues 2 to 18 had a net charge of +1 or +2, the molecule was functional. If the net charge were 0, −2, −3, or, +3, function was lost. Hydrophobic interactions also appeared to be critical. Function was lost if the long alkyl side chains of Val[4], Leu[7], or Ile[12] were replaced by the methyl group of Ala. Thus there is evidence, both in the SERCA2 interaction site sequence and in the PLN interaction site sequence, that electrostatic and hydrophobic interactions are critical. We found no functional role for residues 21–30 in domain Ib.

Conclusion

In our studies of sarcoplasmic reticulum proteins, we have used a strategy of cloning cDNA encoding relevant proteins, mutagenesis of the cDNA, expression or coexpression of the mutated cDNA in heterologous cell culture systems, and assay of the altered function. In the case of SERCA1, we measured partial reactions of the overall reaction of ATP-dependent Ca^{2+} transport. These studies allowed us to define the catalytic domain in the cytoplasmic sector of the Ca^{2+} pump, the Ca^{2+}-binding and translocation domain in the transmembrane sequences, and specific residues, scattered throughout the pump that are involved with conformational changes. With this information, we were able to propose a model for ATP dependent Ca^{2+} transport that is readily understood (MacLennan, 1990; MacLennan et al., 1992).

We have also been able to study the interaction between SERCA2 and PLN by coexpression. This strategy is superior to attempts at reconstitution of purified components, since detergents, which complicate reconstitution systems, are avoided and interactions can be observed with more physiologic ratios of the interacting components. With this system, combined with mutagenesis and measure of function, we have been able to define a relatively few residues in both SERCA2 and PLN that are involved in the interaction between the two proteins.

Acknowledgments

We thank the many colleagues who participated in the work from our laboratory that is described in this review.

Research grants supporting original work from the laboratory of Dr. D.H. MacLennan were from the Medical Research Council of Canada (MRCC), The National Institutes of Health (USA), The Heart and Stroke Foundation of Ontario and The Human Frontier Science Program Organization. Dr. T. Toyofuku was a postdoctoral fellow of the MRCC.

References

Adams, P.D., I.T. Arkin, D.M. Engelman, and A.T. Brünger. 1995. Computational searching and mutagenesis suggest a structure for the pentameric transmembrane domain of phospholamban. *Struct. Biol.* 2:154–162.

Andersen, J.P., and B. Vilsen. 1992. Functional consequences of alterations to Glu[309], Glu[771], and Asp[800] in the Ca^{2+}-ATPase of sarcoplasmic reticulum. *J. Biol. Chem.* 267:19383–19387.

Andersen, J.P., and B. Vilsen. 1994. Amino acids Asn796 and Thr799 of the Ca^{2+}-ATPase of sarcoplasmic reticulum bind Ca^{2+} at different sites. *J. Biol. Chem.* 269:15931–15936.

Andersen, J.P., B. Vilsen, and D.H. MacLennan. 1992. Functional consequences of alterations to Gly[310], Gly[770] and Gly[801] located in the transmembrane domain of the Ca^{2+} ATPase of sarcoplasmic reticulum. *J. Biol. Chem.* 267:2767–2774.

Arkin, I.T., P.D. Adams, K.R. MacKenzie, M.A. Lemmon, A.T. Brünger, and D.M. Engelman. 1994. Structural organization of the pentameric transmembrane α-helices of phospholamban, a cardiac ion channel. *EMBO J.* 13:4757–4764.

Bigelow, D.J., and G. Inesi. 1992. Contributions of chemical derivatization and spectroscopic studies to the characterization of the Ca^{2+} transport ATPase of sarcoplasmic reticulum. *Biochim. Biophys. Acta.* 113:323–338.

Brandl, C.J., N.M. Green, B. Korczak, and D.H. MacLennan. 1986. Two Ca^{2+} ATPase genes: Homologies and mechanistic implications of deduced amino acid sequences. *Cell.* 44:597–607.

Briggs, F.N., K.F. Lee, A.W. Wechsler, and L.R. Jones. 1992. Phospholamban expressed in slow-twitch and chronically stimulated fast-twitch muscle minimally affects calcium affinity of sarcoplasmic reticulum Ca^{2+} ATPase. *J. Biol. Chem.* 267:26056–26061.

Burk, S.E., J. Lytton, D.H. MacLennan, and G.E. Shull. 1989. cDNA cloning, functional expression, and mRNA tissue distribution of a third organellar Ca^{2+} pu264:18561–18568.

Cantilina, T., Y. Sagara, G. Inesi, and L.R. Jones. 1993. Comparative studies of cardiac and skeletal sarcoplasmic reticulum ATPases. Effect of a phospholamban antibody on enzyme activation by Ca^{2+}. *J. Biol. Chem.* 268:17018–17025.

Carafoli, E. 1987. Intracellular calcium homeostatis. *Annu. Rev. Biochem.* 56:395–433.

Catterall, W.A. 1991. Excitation-contraction coupling in vertebrate skeletal muscle: A tale of two calcium channels. *Cell.* 64:871–874.

Chiesi, M., and R. Schwaller. 1989. Involvement of electrostatic phenomena in phospholamban-induced stimulation of Ca uptake into cardiac sarcoplasmic reticulum. *FEBS Lett.* 244:241–244.

Clarke, D.M., T.W. Loo, G. Inesi, and D.H. MacLennan. 1989. Location of high affinity Ca^{2+} binding sites within the predicted transmembrane domain of the sarcopolasmic reticulum Ca^{2+} ATPase. *Nature (Lond.).* 339:476–478.

Clarke, D.M., T.W. Loo, and D.H. MacLennan. 1990*a*. Functional consequences of alterations to polar amino acids located in the transmembrane domain of the Ca^{2+} ATPase of sarcoplasmic reticulum. *J. Biol. Chem.* 265:6262–6267.

Clarke, D.M., T.W. Loo, and D.H. MacLennan. 1990*b*. Functional consequences of alterations to amino acids located in the nucleotide-binding domain of the Ca^{2+}-ATPase of sarcoplasmic reticulum. *J. Biol. Chem.* 265:22223–22227.

Clarke, D.M., T.W. Loo, W. Rice, J.P. Andersen, B. Vilsen, and D.H. MacLennan. 1993. Functional consequences of alterations to hydrophobic amino acids located in the M_4 transmembrane sector of the Ca^{2+} ATPase of sarcoplasmic reticulum. *J. Biol. Chem.* 268:18359–18364.

de Meis, L., and A.L. Vianna. 1979. Energy interconversion by the Ca^{2+}-dependent ATPase of the sarcoplasmic reticulum. *Annu. Rev. Biochem.* 48:275–292.

Ebashi, S., M. Endo, and I. Ohtsuki. 1969. Control of muscle contraction. *Quarterly Rev. Biophys.* 2:351–384.

Fabiato, A. 1983. Calcium-induced release of calcium from the cardiac sarcoplasmic reticulum. *Am. J. Physiol. Cell Physiol.* 14:C1–C14.

Fleischer, S., and M. Inui. 1989. Biochemistry and Biophysics of excitation-contraction coupling. *Annu. Rev. Biophys. Biophys. Chem.* 18:333–364.

Forge, V., E. Mintz, D. Canet, and F. Guillain. 1995. Lumenal Ca^{2+} dissociation from the phosphorylated Ca^{2+}-ATPase of the sarcoplasmic reticulum is sequential. *J. Biol. Chem.* 270:18271–18276.

Fujii, J., M. Kadoma, M. Tada, H. Tada, and F. Sakiyama. 1986. Characterization of structural unit of phospholamban by amino acid sequencing and electrophoretic analysis. *Biochem. Biophys. Res. Commun.* 138:1044–1050.

Fujii, J., A. Ueno, K. Kitano, S. Tanaka, M. Kadoma, and M. Tada. 1987. Complete complementary DNA-derived amino acid sequence of canine cardiac phospholamban. *J. Clin. Invest.* 79:301–304.

Fuji, J., K. Maruyama, M. Tada, and D.H. MacLennan. 1989. Expression and site-specific mutagenesis of phospholamban. Studies of residues involved in phosphorylation and pentamer formation. *J. Biol. Chem.* 264:12950–12955.

Fujii, J., K. Maruyama, M. Tada, and D.H. MacLennan. 1990. Co-expression of slow-twitch/cardiac muscle Ca^{2+}-ATPase (SERCA2) and phospholamban. *FEBS Lett.* 273:232–234.

Hughes, G., J.M. East, and A.G. Lee. 1994. The hydrophilic domain of phospholamban inhibits the Ca^{2+} transport step of the Ca^{2+}-ATPase. *Biochem. J.* 303:511–516.

Inesi, G. 1985. Mechanism of calcium transport. *Annu. Rev. Physiol.* 47:573–601.

Inesi, G. 1987. Sequential mechanism of calcium binding and translocation in sarcoplasmic reticulum adenosine triphosphatase. *J. Biol. Chem.* 262:16338–16342.

Inesi, G., and M.E. Kirtley. 1990. Coupling of catalytic and channel function in the Ca^{2+} transport ATPase. *J. Membr. Biol.* 116:1–8.

Inui, M., B.K. Chamberlain, A. Saito, and S. Fleischer. 1986. The nature of the modulation of

Ca^{2+} transport as studied by reconstitution of cardiac sarcoplasmic reticulum. *J. Biol. Chem.* 261:1794–1800.

James, P., M. Inui, M. Tada, M. Chiesi, and E. Carafoli. 1989. Nature and site of PLB regulation of the Ca^{2+} pump of sarcoplasmic reticulum. *Nature (Lond.).* 342:90–92.

Jones, L.R., H.K.B. Simmerman, W.W. Wilson, F.R.N. Gurd, and A.D. Wegener. 1985. Purification and characterization of phospholamban from canine cardiac sarcoplasmic reticulum. *J. Biol. Chem.* 260:7721–7730.

Kim, H.W., N.A.E. Steenaart, D.G. Ferguson, and E.G. Kranias. 1990. Functional reconstitution of the cardiac sarcoplasmic reticulum Ca^{2+} ATPase with phospholamban in phospholipid vesicles. *J. Biol. Chem.* 265:1702–1709.

Kirchberger, M.A., D. Borchman, and C. Kasinathan. 1986. Proteolytic activation of the canine cardiac sarcoplasmic reticulum calcium pump. *Biochem.* 25:5484–5492.

Kovacs, R.J., M.T. Nelson, H.K.B. Simmerman, and L.R. Jones. 1988. Phospholamban forms Ca^{2+}-selective channels in lipid bilayers. *J. Biol. Chem.* 263:18364–18368.

Lindemann, J.P., L.R. Jones, D.R. Hathaway, H.G. Besch, and A.M. Watanabe. 1983. β-Adrenergic stimulation of phospholamban phosphorylation and Ca^{2+}-ATPase activity in guinea pig ventricles. *J. Biol. Chem.* 258:464–471.

Luo, W., I.L. Grupp, J. Harrer, S. Ponniah, G. Grupp, J.J. Duffy, T. Doetschman, and E.G. Kranias. 1994. Targeted ablation of the phospholamban gene is associated with markedly enhanced myocardial contractility and loss of β-agonist stimulation. *Circ. Res.* 75:401–409.

Lytton, J., and D.H. MacLennan. 1988. Molecular cloning of cDNAs from human kidney coding for two alternatively spliced products of the cardiac Ca^{2+}-ATPase gene. *J. Biol. Chem.* 263:15024–15031.

Lytton, J., M. Westlin, S.E. Burk, G.E. Shull, and D.H. MacLennan. 1992. Functional comparisons between isoforms of the sarcoplasmic or endoplasmic reticulum family of calcium pumps. *J. Biol. Chem.* 267:14483–14489.

MacLennan, D.H. 1990. Molecular tools to elucidate problems in excitation-contraction coupling. *Biophys. J.* 58:1355–1365.

MacLennan, D.H., C.J. Brandl, B. Korczak, and N.M. Green. 1985. Sequence of a Ca^{2+} + Mg^{2+} dependent ATPase from rabbit muscle sarcoplasmic reticulum, deduced from its complementary DNA sequence. *Nature (Lond.).* 316:696–700.

MacLennan, D.H., D.M. Clarke, T.W. Loo, and I. Skerjanc. 1992*a*. Site-directed mutagenesis of the Ca^{2+} ATPase of sarcoplasmic reticulum. *Acta Physiol. Scand.* 146:141–150.

MacLennan, D.H., T. Toyofuku, and J. Lytton. 1992*b*. Structure-function relationships in sarcoplasmic or endoplasmic reticulum type Ca^{2+} pumps. *Ann. NY Acad. Sci.* 671:1–10.

Makinose, M., and W. Hasselbach. 1971. ATP synthesis by the reverse of the sarcoplasmic calcium pump. *FEBS Lett.* 12:271–272.

Maruyama, K., and D.H. MacLennan. 1988. Mutation of aspartic acid-351, lysine-352 and lysine-515 alters the Ca^{2+} transport activity of the Ca^{2+} ATPase expressed in COS-1 cells. *Proc. Natl. Acad. Sci. USA.* 85:3314–3318.

Maruyama, K., D.M. Clarke, J. Fujii, G. Inesi, T.W. Loo, and D.H. MacLennan. 1989. Functional consequences of alterations to amino acids located in the catalytic center (isoleucine 348 to threonine 357) and nucleotide binding domain of the Ca^{2+} ATPase of sarcoplasmic reticulum. *J. Biol. Chem.* 264:13038–13042.

Matthews, I., J. Colyer, A.M. Mata, N.M. Green, R.P. Sharma, A.G. Lee, and J.M. East. 1989. Evidence for the cytoplasmic location of the N- and C-terminal segments of sarcoplasmic reticulum (Ca^{2+}-Mg^{2+})-ATPase. *Biochem. Biophys. Res. Commun.* 161:683–688.

Morris, G.L., H.-C. Cheng, J. Colyer, and J.H. Wang. 1991. Phospholamban regulation of cardiac sarcoplasmic reticulum (Ca^{2+}-Mg^{2+})-ATPase. Mechanism of regulation and site of monoclonal antibody interaction. *J. Biol. Chem.* 266:11270–11275.

Mortishire-Smith, R.J., S.M. Pitzenberger, C.J. Burke, C.R. Middaugh, J.V.M. Garsky, and R.G. Johnson. 1995. Solution structure of the cytoplasmic domain of phospholamban: Phosphorylation leads to a local perturbation in secondary structure. *Am. Chem. Soc.* 34:7603–7613.

Petithory, J.R., and W.P. Jencks. 1988. Sequential dissociation of Ca^{2+} from the calcium adenosinetriphosphatase of sarcoplasmic reticulum and the calcium requirement for its phosphorylation by ATP. *Biochem.* 27:5553–5564.

Reddy, L.G., L.R. Jones, S.E. Cala, J.J. O'Brian, S.A. Tatulian, and D.L. Stokes. 1995. Functional reconstitution of recombinant phospholamban with rabbit skeletal Ca^{2+}-ATPase. *J. Biol. Chem.* 270:9390–9397.

Reithmeier, R.A.F., and D.H. MacLennan. 1981. The NH_2-terminus of the ($Ca^{2+}Ca^{2+}+Mg^{2+}$)-adenosine triphosphatase is located on the cytoplasmic surface of the sarcoplasmic reticulum membrane. *J. Biol. Chem.* 256:5957–5960.

Sasaki, T., M. Inui, Y. Kimura, T. Kuzuya, and M. Tada. 1992. Molecular mechanism of regulation of Ca^{2+} pump ATPase by phospholamban in cardiac sarcoplasmic reticulum. Effects of synthetic phospholamban peptides on Ca^{2+} pump ATPase. *J. Biol. Chem.* 267:1674–1679.

Simmerman, H.K.B., J.H. Collins, J.L. Thiebert, A.D. Wegener, and L.R. Jones. 1986. Sequence analysis of phospholamban: Identification of phosphorylation sites and two major structural domains. *J. Biol. Chem.* 261:13333–13341.

Skerjanc, I.S., T. Toyofuku, C. Richardson, and D.H. MacLennan. 1993. Mutation of glutamate 309 to glutamine alters one Ca^{2+} binding site in the Ca^{2+} ATPase of sarcoplasmic reticulum expressed in Sf9 cells. *J. Biol. Chem.* 268:15944–15950.

Suzuki, T., and J.H. Wang. 1986. Stimulation of bovine cardiac sarcoplasmic reticulum Ca^{2+} pump and blocking of phospholamban phosphorylation and dephosphorylation by a phospholamban monoclonal antibody. *J. Biol. Chem.* 261:7018–7023.

Szymanska, G., H.W. Kim, J. Cuppoletti, and E.G. Kranias. 1992. Regulation of the skeletal sarcoplasmic reticulum Ca^{2+}-pump by phospholamban in reconstituted vesicles. *Membr. Biochem.* 9:191–202.

Tada, M., and A.M. Katz. 1982. Phosphorylation of the sarcoplasmic reticulum and sarcolemna. *Annu. Rev. Physiol.* 44:401–423.

Tada, M., M.A. Kirchberger, and A.M. Katz. 1975. Phosphorylation of a 22,000-dalton component of the cardiac sarcoplasmic reticulum by adenosine 3'-5'-monophosphate-dependent protein kinase. *J. Biol. Chem.* 250:2640–2647.

Takisawa, H., and M. Makinose. 1981. Occluded bound calcium on the phosphorylated sarcoplasmic transport ATPase. *Nature (Lond.).* 290:271–273.

Tatulian, S.A., L.R. Jones, L.G. Reddy, D.L. Stokes, and L.K. Tamm. 1995. Secondary structure and orientation of phospholamban reconstituted in supported bilayers from polarized attenuated total reflection FTIR spectroscopy. *Biochem.* 34:4448–4456.

Taylor, W.R., and N.M. Green. 1989. The homologous secondary structures of the nucleotide-binding sites of six cation-transporting ATPases lead to a probable tertiary fold. *Eur. J. Biochem.* 179:241–248.

Toyofuku, T., K. Kurzydlowski, J. Lytton, and D.H. MacLennan. 1992. The nucleotide binding/hinge domain plays a crucial role in determining isoform specific dependence of organellar Ca^{2+} ATPases. *J. Biol. Chem.* 267:14490–14496.

Toyofuku, T., K. Kurzydlowski, M. Tada, and D.H. MacLennan. 1993. Identification of regions in the Ca^{2+} ATPase of sarcoplasmic reticulum that affect functional association with phospholamban. *J. Biol. Chem.* 268:2809–2815.

Toyofuku, T., K. Kurzydlowski, M. Tada, and D.H. MacLennan. 1994a. Amino acids Glu^2 to Ile^{18} in the cytoplasmic domain of phospholamban are essential for functional association with the Ca^{2+} ATPase of sarcoplasmic reticulum. *J. Biol. Chem.* 269:3088–3094.

Toyofuku, T., K. Kurzydlowski, M. Tada, and D.H. MacLennan. 1994b. Amino acids Lys-Asp-Asp-Lys-Pro-Val^{402} in the Ca^{2+}-ATPase of cardiac sarcoplasmic reticulum are critical for functional association with phospholamban. *J. Biol. Chem.* 269:22929–22932.

Toyoshima, C., H. Sasake, and D.L. Stokes. 1993. Three-dimensional cryo-electron microscopy of the calcium ion pump in the sarcoplasmic reticulum membrane. *Nature (Lond.).* 362:469–471.

Vilsen, B., and J.P. Andersen. 1992a. CrATP-induced Ca^{2+} occlusion in mutants of the Ca^{2+}-ATPase of sarcoplasmic reticulum. *J. Biol. Chem.* 267:25739–25743.

Vilsen, B., and J.P. Andersen. 1992b. Mutational analysis of the role of Glu^{309} in the sarcoplasmic reticulum Ca^{2+}-ATPase of frog skeletal muscle. *FEBS Lett.* 306:247–250.

Wegener, A.D., and L.R. Jones. 1984. Phosphorylation-induced mobility shift in phospholamban in sodium dodecyl sulfate polyacrylamide gels. Evidence for a protein structure consisting of multiple identical phosphorylatable subunits. *J. Biol. Chem.* 259:1834–1841.

Xu, Z.-C., and M.A. Kirchberger. 1989. Modulation by polyelectrolytes of canine cardiac microsomal calcium uptake and the possible relationship of phospholamban. *J. Biol. Chem.* 264:16644–16651.

Yu, X., S. Carroll, J-L. Rigaud, and G. Inesi. 1993. H$^+$ countertransport and electrogenicity of the sarcoplasmic reticulum Ca^{2+} pump in reconstituted proteoliposomes. *Biophys. J.* 64:1232–1242.

Zot, A.S., and J.D. Potter. 1987. Structural aspects of troponin-tropomyosin regulation of skeletal muscle contraction. *Annu. Rev. Biophys. Biophys. Chem.* 16:535–559.

Transporters of Nucleotides and Nucleotide Derivatives in the Endoplasmic Reticulum and Golgi Apparatus

Carlos B. Hirschberg

Department of Biochemistry and Molecular Biology, University of Massachusetts Medical School, Worcester, Massachusetts 01655

The lumen of the endoplasmic reticulum (ER) and Golgi apparatus are the subcellular sites where glycosylation, sulfation, and phosphorylation of secretory and membrane-bound proteins, proteoglycans, and lipids occur. Nucleotide sugars, adenosine 3'-phosphate 5'-phosphosulfate (PAPS) and ATP are substrates for these reactions. ATP is also used as an energy source in the lumen of the endoplasmic reticulum during protein folding and degradation. The above nucleotide derivatives and ATP must first be translocated across the membranes of the endoplasmic reticulum and/or Golgi apparatus before they can serve as substrates in the above lumenal reactions. Translocation of these solutes is mediated by highly specific transporters, which are antiporters with the corresponding nucleoside monophosphate, as shown by genetic and biochemical approaches. Studies in mammalian and yeast mutants showed that a defect in a specific translocator activity results in selective impairment of glycosylation of lipids, proteins, and proteoglycans. Several of these transporters have been purified from mammalian cells. The Golgi membrane UDP-N-acetylglucosamine (UDP-GlcNAc) transporter from the yeast *Kluyveromyces lactis* has been cloned. Experiments with yeast and mammalian cells demonstrate that these transporters play a regulatory role in the above reactions.

The Need for Transporters in the Golgi and Endoplasmic Reticulum Membrane

The existence of a topographic problem arose since the realization that proteins are compartmentalized in the lumen of the ER and Golgi apparatus while in transit toward the cell surface, organellar membranes such as lysosomes, or the outside of the cell (Palade, 1975). These proteins arrive in the Golgi lumen following translocation of their nascent polypeptides into the lumen of the ER (Katz et al., 1977; Lingappa, et al., 1978), budding of vesicles from this organelle, and fusion with elements of the Golgi apparatus (Pryer, et al., 1992). Within the Golgi, some of these proteins, as well as the glycolipids and proteoglycans, are glycosylated, sulfated, and phosphorylated. The substrates for these reactions—nucleotide sugars, PAPS, and ATP—are not synthesized in the lumen of the Golgi, but in the cytosol, with the exception of CMP-sialic acid, which is synthesized in the nucleus (Coates et al., 1980) and ATP, most of which is synthesized in mitochondria.

How do these highly charged substrates cross the Golgi membrane and enter the lumen? Beginning with the pioneering studies by Kuhn and White (1975), assays in vitro were developed to study this question. Rat liver and mammary gland

Organellar Ion Channels and Transporters © 1996 by The Rockefeller University Press

Golgi vesicles, which were sealed and of the same membrane topology as in vivo, were used to study the biosynthesis of glycoproteins and lactose. Transport of solutes into the lumen of these vesicles was measured by use of filtration and centrifugation assays (Kuhn and White, 1975; Perez and Hirschberg, 1987; Capasso et al., 1989; Waldman and Rudnick, 1990). Both assays yielded comparable values for K_{mapp} and V_{max} (Hirschberg and Snider, 1987).

General Characteristics of Nucleotide Sugars, PAPS, and ATP Transport into Golgi and Endoplasmic Reticulum Vesicles

1. Transport of nucleotide sugars, PAPS, and ATP is organelle-specific. Many nucleotides and derivatives are transported solely or much faster into Golgi vesicles than into those from the ER (Table 1 and Figs. 1, 3, and 6): ATP (but not GTP), UDP-GlcNAc, UDP-glucuronic acid, and UDP-*N*-acetylgalactosamine (UDP-GalNAc), are transported into vesicles form the Golgi apparatus and the endoplasmic reticulum (Table 1, Figs. 1, 3, and 6). UDP-glucose is transported mainly into the ER (Perez and Hirschberg, 1986; Hauser et al., 1988). The physiologic significance of transport of a given nucleotide derivative into both of these organelles is not always clear, although it cannot be explained by simple organellar cross-contamination. In some instances enzymes, such as specific glycosyltransferases, that use a given nucleotide sugar as substrate have been detected only in the Golgi membrane (Nuwayhid et al., 1986; Abeijon and Hirschberg, 1987) although it is possible that other reactions may use the same substrate in the ER. This happens with ATP, which is used for energy-requiring reactions in the lumen of the ER and as donor of phosphate in the lumen of the ER and Golgi apparatus. Most of these studies have been done with rat liver; in other cells, these transporters may have somewhat different distributions in these organelles. GDP-mannose is not transported into mam-

TABLE I

Mammalian Intracellular Organelle Specificity of Nucleotides and Nucleotide Derivatives Transport

Nucleotides and derivatives	Golgi	ER	References
CMP-Sialic Acid	++++	−	Sommers and Hirschberg, 1982
GDP-Fucose	++++	−	Sommers and Hirschberg, 1982
GDP-Mannose	−	−	Perez and Hirschberg, 1986
PAPS	++++	−	Schwarz et al., 1984
UDP-Galactose	++++	−	Kuhn and White, 1976; Perez and Hirschberg, 1985; Abeijon and Hirschberg, 1987
UDP-*N*-Acetylgalactosamine	++++	++	Abeijon and Hirschberg, 1987
UDP-*N*-Acetylglucosamine	++++	++	Perez and Hirschberg, 1985
UDP-Glucuronic Acid	++++	++	Nuwayhid et al., 1986; Hauser et al., 1988; Bossuyt and Blanchaert, 1994
UDP-Xylose	++++	++	Nuwayhid et al., 1986
ATP	++++	+++	Capasso et al., 1989; Clairmont et al., 1992
UDP-Glucose	+	++++	Perez and Hirschberg, 1986; Vanstapel and Blanchaert, 1988

malian ER or Golgi vesicles (Perez and Hirschberg, 1986) but into those from yeast Golgi (Abeijon et al., 1989) (see next section).

2. The entire molecule of nucleotide sugar, PAPS, and ATP is transported into the lumen of the Golgi apparatus and ER.

3. Transport is saturable. The apparent K_m values are between 1 and 10 μM.

4. Transport is temperature-dependent, with that at 30°C being 4–10–fold more rapid than at 4°C, depending on the individual nucleotide or derivative.

5. Transport is competitively inhibited by the corresponding nucleoside mono- and di-phosphate; transport is not inhibited by sugars or sulfate (Capasso and Hirschberg, 1984*b*; Berninsone et al., 1994).

6. Transport is protease-sensitive under conditions in which the enzymes facing their active sites towards the lumen of the Golgi vesicles, such as sialyltransferases, remain active (Hirschberg and Snider, 1987).

7. Transport does not require ATP as an energy source and is neither inhibited nor stimulated by ionophores (Capasso and Hirschberg, 1984*a*; Berninsone et al., 1994).

8. The PAPS transporter has structural similarities with the mitochondrial ATP/ADP antiporter (Capasso and Hirschberg, 1984*c*).

The above characteristics demonstrate that nucleotide sugars, PAPS, and ATP are transported into the Golgi and ER lumen by transporter proteins that are or- ganelle-specific and have a domain facing the cytosolic side of the membrane. The next sections will describe experiments which demonstrate that the Golgi transport- ers are important in vivo, function as an antiporter, and play a pivotal role in the regulation of posttranslational modifications.

Transport of Nucleotide Sugars into the Golgi Lumen Is Essential for Glycosylation of Proteins and Lipids In Vivo

The occurrence of mutant mammalian and yeast cells defective in nucleotide sugar translocation into the Golgi lumen has demonstrated the physiologic importance of this event. Chinese hamster ovary (CHO) cells and Madin-Darby canine kidney (MDCK) cells that were isolated by their resistance to plant lectins, have specific nucleotide sugar transporter defects that result in a distinct phenotype. One group of cells, belonging to the same genetic complementation group, CHO Lec8 (Stan- ley, 1980), clone 13 (Briles et al., 1977), and MDCK II-RCA[r] (Brandli et al., 1988), have a 70–90% deficiency of sialic acid and galactose in their glycoproteins, gly- cosphingolipids, and selective proteoglycans (Brandli et al., 1988; Toma et al., 1996). Detailed biochemical studies with extracts from these cell lines showed that the resulting phenotype was not due to defective biosynthesis of nucleotide sugars, macromolecular and lipid acceptors, or corresponding glycosyltransferases (Briles et al., 1977; Stanley, 1980; Brandli et al., 1988). Transport of UDP-galactose into Golgi vesicles from these cell lines was found to be 90% defective; transport of other uridine nucleotide sugars and CMP-sialic acid was normal (Deutscher and Hirschberg, 1986; Brandli et al., 1988). Together, these in vivo and in vitro results demonstrate that the observed phenotype is the result of impaired entry of UDP- galactose into the Golgi lumen and subsequent impaired galactosylation of pro- teins, lipids, and some, but not all, proteoglycans; this, in turn, leads to defective sial-

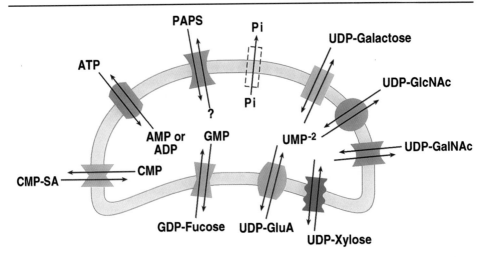

Figure 1. Mammalian Golgi nucleotide antiporters. Nucleotide sugar, nucleotide sulfate, and ATP transporters are antiporters with the corresponding nucleoside monophosphate. Exceptions (to date) are ATP—where it is not clear whether AMP, ADP, or both are antiporters—and PAPS, where the antiporter is unknown. No direct evidence for an inorganic phosphate carrier has been obtained. CMP-SA, CMP-sialic acid; UDP-GluA, UDP-glucuronic acid; UDP-GalNAc, UDP-N-acetylgalactosamine; UDP-GlcNAc, UDP-N-acetylglucosamine; PAPS, adenosine 3′ phosphate 5′ phosphosulfate.

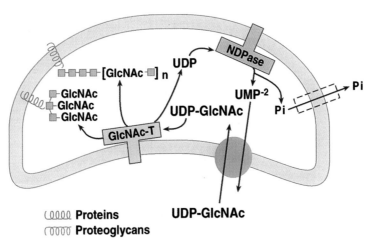

Figure 2. Mechanism of mammalian Golgi antiporters. Following transport into the lumen of the Golgi of UDP-GlcNAc, transfer of N-acetylglucosamine to proteins and proteoglycans is mediated by specific N-acetylglucosaminyltransferases. The other reaction product, UDP, is a substrate for a nucleotide diphosphatase yielding UMP^{-2} and inorganic phosphate (*Pi*). UMP^{-2} is the antiporter that is coupled to entry of additional UDP-GlcNAc while inorganic phosphate presumably leaves the Golgi lumen via its specific carrier. UDP-GlcNAc, UDP-N-acetylglucosamine; GlcNAc-T, N-acetylglucosaminyltransferases; NDPase, nucleotide diphosphatase.

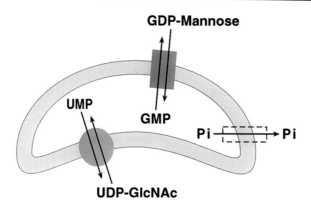

GDP-Mannose

UMP

GMP

Pi → Pi

UDP-GlcNAc

Figure 3. Yeast Golgi antiporters. GDP-mannose and UDP-*N*-acetylglucosamine are antiporters with the corresponding nucleoside monophosphates. The GDP-mannose antiporter has only been detected in *S. cerevisiae* while the UDP-GlcNAc transporter has only been detected in *K. lactis*. No direct evidence for the latter antiporter or an inorganic phosphate transporter has been obtained. Abbreviations are the same as in Fig. 2.

ylation because sialic acid is usually covalently linked to terminal galactose of proteins and lipids.

A different group of mutants, CHO cells Lec2 (Stanley, 1980; 1985) and clone 1021 (Briles et al., 1977), which belong to the same complementation group, have a 70%–90% deficiency of sialic acid in glycoproteins and gangliosides. Extracts from these cell lines showed no defect in the biosynthesis of CMP-sialic acid, levels of sialyltransferases, asialoglycoproteins, or asialoglycosphingolipids. Transport of CMP-sialic acid into Golgi vesicles from these mutants was 90% defective, while transport of other nucleotide sugars was normal (Deutscher et al., 1984); this shows that the resulting phenotype is the consequence of impaired entry of CMP-sialic acid into the Golgi lumen in vivo.

Recently, a mutant of the yeast *K. lactis* was found to be defective in transport of UDP-GlcNAc into the Golgi lumen (Abeijon et al., 1996*a*). The mutant had been characterized as defective in the addition of *N*-acetylglucosamine to its outer mannan chain. Detailed biochemical studies ruled out that the defect was a consequence of impaired biosynthesis of UDP-GlcNAc, endogenous macromolecular acceptors, or *N*-acetylglucosaminyltransferase (Douglas and Ballou, 1982). Isolation of Golgi-enriched vesicles from these cells showed that transport of UDP-GlcNAc was virtually zero; however, transport of GDP-mannose was essentially the same as into wild-type cells' vesicles (Abeijon et al., 1996*a*).

Together, the above results and those of more recent studies (Hayes et al., 1993; Hayes and Varki, 1993*a*; Hayes and Varki, 1993*b*) demonstrate that transport of nucleotide sugars into the Golgi lumen is mediated by highly specific (nucleotide sugar transporter) proteins and is required for subsequent glycosylation of proteins, lipids, and proteoglycans in vivo. Although to date no mutants in Golgi transport of ATP and PAPS have been described, we believe by inference that their transport into the Golgi lumen is of physiologic relevance and necessary for lumenal reactions requiring these substrates.

Nucleotide Sugars and ATP Enter the Golgi Lumen via Antiporters

Results of biochemical and genetic approaches strongly suggest that entry of nucleotide sugars and ATP into the Golgi lumen is coupled to exit of the corresponding nucleoside monophosphate (Figs. 2 and 4). When transport of nucleotide sugars, ATP, and PAPS into mammalian and/or yeast Golgi vesicles was measured, these solutes were concentrated in the lumen relative to the incubation medium, a finding that suggests active transport (Capasso and Hirschberg, 1984a; Waldman and Rudnick, 1990; Berninsone et al., 1994). For such concentration to occur, no effect by ATP or different ionophores was observed; this led to the hypothesis that at least part of the driving force for the concentration of nucleotides and derivatives in the Golgi lumen was provided by the exit of solutes, down a concentration gradient, from the lumen into the cytosol. Evidence for this was obtained by demonstration that following the loading of Golgi vesicles with radioactively labeled nucleoside monophosphate, exit of this radiolabel could only be effected when the vesicles were subsequently incubated with a nucleotide derivative containing the same nucleotide base. For example, GDP-fucose could displace GMP from the lumen of mammalian Golgi vesicles; GDP-mannose, which does not enter these Golgi vesicles, could not. This specificity and the apparent 1:1 stoichiometry of the exchange (based on equilibration specific activity assumptions) suggested the scheme shown in Figs. 2 and 4: following entry into the Golgi lumen against a concentration gradient, ATP, nucleotide sugars, or PAPS transfer phosphate, sugars, or sulfate, respectively, to endogenous acceptors in reactions catalyzed by the corresponding kinases, glycosyltransferases, or sulfotransferases. The resulting nucleoside diphosphates are substrates for lumenal nucleoside diphosphatases (Kuhn and White, 1977 and 1976; Brandan and Fleischer, 1982; Novikoff and Goldfischer, 1961), which give rise to nucleoside monophosphates and inorganic phosphate. Exit of nucleoside monophosphates and phosphate, down their concentration gradient, produces the necessary energy for entry and lumenal concentration of the corresponding nucleotide sugar, PAPS, or ATP (Capasso and Hirschberg, 1984a).

The majority of mammalian nucleotide sugars contain uridine and give rise to UDP in the Golgi lumen: Because the preloading of Golgi vesicles with UMP or UDP-GlcNAc markedly stimulated the accumulation of UDP-GlcNAc relative to vesicles loaded only with buffer, ATP, uridine, or uracyl, this conclusively demonstrated that UDP-GlcNAc exchanges for lumenal UMP (Waldman and Rudnick, 1990). This exchange is electroneutral with dianionic UMP because the rate of exchange is faster when the vesicles are preloaded with UMP at pH 7.5 (dianionic) vs. pH 5.45 (monoanionic). The highest stimulation of UDP-GlcNAc transport by internal UMP occurs when the internal pH is 7.5 and the external pH is 5.45. Under these conditions, UMP^{2-} arriving in the medium becomes protonated to the monoanionic form. UDP-GlcNAc is dianionic between pH 5.45 and pH 7.5. Further evidence for this mechanism was the demonstration that exit of UDP-GlcNAc from the lumen of vesicles is faster when external UMP is dianionic rather than monoanionic (Waldman and Rudnick, 1990). These results also strongly suggest that the Golgi membrane from mammals must have a transporter for inorganic phosphate from the lumen to the cytosol. No evidence for this has been reported.

Reconstitution experiments provided independent support that antiporters are the mechanism for nucleotide sugar entry into the Golgi lumen. When solubilized Golgi membrane proteins reconstituted into unilamellar phosphatidylcholine vesicles are in the presence of lumenal CMP, the rate of CMP-sialic acid entry into the proteoliposomes is stimulated approximately threefold over that into proteoliposomes containing buffer (Milla and Hirschberg, 1989). In a similar manner, entry of

UDP-xylose, UDP-glucuronic acid, and UDP-galactose into proteoliposomes is stimulated by lumenal UMP (Milla et al., 1992). A summary of the mechanisms of nucleotide sugar entry into the mammalian Golgi lumen is shown in Fig. 2.

A combination of genetic and biochemical experiments with yeast also strongly supports the idea that nucleotide sugar entry into the Golgi lumen is coupled to exit of nucleoside monophosphate. Golgi vesicles from *S. cerevisiae* contain a GDPase facing the lumen of the membrane (Fig. 4; Abeijon et al., 1989). This enzyme hydrolyzes GDP derived from GDP-mannose after its entry into the Golgi lumen and transfer of mannose to endogenous (mannan) acceptors, to GMP; exit of this nucleoside monophosphate from the Golgi lumen is required for entry of additional GDP-mannose (Fig. 4). The GDPase has been purified to homogeneity (Yanagisawa et al., 1990) and functions in the membrane as a homodimer (Berninsone et al., 1995). In the presence of Mn^{+2} it has 30% of UDPase activity (Yanagisawa et al., 1990). Its gene, GDA1, has been cloned and found to encode for a type-II membrane protein. Null mutants in this gene showed a block in Golgi mannosylation of lipids and proteins in vivo (Abeijon et al., 1993) and a 5-fold lower rate of entry of GDP-mannose into Golgi vesicles in vitro (Berninsone et al., 1994). The Golgi GDPase is therefore essential for Golgi mannosylation reactions. These results very strongly support the existence of a GDP-mannose/GMP antiporter in the yeast Golgi membrane. These studies also strongly suggest that there must be a transporter for inorganic phosphate from the Golgi lumen to the cytosol; no evidence for this has been reported (Fig. 4).

Reconstitution of the Golgi Nucleotide and Nucleotide Derivative Transporters into Proteoliposomes

Reconstitution of membrane transporters into proteoliposomes can be used for several important objectives: to assay for transporter purification; to study the mechanism of translocation, including the arrangement of the transporters within the membrane; and to understand possible regulation of the transporter proteins, per se. Our initial interest in reconstitution of Golgi transporters was as a means towards their purification, although as described in the previous section, this approach also provided support for CMP and UMP as antiporters in transport of CMP-sialic acid and several uridine diphosphate nucleotide sugars.

The general reconstitution strategy used for Golgi transporter proteins consisted of dissolving Golgi integral membrane proteins in buffer containing Triton X-100, removing most of the detergent with Extracti Gel D, and intercalating these proteins into unilamellar phosphatidylcholine liposomes during five freeze-thaw cycles. To date, the following transporters of the Golgi membrane have been reconstituted into proteoliposomes: CMP-sialic acid (Milla and Hirschberg, 1989), PAPS (Milla and Hirschberg, 1989), UDP-galactose (Milla et al., 1992), UDP-glucuronic acid (Milla et al., 1992), UDP-xylose (Milla et al., 1992), and ATP (Berninsone et al., 1995).

Several biochemical parameters were measured with these proteoliposomes: solute transport specificity, saturability, temperature dependence, solute inhibition, and membrane protein specificity. All were found to be very similar to those previously measured in sealed, "right-side out," rat liver Golgi vesicles (Milla and

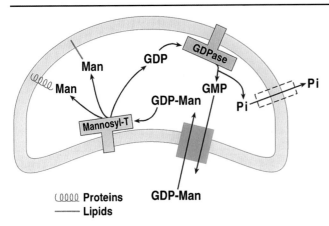

Figure 4. Mechanism of yeast Golgi antiporters. Following entry of GDP-mannose into the yeast Golgi lumen, mannose is transferred to proteins and lipids in a reaction catalyzed by mannosyl-transferases. The other re-action product, GDP, is a substrate for a lumenal GDPase yielding GMP, the antiporter for GDP-mannose entry and inor-ganic phosphate, which presumable leaves the Golgi lumen via its own transporter. GDP-man, GDP-mannose; man-nosyl-T, mannosyltransferases; GDPase, guanosine diphosphatase.

Hirschberg, 1989; Milla et al., 1992). These studies with proteoliposomes demon-strated that the K_m and V_{max} previously measured with Golgi vesicles—where there is coupling of transport of nucleotide sugars, PAPS, and ATP, and transfer of sug-ars, sulfate, and phosphate to endogenous lipids and macromolecules—are those of the transporters, and are not determined by the glycosyl- or sulfo- transferases or kinases. This suggests that the transporters and not the corresponding transferases or kinases are rate-limiting and that the former are possible candidates for regula-tion of the particular posttranslational modifications.

As previously mentioned, Golgi proteoliposomes preloaded with the corre-sponding nucleoside monophosphate showed a 2–5-fold enhancement in the rate of transport of nucleotide sugars into their lumen, an observation strongly supporting an antiporter mechanism. As will be shown below, these proteoliposomes can be used as an assay system for the purification of several Golgi nucleotide sugar, PAPS, and ATP transporters. The above approach, while highly successful for re-constitution of several Golgi transporter proteins, was not successful with ER trans-porter proteins, such as that for ATP (Guillen and Hirschberg, 1995a, b). In addi-tion, the UDP-xylose transporter is apparently the only Golgi nucleotide derivative that cannot be functionally intercalated with phosphatidylcholine liposomes and appears to require Golgi lipids for its proper reconstitution (Milla et al., 1992).

Structure of Golgi Nucleotide Sulfate and Nucleotide Sugar Transporters

To date, the PAPS transporter (Mandon et al., 1994) has been purified to apparent homogeneity, and those for CMP-sialic acid and Golgi ATP have been partially pu-rified (Berninsone et al., 1995). The strategy for purification in all of these cases consisted of conventional and affinity chromatographic steps in the presence of de-tergent and reconstitution into phosphatidylcholine liposomes of the different frac-tions to assess the activity of the transporter. Because of the low abundance of

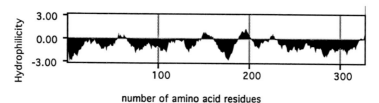

Figure 5. Kyte-Doolittle Plot of the MNN2-2 open reading frame. Window size is 18 amino acids.

these proteins in the cell, analyses of the more purified fractions was done by iodination of the proteins with chloramine T, followed by SDS-PAGE and autoradiography. By correlation of the protein profile on gels with PAPS transport activity, this transporter was found to be a protein of apparent mobility of 75 kD. A second criteria for identification of this transporter was photolabeling with adenosine 3′,5′ bisphosphate, a competitive inhibitor of the transporter. A protein of the same apparent mobility as the one previously identified as the PAPS transporter was photolabeled. This protein was not photolabeled in fractions that were inactive in PAPS transport activity or fractions that had had transport activity but lost it as a result of inactivation.

Radiation target inactivation of the PAPS transport activity measured in rat liver Golgi vesicles yielded a target size of 150 kD (Mandon et al., 1994). This, to-

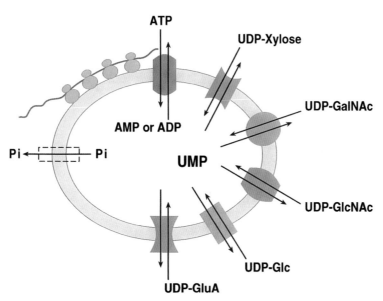

Figure 6. Mammalian endoplasmic reticulum nucleotide antiporters. Mammalian nucleotide sugar and ATP transporters are antiporters with the corresponding nucleoside monophosphates. The exception (to date) is ATP, where it is not clear whether AMP or ADP or both are antiporters. No direct evidence for inorganic phosphate transporter has been obtained. UDP-GluA, UDP-glucuronic acid; UDP-Glc, UDP-glucose; UDP-GlcNAc, UDP-*N*-acetylglucosamine; UDP-GalNAc, UDP-*N*-acetylgalactosamine.

gether with the previous results, strongly suggests that the PAPS transporter in situ functions as a homodimer. To date, all antiporters in cellular membranes appear to function as homodimers.

The CMP-sialic acid transporter has been partially purified. An important breakthrough in the purification was the realization that this transporter co-purifies with the PAPS and Golgi ATP transporters through the first two chromatographic steps and elutes in the third step, the red Sepharose column, at a higher NaCl concentration than the above transporter (Berninsone et al., 1995).

The UDP-GlcNAc Transporter of the Golgi Membrane of *K. lactis*

A mutant of *K. lactis* (MNN 2-2), which has a specific defect in the transport of UDP-GlcNAc into Golgi vesicles has been characterized (Abeijon et al., 1996*a*). This mutant lacks *N*-acetylglucosamine in its outer chain oligosaccharides (Douglas and Ballou, 1982), can transport GDP-mannose into its Golgi lumen (Abeijon et al., 1996*a*), and is not impaired in the biosynthesis of macromolecular acceptors and UDP-GlcNAc or in *N*-acetylglucosaminyltransferase activity (Douglas and Ballou, 1982).

The UDP-GlcNAc transporter was cloned by phenotypic correction of the mutant with a wild-type genomic library of *K. lactis* in a pKD1 vector (Abeijon et al., 1996*b*). Screening for phenotypic correction was done by use of FITC-conjugated GSII lectin, which binds to terminal *N*-acetylglucosamine in wild-type cells and allows their separation from the mutant population in a cell sorter. The gene encoding for the transporter has 1.4 kb. It encodes for a protein of 328 amino acids. A Kyte-Doolittle plot shows a very hydrophobic protein with multiple putative transmembrane domains (Fig. 5), consistent with the protein being a transporter. Future studies will determine its precise topology, subcellular localization, and possible homology with other uridine sugar transporters.

Transporters of ATP and Nucleotide Sugars in the Endoplasmic Reticulum

To date, transporters for ATP (Clairmont et al., 1992; Mayinger and Meyer, 1993; Jungnickel and Rapoport, 1993; Guillen and Hirschberg, 1995), UDP-glucose (Perez and Hirschberg, 1986; Vanstapel and Blanckaert, 1988), UDP-GlcNAc (Perez and Hirschberg, 1985), UDP-glucuronic acid (Nuwayhid et al., 1986; Hauser et al., 1988; Bossuyt and Blanchaert, 1994), UDP-xylose (Nuwayhid et al., 1986) and UDP-GalNAc (Abeijon and Hirschberg, 1987) have been detected in the ER of rat liver and/or yeast (Fig. 6). The ATP transporter, which has been reconstituted into proteoliposomes and partially purified (Guillen and Hirschberg, 1995*a*, 1995*b*) is thought to make this nucleoside triphosphate, which is synthesized primarily in mitochondria, available in the lumen of the ER for energy-requiring reactions (Pfeffer and Rothman, 1987) including the association of complexes between BiP and correctly folded and assembled proteins (Munro and Pelham, 1986; Flynn et al., 1989), disulfide bond formation (Braakman et al., 1992), protein polymerization (Braakman et al., 1992) and degradation. ATP is also used in lumenal phosphorylation reactions for proteins such as BiP and protein disulfide isomerase

(Hendershot et al., 1988; Quemeneur et al., 1994). UDP-glucose is required for re-glucosylation of proteins during folding (Sousa et al., 1992; Helenius, 1994). Transport of UDP-GlcNAc is required for the synthesis of *O-N*-acetylglucosamine-linked proteins that face the lumenal side of integral membrane proteins of rat liver rough and smooth endoplasmic reticulum (Abeijon and Hirschberg, 1988); it is not required for initial *N*-glycosylation (Abeijon and Hirschberg, 1992). UDP-glucuronic acid is required for hepatic glucuronidation of bile acids and xenobiotics (Berg et al., 1995).

Some of the above transporters have a known function, such as making ATP or nucleotide sugar available in the ER lumen as substrate for kinases or glycosyltransferases in reactions that occur in the lumen of the ER (Abeijon and Hirschberg, 1992). However, in some instances, the functions of the transporters are less clear; thus, while transport of UDP-xylose and UDP-GalNAc has been detected in the membrane of rat liver ER (Table I), so far, no corresponding xylosyl- or *N*-acetylgalactosaminyl-transferase or endogenous acceptors have been detected in the ER. These transferases and endogenous acceptors have been detected in the Golgi apparatus. This raises the question of whether the putative rat liver ER UDP-xylose and UDP-GalNAc transporters are the result of incomplete sorting during their biogenesis towards the Golgi membrane, whether there are yet unknown functions for these transporters and the corresponding nucleotide sugars in the lumen of the ER, or whether some uridine transporter such as UDP-glucose may also function, to some extent, with UDP-xylose or UDP-GalNAc. Experiments described in the next section should help answer some of these questions.

Future Directions

With the ongoing purification and molecular cloning of the different Golgi and ER transporters for nucleotide sugars, PAPS, and ATP, answers to important questions should be forthcoming in three general areas:

1. Structural organization. Are there common elements of primary and secondary structure among the different transporters? Do all or most of them have similar number of transmembrane domains? We have shown that the PAPS transporter is functional as a homodimer. Is this a general property of these transporters? Do the different uridine nucleotide sugar transporters have common structural domains? Because they all appear to use UMP^{-2} as antiporter, it is reasonable to infer that they may all have similar lumenal binding domains for this nucleoside monophosphate. UMP has also been shown to be a competitive inhibitor of transport for all the uridine nucleotide sugar transporters (Capasso and Hirschberg, 1984*b*); thus it is also possible that they may have common cytosolic structural domains. Do yeast Golgi nucleotide sugar transporters have common structural features among themselves and with mammalian ones? What are the structural differences between a specific transporter that occurs both in the ER and Golgi apparatus? The ATP transporter occurs in the ER and the Golgi apparatus of rat liver and is required for different functions in the lumen of these organelles, thus it is unlikely that its presence in both membranes may be the result of incomplete sorting.

2. Subcellular localization and targeting. How are these transporters targeted to the Golgi apparatus and ER membrane? By analogy to current postulated mechanisms of Golgi membrane protein targeting, one may hypothesize that the first amino terminal transmembrane domain and flanking sequences (Dahdal and Colley, 1993; Burke et al., 1994) and/or kin recognition (Nilsson et al., 1994) may be critical for Golgi retention. The activities of the transporters for UDP-xylose, UDP-glucuronic acid, UDP-GalNAc, and UDP-GlcNAc are less in the ER than in the Golgi membrane; is there incomplete sorting or do they have different functions in the two membranes? What is the Golgi sub-localization of the different transporters? Are they polarized within the Golgi apparatus? Epitope tagging should provide a simple, adequate means of answering this question. What is the relative sub-Golgi localization of a given transporter with the corresponding transferases, i.e., do they overlap in their entirety or are there regions in the membrane where only one or the other exist? Is the transporter for a given derivative always in an overlapping or *cis* position relative to the corresponding transferases? If not, what is the role of a transporter in regions *trans* in relation to the corresponding transferases?

   3. Regulation of activity and expression. What are the consequences of regulating the different transporters? Initial results suggest that these transporters limit the amount of nucleotide derivatives entering the lumen of these organelles and thereby favor those reactions where the K_m for the nucleotide derivatives are lower (Toma et al., 1996). A combination of overexpression of these transporters and RNA antisense experiments against such transporters should help answer this question. Are "knock-out" mice of any of these transporters viable? Our hypothesis is that these transporters are products of single genes and therefore disruption of them will probably not lead to further development of embryos, in a similar manner to the recently described knock-out of the *N*-acetylglucosaminyltransferase I gene (Ioffe and Stanley, 1994). What is the organization of the transporter genes in mammals and yeast? Is gene splicing involved? What are the signals and mechanisms involved in their transcriptional and translational regulation? It is clear that we have just begun to understand the structure and function of the above transporters and that the near future will yield answers to many of the above questions.

Acknowledgments

I thank Drs. C. Abeijon, P. Berninsone, E. Guillen, E. Mandon, and M. Milla for helpful suggestions and critical reading of this manuscript and Karen Welch and Annette Stratton for excellent secretarial assistance.

   This work has been supported by grants from the National Institute of General Medical Sciences, NIH GM 30365 and GM 34396.

References

Abeijon, C., and C.B. Hirschberg. 1987. Subcellullar site of synthesis of the *N*-acetylgalactosamine (α1-*0*) serine (or Threonine) linkage in rat liver. *J. Biol. Chem.* 262:4153–4159.

Abeijon, C., and C.B. Hirschberg. 1988. Intrinsic membrane glycoproteins with cytosol-oriented sugars in the endoplasmic reticulum. *Proc. Natl. Acad. Sci. USA.* 85:1010–1014.

Abeijon, C., P. Orlean, R.W. Robbins, and C.B. Hirschberg. 1989. Topography of glycosylation in yeast. Characterization of GDP-mannose transport and lumenal guanosine diphosphatase activities in Golgi-like vesicles. *Proc. Natl. Acad. Sci. USA.* 86:6935–6939.

Abeijon, C., and C.B. Hirschberg. 1992. Topography of glycosylation reactions in the endoplasmic reticulum. *Trends Biochem. Sci.* 17:31–36.

Abeijon, C., K. Yanagisawa, E. Mandon, A. Hausler, K. Moreman, C.B. Hirschberg, and P.W. Robbins. 1993. Guanosine diphosphatase is required for protein and sphingolipid glycosylation in the Golgi lumen of *Saccharomyces cerevisiae. J. Cell Biol.* 122:307–323.

Abeijon, C., E.C. Mandon, P.W. Robbins, and C.B. Hirschberg. 1996*a.* A mutant yeast deficient in Golgi transport of uridine diphoshate *N*-acetylglucosamine. *J. Biol. Chem.* 271:8851–8854.

Abeijon, C., P.W. Robbins, and C.B. Hirschberg. 1996*b.* Molecular cloning of the Golgi apparatus uridine diphosphate *N*-acetylgucosamine transporter from *Kluyveromyces lactis. Proc. Natl. Acad. Sci. USA.* In press.

Berg, C.L., A. Radominska, R. Lester, and J.L. Gollan. 1995. Membrane translocation and regulation of uridine diphosphate-glucuronic acid uptake in rat liver microsomal vesicles. *Gastroenterology.* 108:183–192.

Berninsone, P., J.J. Miret, and C.B. Hirschberg. 1994. The Golgi guanosine diphosphatase is required for transport of GDP-mannose into the lumen of *Saccharomyces cerevisiae* Golgi vesicles. *J. Biol. Chem.* 269:207–211.

Berninsone, P., Z.Y. Lin, E. Kempner, and C.B. Hirschberg. 1995. Regulation of yeast Golgi glycosylation: Guanosine diphosphatase functions as a homodimer in the membranes. *J. Biol. Chem.* 270:14564–14567.

Bernisone, P., E.C. Mandon, and C.B. Hirschberg. 1995. Purification of the Golgi CMP-*N*-acetylneuraminic acid/CMP antiporter. *J. Gen. Physiol.* 105:29a.

Boussuyt, X., and N. Blanchaert. 1994. Carrier-mediated transport of intact UDP-glucuronic acid into the lumen of endoplasmic reticulum-derived vesicles from rat liver. *Biochem. J.* 302:261–269.

Braakman, I., J. Helenius, and A. Helenius. 1992. Role of ATP and disulfide bonds during protein folding in the endoplasmic reticulum. *Nature (Lond.).* 356:260–262.

Brandan, E., and B. Fleischer. 1982. Orientation and role of nucleosidediphosphatase and 5′ nucleotidase in Golgi vesicles from rat liver. *Biochemistry.* 21:4640–4635.

Briles, E.B., E. Li, and S. Kornfeld. 1977. Isolation of wheat germ agglutinin-resistant clones of chinese hamster ovary cells deficient in membrane sialic acid and galactose. *J. Biol. Chem.* 252:1107–1116.

Burke, J., J.M. Pettit, D. Humphris, and P. Gleeson. 1994. Medial Golgi retention of *N*-acetylglucosaminyltransferase I. Contributions from all domains of the enzyme. *J. Biol. Chem.* 269:12049–12059.

Brandli, A.W., G.C. Hansson, E. Rodriguez-Boulan, and K. Simons. 1988. A polarized epithelial cell mutant deficient in translocation of UDP-galactose into the Golgi complex. *J. Biol. Chem.* 264:16283–16290.

Capasso, J.M., and C.B. Hirschberg. 1984*a.* Mechanisms of glycosylation and sulfation in the Golgi apparatus: evidence for nucleotide sugar/nucleoside monophosphate and nucleotide sulfate/nucleoside monophosphate antiports in the Golgi apparatus membrane. *Proc. Natl. Acad. Sci. USA.* 81:7051–7055.

Capasso, J.M. and C.B. Hirschberg. 1984*b.* Effect of nucleotides on translocation of sugar nucleotides and adenosine 3′ phosphate 5′ phosphosulfate into Golgi apparatus vesicles. *Biochim. Biophys. Acta.* 777:133–139.

Capasso, J.M. and C.B. Hirschberg. 1984c. Effect of atractylosides, palmitoyl coenzyme A, and anion transport inhibitors on translocation of nucleotide sugars and nucleotide sulfate into Golgi vesicles. *J. Biol. Chem.* 259:4263–4266.

Capasso, J.M., T.W. Keenan, C. Abeijon, and C.B. Hirschberg. 1989. Mechanism of phosphorylation in the lumen of the Golgi apparatus: Translocation of adenosine 5′ triphosphate into Golgi vesicles from rat liver and mammary gland. *J. Biol. Chem.* 264:5233–5240.

Clairmont, C.A., A. DeMaio, and C.B. Hirschberg. 1992. Translocation of ATP into the lumen of the rough endoplasmic reticulum-derived vesicles and its binding to lumenal proteins including BiP (GRP 78) and GRP 94. *J. Biol. Chem.* 267:3983–3990.

Coates, S.W., T. Gurney, L.W. Sommers, M. Yeh, and C.B. Hirschberg. 1980. Subcellular localization of sugar nucleotide synthetases. *J. Biol. Chem.* 255:9225–9229.

Dahdal, R.Y., and K.J. Colley. 1993. Specific sequences in the signal anchor of the β-galactoside α2,6 sialyltransferases are not essential for Golgi localization. Membrane flanking sequence may specify Golgi retention. *J. Biol. Chem.* 268:26310–26319.

Deutscher, S.L., N. Nuwayhid, P. Stanley, E.I.B. Briles, and C.B. Hirschberg. 1984. Translocation across Golgi vesicle membranes. A CHO glycosylation mutant deficient in CMP-sialic acid transport. *Cell.* 39:295–299.

Deutscher, S.L., and C.B. Hirschberg. 1986. Mechanism of galactosylation in the Golgi apparatus: A Chinese hamster ovary cell mutant deficient in translocation of UDP-galactose across Golgi vesicle membranes. *J. Biol. Chem.* 261:96–100.

Douglas, R.H., and C.E. Ballou. 1982. Purification of an α-*N*-acetylglucosaminyltransferase from yeast *Kluyveromyces lactis* and a study of mutants defective with enzyme activity. *Biochemistry.* 21:1561–1570.

Flynn, G.C., T.G. Chappell, and J.E. Rothman. 1989. Peptide binding and release by proteins implicated as catalysts of protein assembly. *Science (Wash. DC).* 245:385–390.

Guillen, E., and C.B. Hirschberg. 1995a. Transport of adenosine triphosphate into rat liver endoplasmic reticulum proteoliposomes. *Biochemistry.* 34:5472–5476.

Guillen E., and C.B. Hirschberg. 1995b. Reconstitution and purification of the endoplasmic reticulum ATP transporter. *J. Gen. Physiol.* 105:27a.

Hauser, S.C., J.C. Ziurys, and J.L. Golan. 1988. A membrane transporter mediates access of uridine 5′-diphosphoglucuronic acid from the cytosol into the endoplasmic reticulum of rat hepatocytes: Implications for glucuronidation reactions. *Biochim. Biophys. Acta.* 967:149–157.

Hayes, B.K., H.H. Freeze, and A. Varki. 1993. Biosynthesis of oligosaccharides in intact Golgi preparations from rat liver. Analysis of *N*-linked glycans labeled by UDP-[6-^{3}H]*N*-acetylglucosamine. *J. Biol. Chem.* 268:16139–16154.

Hayes, B.K., and A. Varki. 1993a. Biosynthesis of oligosaccharides in intact Golgi apparatus from rat liver. Analysis of *N*-linked glycans labeled by UDP-[6-^{3}H] galactose, CMP-[9-^{3}H]*N*-acetylneuraminic acid and [acetyl ^{3}H]acetyl-coenzyme A. *J. Biol. Chem.* 268:16155–16169.

Hayes, B.K., and A. Varki. 1993b. The biosynthesis of oligosaccharides in intact Golgi preparations from rat liver. Analysis of *N*-linked glycans labeled by UDP-[6-^{3}H]*N*-acetylgalactosamine. *J. Biol. Chem.* 261:16170–16178.

Helenius, A. 1994. How *N*-linked oligosaccharides affect glycoprotein folding in the endoplasmic reticulum. *Mol. Cell. Biol.* 5:253–265.

Hendershot, L.M., J. Ting, and A.S. Lee. 1988. Identity of the immunoglobulin heavy chain binding protein with the 78,000 Dalton glucose regulated protein and the role of posttranslational modifications in its binding function. *Mol. Cell. Bio.* 8:4250–4256.

Hirschberg, C.B., and M.D. Snider. 1987. Topography of glycosylation in the rough endoplasmic reticulum and Golgi apparatus. *Annu. Rev. Biochem.* 56:63–88.

Ioffe, E., and P. Stanley. 1994. Mice lacking *N*-acetylglucosaminyltransferase I activity die at mid-gestation revealing an essential role for complex or hybrid *N*-linked carbohydrates. *Proc. Nat. Acad. Sci. USA.* 91:728–732.

Jungnickel, B., and T.A. Rapoport. 1993. DIDS (4,4′ diisothiocyanato-stilbene-2,2′ disulfonic acid) inhibits an early step of protein translocation across the mammalian ER membrane. *Fed. Eur. Biochem. Soc. Lett.* 329:268–272.

Katz, R.N., J.E. Rothman, V.R. Lingappa, G. Blobel, and H.F. Lodish. 1977. Membrane assembly *in vitro*. Synthesis, glycosylation and asymmetric insertion of a transmembrane protein. *Proc. Natl. Acad. Sci. USA.* 74:3278–3282.

Kuhn, N.J., and A. White. 1975. The topography of lactose synthesis. *Biochem. J.* 148:77–84.

Kuhn, N.J., and A. White. 1976. Evidence for specific transport of uridine diphosphate galactose across the Golgi membrane of rat mammary gland. *Biochem. J.* 154:243–244.

Kuhn, N.J., and A. White. 1977. The role of nucleoside diphosphatase in a uridine nucleotide cycle associated with lactose synthesis in rat mammary gland Golgi apparatus. *Biochem. J.* 168:423–433.

Lingappa, V.R., J.R. Lingappa, R. Prassad, K. Ebner, and G. Blobel. 1978. Coupled cell-free synthesis, segregation and core glycosylation of a secretory protein. *Proc. Natl. Acad. Sci. USA.* 75:2338–2342.

Mandon, E.C., M.E. Milla, E. Kempner, and C.B. Hirschberg. 1994. Purification of the Golgi adenosine 3′ phosphate 5′-phosphosulfate transporter, a homodimer within the membrane. *Proc. Natl. Acad. Sci. USA.* 91:10707–10711.

Mayinger, P., and D.I. Meyer. 1993. An ATP transporter is required for protein translocation into the yeast endoplasmic reticulum. *EMBO (Eur. Mol. Biol. Organ.) J.* 12:659–666.

Milla, M.E., and C.B. Hirschberg. 1989. Reconstitution of Golgi vesicle CMP-sialic acid and adenosine 3′ phosphate 5′phosphosulfate transport into proteoliposomes. *Proc. Natl. Acad. Sci. USA.* 86:1786–1790.

Milla, M.E., C.A. Clairmont, and C.B. Hirschberg. 1992. Reconstitution into proteoliposomes and partial purification of the Golgi apparatus membrane UDP-galactose, UDP-xylose and UDP-glucuronic acid transport activities. *J. Biol. Chem.* 267:103–107.

Munro, S., and H.R.B. Pelham. 1986. An Hsp 70-like protein in the ER: Identity with 78 kD glucose-regulated protein and immunoglobulin heavy chain binding protein. *Cell.* 46:291–300.

Nilsson, T., M.H. Hoe, P. Slusarewicz, C. Rabouille, R. Watson, F. Hunter, G. Watzele, E.G. Berger, and G. Warren. 1994. Kin recognition between medical Golgi enzymes in HeLa Cells. *EMBO (Eur. Mol. Biol. Organ.) J.* 13:562–574.

Novikoff, A.B., and S. Goldfischer. 1961. Nucleosidediphosphatase activity in the Golgi apparatus and its usefulness for cytological studies. *Proc. Natl. Acad. Sci. USA.* 47:802–810.

Nuwayhid, N., J.H. Glaser, J.C. Johnson, H.E. Conrad, S.C. Hauser, and C.B. Hirschberg. 1986. Xylosylation and glucuronosylation reactions in rat liver Golgi apparatus and endoplasmic reticulum. *J. Biol. Chem.* 261:12936–12941.

Palade, G. 1975. Intracellular aspects of the process of protein synthesis. *Science (Wash. DC).* 189:347–358.

Perez, M., and C.B. Hirschberg. 1985. Translocation of UDP-*N*-acetylglucosamine into vesicles derived from rat liver endoplasmic reticulum and Golgi apparatus. *J. Biol. Chem.* 260:4671–4678.

Perez, M., and C.B. Hirschberg. 1986. Topography of glycosylation reactions in the rough endoplasmic reticulum membrane. *J. Biol. Chem.* 261:6822–6830.

Perez, M., and C.B. Hirschberg. 1987. Transport of sugar nucleotides into the lumen of vesicles derived from rat liver rough endoplasmic reticulum and Golgi apparatus. *Methods Enzymol.* 138:709–715.

Pfeffer, S.R., and J.E. Rothman. 1987. Biosynthetic protein transport and sorting by the endoplasmic reticulum and Golgi. *Annu. Rev. Biochem.* 56:833–851.

Pryer, N.K., L.J. Wuestehube, and R. Schekman. 1992. Vesicle mediated protein sorting. *Annu. Rev. Biochem.* 61:471–516.

Quemeneur, E., R. Guthapfel, and P. Gueguen. 1994. A major phosphoprotein of the endoplasmic reticulum is protein disulfide isomerase. *J. Biol. Chem.* 269:5485–5488.

Schwarz, J.K., J.M. Capasso, and C.B. Hirschberg. 1984. Translocation of adenosine 3'-phosphate 5'-phosphosulfate into rat liver Golgi vesicles. *J. Biol. Chem.* 259:3554–3559.

Sommers, L.W., and C.B. Hirschberg. 1982. Transport of sugar nucleotides into rat liver Golgi: A new Golgi marker activity. *J. Biol. Chem.* 257:10811–10817.

Sousa, M.C., M.A. Ferrero-Garcia, and A.J. Parodi. 1992. Recognition of the oligosaccharide and protein moieties of glycoproteins by the UDP-Glc:glycoprotein glucosyltransferase. *Biochem.* 31:97–105.

Stanley, P. 1980. Altered glycolipids of CHO cells resistant to wheat germ agglutinin. *Am. Chem. Soc. Symp. Ser. B.* 128:213–221.

Stanley, P. 1985. Membrane mutants of animal cells: Rapid identification of those with a primary defect in glycosylation. *Mol. Cell. Biol.* 5:923–929.

Toma, L., M.A.S. Pinhal, C.P. Dietrich, H.B. Nader, and C.B. Hirschberg. 1996. Transport of UDP-galactose into the Golgi lumen regulates the biosynthesis of proteoglycans. *J. Biol. Chem.* 271:3897–3901.

Vanstapel, F., and N. Blanckaert. 1988. Carrier-mediated translocation of uridine diphosphate glucose into the lumen of the endoplasmic reticulum-derived vesicles from rat liver. *J. Clin. Invest.* 82:1113–1122.

Waldman, B.C., and G. Rudnick. 1990. UDP-GlcNAc transport across the Golgi membrane: Electroneutral exchange for dianionic UMP. *Biochemistry.* 29:44–52.

Yanagisawa, K., D. Resnick, C. Abeijon, P.W. Robbins, and C.B. Hirschberg. 1990. A guanosine diphosphatase enriched in Golgi vesicles of *Saccharomyces cerevisiae*: purification and characterization. *J. Biol. Chem.* 265:19351–19355.

Regulation of Vacuolar Acidification

Michael Forgac

Department of Cellular and Molecular Physiology, Tufts University School of Medicine, Boston, Massachusetts 02111

Vacuolar acidification plays an essential role in a variety of cellular processes, including receptor-mediated endocytosis, intracellular membrane traffic, protein processing and degradation, and coupled transport. Vacuolar compartments are acidified by the vacuolar class of (H^+)-ATPases (or V-ATPases), which are present in many intracellular organelles in eukaryotic cells. The V-ATPase is a multisubunit complex of molecular mass 750 kD, which is composed of two functional domains. The 500-kD peripheral V_1 domain, which has the structure $73_358_340_134_133_1$ contains all of the nucleotide-binding sites, which are located on the 73-kD A and 58-kD B subunits. The 250 kD integral V_0 domain, which has the structure $100_138_119_117_6$, is responsible for proton translocation, with the 17-kD c subunit playing a direct role in proton movement.

We have demonstrated that V-ATPase activity can be controlled through disulfide bond formation between two cysteine residues located at the catalytic site on the A subunit (Feng and Forgac, 1994). We have further characterized the structure of the nucleotide binding sites by use of 2-azido-ATP (Zhang, et al., 1995). Dissociation and reassembly of the integral V_0 domain has provided information concerning the role of individual V_0 subunits in proton conduction and bafilomycin binding (Zhang et al., 1994). Finally, we have demonstrated that the 50-kD polypeptide, which is identical to the 50-kD subunit of the AP-2 adaptor complex, is required for activity and in vitro reassembly of the coated vesicle V-ATPase (Liu et al., 1994). These results may have important implications for targeting and assembly of V-ATPases as well regulation of vacuolar acidification in vivo.

Functions of Vacuolar Acidification

Vacuolar acidification, which is carried out by the vacuolar (H^+)-ATPases, or V-ATPases, plays an important role in a variety of cellular processes (for review, see Forgac, 1989; Forgac, 1992). In the process of receptor-mediated endocytosis, exposure to a low pH within the endocytic structure termed *CURL* (for compartment of uncoupling of receptor and ligand) activates dissociation of internalized ligands from their receptors, thus facilitating recycling of receptors to the plasma membrane (Fig. 1). Neutralization of CURL with weak bases, such as chloroquine or ammonia, results in accumulation of ligand-receptor complexes within endocytic structures and depletion of receptors from the cell surface. A low endosomal pH is also required for formation of carrier vesicles that mediate transport from endosomes to lysosomes (Clague et al., 1994). Vacuolar acidification plays a similar role in the intracellular targeting of newly synthesized lysosomal enzymes from the

Golgi to the lysosome. Exposure of lysosomal enzyme/mannose-6-phosphate receptor complexes to a low pH within a late uncoupling compartment facilitates recycling of mannose-6-phosphate receptors to the trans-Golgi (Fig. 1). Neutralization of this compartment with weak bases results in secretion of lysosomal enzymes. Thus, in both cases, cells employ low pH as a signal to facilitate receptor recycling.

Acidification of secretory vesicles is necessary for the coupled transport of various small molecules, such as neurotransmitters, whose uptake is coupled to either the proton gradient or the membrane potential generated by the V-ATPases. Acidification of lysosomes and other degradative and processing compartments is required for the activity of acid hydrolases located in their lumen, such that both protein breakdown and processing are sensitive to weak bases. Finally, V-ATPases

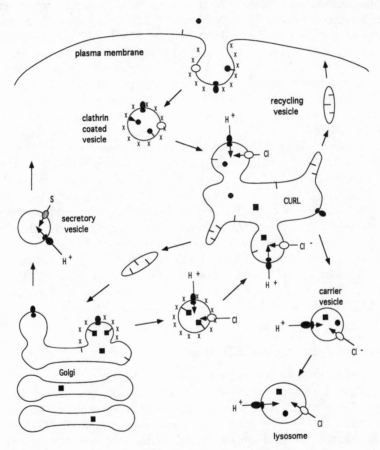

Figure 1. Function of vacuolar acidification in receptor-mediated endocytosis and intracellular targeting of lysosomal enzymes. Following internalization of ligand-receptor complexes (●), exposure to a low pH within CURL causes dissociation of ligands from their receptors, thus facilitating recycling of the unoccupied receptors to the cell surface. Lysosomal enzymes (■) bind to Man-6-P receptors in the *trans*-Golgi and these complexes are also delivered to an acidic recycling compartment, which activates their dissociation and allows recycling of Man-6-P receptors to the Golgi. In both cases ligands released into the lumen of CURL are targeted to lysosomes via carrier vesicles whose formation is also dependent on an acidic vacuolar pH.

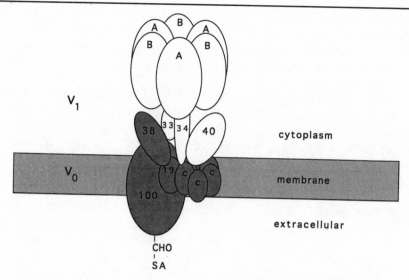

Figure 2. Structural model of the coated vesicle V-ATPase. The V-ATPase complex is composed of two domains. The V_1 domain, which has the structure $A_3B_340_134_133_1$ (Arai et al., 1988), is a 500-kD peripheral complex that contains all of the nucleotide binding sites, which are located on the 73-kD A (catalytic) and 58-kD B (noncatalytic) subunits (Feng and Forgac, 1992a). The integral V_0 domain is a 250-kD complex (Zhang et al., 1992) which has the structure $100_138_119_1c_6$ and is responsible for proton translocation across the membrane (Zhang et al., 1994).

also function in the plasma membrane of various specialized cells, including renal intercalated cells (Brown et al., 1987), osteoclasts (Chaterjee et al., 1992), macrophages (Swallow et al., 1990), and tumor cells (Martinez-Zaguilan et al., 1993), where they function in renal acidification, bone resorption, cytoplasmic alkalinization, and metastasis, respectively.

Structure and Subunit Function of V-ATPases

Our current model for the structure of the coated vesicle V-ATPase (Arai et al., 1987b) is shown in Fig. 2. The V-ATPase is a multisubunit complex composed of two functional domains. The V_1 domain, which has the structure $73_358_340_134_133_1$ (Arai et al., 1988), is a 750-kD peripheral complex that is oriented towards the cytoplasmic side of the membrane (Adachi et al., 1990a) and can be dissociated from the membrane with chaotropic agents (Arai et al., 1989; Adachi et al., 1990b). This domain possesses all of the nucleotide binding sites, which are located on the 73-kD A subunits (catalytic sites) and the 58-kD B subunits (noncatalytic sites).

The integral V_0 domain, which has the structure $100_138_119_117_6$ (Arai et al., 1988), is a 250-kD complex that is responsible for proton translocation across the membrane. The 17-kD c subunit, which possesses four transmembrane helices (Mandel et al., 1988), the last of which contains a buried carboxyl group that is the site of reaction with DCCD, is essential for proton conductance (Arai et al., 1987a). The 100-kD subunit is a transmembrane glycoprotein (Adachi et al., 1990b) possessing an amino terminal hydrophilic domain and a carboxy terminal hydrophobic domain containing six transmembrane helices (Perin et al., 1991). This subunit also appears to possess the binding site for bafilomycin (Zhang et al., 1994), a specific inhibitor of the V-ATPases (Bowman, E.J., 1988). The 38-kD subunit possesses no transmembrane helices but remains tightly bound to the V_0 domain (Wang et al., 1988).

The V-ATPases thus resemble the F-ATPases of mitochondria, chloroplasts, and bacteria that are responsible for ATP synthesis (Senior, 1990; Penefsky and Cross, 1991; Pedersen and Amzel, 1993). This is further demonstrated by sequence homology between the A and B subunits of the V-ATPase and the alpha and beta subunits of F_1 (Zimniak et al., 1988; Bowman et al., 1988; Puopolo et al., 1991; Puopolo et al., 1992a) and between the DCCD-reactive c subunits (Mandel et al., 1988). Structural similarity between the V and F-ATPases has also been observed from electron microscopic studies (Dschida and Bowman, 1992), although in addition to the ball-and-stalk appearance of F_1F_0, the V-ATPases possess two arms projecting from the base of the stalk. In vitro studies have demonstrated that it is possible to dissociate and reassemble the V_1 and V_0 domains (Puopolo et al., 1990) and have begun to address the role of individual V_1 subunits. Thus, the 40-kD subunit has been shown to be required for maximum activity and stability of the V-ATPase complex (Puopolo et al., 1992b).

Homology between the nucleotide binding subunits of the V- and F-ATPases makes the recent X-ray crystal structure of F_1 (Abrahams et al., 1994) particularly relevant to the V-ATPases. This structure demonstrates an alternating hexamer of alpha and beta subunits with the nucleotide binding sites located at the interfaces between subunits and the gamma subunit existing as an extended alpha helical rod through the center of the hexamer. The catalytic sites are located principally on the beta subunits, while the noncatalytic sites are located principally on the alpha subunits.

Studies of the coated-vesicle V-ATPase have identified Cys254 of the A subunit as the residue responsible for the sensitivity of the V-ATPases to sulfhydryl reagents (Feng et al., 1992a). This cysteine is conserved in all of the A subunit sequences and is located in the glycine-rich loop consensus sequence GXGKTV, which, from the crystal structure of F_1, appears to be in close proximity to the triphosphates of ATP bound at the catalytic site (Abrahams et al., 1994). It has also recently been shown that Cys254 is able to form a disulfide bond with a second conserved cysteine residue, Cys532, near the carboxyl terminus of the protein (Feng et al., 1994). The ability of these two cysteines to form a disulfide bond indicates that these residues must be within 5–6 Å of each other in the tertiary structure of the A subunit, a distance consistent with that observed between the corresponding positions in the beta subunit of F_1 (Abrahams et al., 1994). Aromatic residues in the vicinity of Cys532 are also labeled upon occupation of rapidly exchangeable sites on the V-ATPase with 2-azido-[^{32}P]-ATP (Zhang et al., 1995); this suggests that these residues may stabilize the adenine ring in the nucleotide-binding pocket. A model of the catalytic nucleotide-binding site on the V-ATPase A subunit based on these data and homology to the F-ATPase beta subunit is shown in Fig. 3.

One significant difference between the V- and F-ATPases is in the activity of the separate domains. Thus, unlike the F_1 domain, the dissociated V_1 domain is inactive as a MgATPase (Puopolo et al., 1990; Puopolo et al., 1992b). Similarly, the free V_0 domain is not functional as a passive proton channel (Zhang et al., 1992).

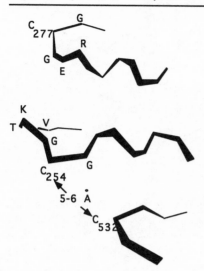

Figure 3. Model for the structure of the catalytic nucleotide binding site on the V-ATPase A subunit. The model is based on the X-ray crystal structure of the homologous beta subunit of the mitochondrial F-ATPase (Abrahams et al., 1994), the localization of Cys254 to the catalytic site of the V-ATPase A subunit (Feng and Forgac, 1992a), and the demonstration that Cys254 and Cys532 are able to form a disulfide bond (Feng and Forgac, 1994); these indicate a separation of 5–6 Å in the tertiary structure of the A subunit. ATP binds such that the triphosphates are surrounded by the glycine-rich loop (GXGKTV) and the adenine ring extends towards the bottom of the figure (near Cys532).

Nevertheless, dissociation and reassembly studies indicate that the V_0 domain does possess the information necessary to form a DCCD-inhibitable proton channel (Zhang et al., 1994). The lack of activity of the separate V_1 and V_0 domains may have relevance to the utilization of assembly and disassembly of the V-ATPase complex as a mechanism for regulation of vacuolar acidification in vivo (see below).

Regulation of Vacuolar Acidification

Considerable evidence indicates that cells are able to control the pH of the various intracellular compartments (Forgac, 1989). Thus, along the endocytic pathway, endocytic coated vesicles are near neutral pH while endosomes are mildly acidic and lysosomes are more acidic still (Anderson and Orci, 1988). A similar gradation of pH exists from the ER and *cis* and medial Golgi (neutral pH) to the *trans* Golgi and Golgi-derived vesicles (mildly acidic) and to the lysosomes (pH < 5). The following sections discuss a number of possible mechanisms that may be involved in the control of vacuolar pH in vivo.

Disulfide-Bond Formation

It has been demonstrated that disulfide-bond formation between Cys254 and Cys532 of the A subunit results in reversible inactivation of the V-ATPase (Feng and Forgac, 1994). Moreover, a significant fraction (approximately 50%) of the V-ATPase in native clathrin-coated vesicles exists in this reversibly inactivated, disulfide-bonded state (Feng and Forgac, 1992b). Because the protein tends to become spontaneously activated after isolation, even in the absence of reducing agents, this value represents a lower limit to the fraction of V-ATPase that exists in the disulfide-bonded state in vivo. These observations also suggest that activation occurs through thio-disulfide exchange with another cysteine residue in the A subunit rather than by simple reduction. The fact that both of these cysteine residues are conserved in all V-ATPase A subunits thus far sequenced, from yeast to mam-

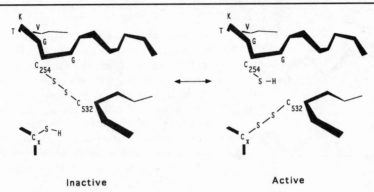

Inactive   Active

Figure 4. Model for the role of disulfide-bond formation in regulation of V-ATPase activity. The V-ATPase is postulated to exist in two states, an inactive state in which Cys254 and Cys532 are disulfide bonded and an active state in which Cys254 is reduced, most likely through thio-disulfide exchange with another sulfhydryl in the V-ATPase A subunit (Feng and Forgac, 1992b; 1994).

malian species, suggests that their function has been highly conserved throughout evolution.

A model for the involvement of disulfide-bond formation in regulation of vacuolar acidification is shown in Fig. 4. According to this model, the enzyme exists in an equilibrium between an active state, in which Cys254 is reduced, and an inactive state, in which Cys254 and Cys532 are disulfide bonded. Thus, the V-ATPase at the plasma membrane and in endocytic coated vesicles would be predicted to be in the oxidized state, whereas the V-ATPase in CURL would be reduced. Because the cytoplasm of the cell is strongly reducing, the catalytic site on the A subunit must be shielded to prevent reduction of this disulfide bond under conditions where it remains oxidized. The cellular signals that control the equilibrium between the oxidized and reduced states remain to be determined.

Insight into how disulfide-bond formation between Cys254 and Cys532 inactivates the V-ATPase has come from studies in which 2-azido[^{32}P]ATP is used (Feng and Forgac, 1994). It was found that disulfide-bond formation does not block nucleotide binding, a result suggesting that oxidation instead disrupts catalysis. The X-ray crystal structure of the F-ATPase indicates that the catalytic beta subunit undergoes a considerable movement between the amino and carboxyl terminal domains during catalysis. Thus the empty form of the beta subunit shows a 20-Å separation of these two domains when compared with the ATP- and ADP-bound forms (Abrahams et al., 1994). If one assumes that a similar conformational change must occur during each catalytic cycle of the V-ATPases, disulfide-bond formation may inhibit catalysis by locking the A subunit into a form in which the two domains are close to each other, thus preventing the domain separation that must occur to complete the cycle.

Assembly of V_1 and V_0 Domains

Studies on the coated-vesicle V-ATPase have revealed the presence in native clathrin-coated vesicles of a significant population (approximately 50%) of free V_0 domains (Zhang et al., 1992). The stability of the fully assembled V-ATPase complex under these conditions suggests that this is not an artifact of dissociation of the V_1 and V_0 domains during isolation of the vesicles. These V_0 domains were shown to be silent with respect to proton conductance activity (Zhang et al., 1992). Similarly, a significant pool of free V_1 domains have been identified by immunoprecipitation from the cytoplasm of MDBK cells (Myers and Forgac, 1993a). These results suggest that assembly of the V_1 and V_0 domains may play a role in regulation of vacuolar acidification in vivo.

The strongest evidence in favor of this mechanism comes from studies of yeast (Kane, 1995). Thus, growth of yeast in the absence of glucose results in the rapid (within minutes) dissociation of the V_1 and V_0 domains. This effect is rapidly reversible and is not effected by inhibition of protein synthesis, an observation indicating that the same peripheral and integral domains which had been dissociated are reassembling. The intracellular signals that control the assembly state of the V-ATPase remain to be determined.

Targeting of V-ATPases

Epithelial cells in the kidney and related tissues are able to control proton transport across the apical membrane through reversible exocytosis of intracellular vesicles containing a high density of V-ATPases (Gluck et al., 1982; Brown et al., 1987). While the mechanisms by which V-ATPases are selectively targeted to particular intracellular membranes have not been completely elucidated, there are a number of relevant observations. First, multiple isoforms of several V-ATPase subunits exist that may contain targeting information. In plants, distinct A-subunit isoforms are required for acidification of the central vacuole and the Golgi compartment (Gogarten et al., 1992), while in yeast the vph1 and stv1 isoforms of the 100-kD subunit appear to be targeted to distinct intracellular compartments (Manolson et al., 1994). In animal cells, multiple isoforms of the B subunit have been identified (Bernasconi et al., 1990; Puopolo et al., 1992a), with one of these isoforms expressed predominantly in renal cells that target V-ATPases to the apical membrane (Nelson et al., 1992). Whether the apical membrane targeting of the V-ATPase in these cells is directly attributable to the B subunit isoform expressed remains to be determined.

Further information relevant to the selective targeting of V-ATPases has come from studies of the coated vesicle V-ATPase. It has been found that the V-ATPase in coated vesicles contains a single copy of the 50-kD subunit of the AP-2 adaptor complex (Myers et al., 1993b). The adaptors are multisubunit complexes involved in bridging the cytoplasmic tails of internalized receptors with the heavy chain of clathrin (Pearse and Robinson, 1990). They thus provide for the selectivity of clathrin-mediated membrane traffic. AP-2 is specific for the plasma membrane while the homologous AP1 complex is specific for the Golgi. The association of the V-ATPase complex with one of the adaptor subunits suggests a possible mechanism by which V-ATPases may become internalized via clathrin-coated pits (see Fig. 5). More recent studies have indicated that AP50 is essential both for activity and in vitro assembly of the coated vesicle V-ATPase (Liu et al., 1994). These results suggest that V-ATPase/adaptor interactions may also play a role in assembly and/or regulation of the V-ATPase complex.

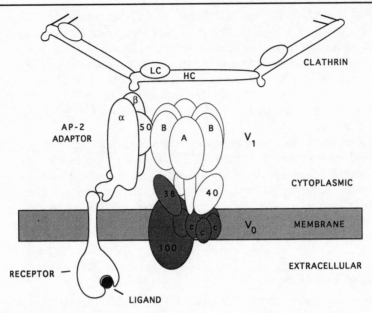

Figure 5. Model for the role of the V-ATPase/AP-2 interaction in the internalization and/or assembly of the V-ATPase complex in clathrin-coated pits. The AP-2 adaptor complex, which bridges internalized receptors with clathrin (Pearse and Robinson, 1990), is postulated to bind to the V-ATPase complex via AP50, which is present stoichiometrically in the purified V-ATPase (Myers and Forgac, 1993b) and is required for both activity and in vitro assembly of the V-ATPase complex (Liu et al., 1994). AP50 may become transferred from AP-2 to the V-ATPase at some point following internalization. *HC*, clathrin heavy chain; *LC*, clathrin light chain.

Other Mechanisms

Several other mechanisms have been suggested for control of vacuolar acidification. The "slip" mechanism postulates that changes in the tightness of coupling between ATP hydrolysis and proton transport can control vacuolar pH (Nelson, 1992). In fact, several conditions, including detergent solubilization (Arai et al., 1987a), high concentrations of ATP (Arai et al., 1989), and mild proteolysis (Adachi et al., 1990a) have been shown to alter the coupling efficiency; this suggests that the enzyme is poised to exist in a state of altered coupling. Several activator and inhibitor proteins have also been identified that have effects on V-ATPase activity in vitro (Zhang et al., 1992a, b; Xie et al., 1993). Finally, because the V-ATPase is electrogenic, proton transport is dependent upon the activity of a parallel chloride channel (Glickman et al., 1983; Arai et al., 1989), and this channel has been shown to be regulated by protein kinase A–dependent phosphorylation (Bae and Verkman, 1990; Mulberg et al., 1991).

Conclusions

The V-ATPases play an important role in a variety of processes in eukaryotic cells, including receptor-mediated endocytosis, intracellular membrane traffic, protein processing and degradation, coupled transport, and certain functions in the plasma membrane of specialized cells. For all of these cellular functions, regulation of the level of V-ATPase activity is crucial. Among the mechanisms that may be involved in regulation of vacuolar acidification are disulfide-bond formation at the catalytic site, control of assembly of the peripheral and integral domains, selective targeting of V-ATPases to particular cellular sites, and control of anion conductance. Further work will be required to determine the relative importance of these mechanisms in vivo.

References

Abrahams, J.P., A.G. Leslie, R. Lutter, and J.E. Walker. 1994. Structure at 2.8 Å resolution of F_1-ATPase from bovine heart mitochondria. *Nature (Lond.)*. 370:621–628.

Adachi, I., H. Arai, R. Pimental, and M. Forgac. 1990a. Proteolysis and orientation on reconstitution of the coated vesicle proton pump. *J. Biol. Chem.* 265:960–966.

Adachi, I., K. Puopolo, N. Marquez-Sterling, H. Arai, and M. Forgac. 1990b. Dissociation, crosslinking and glycosylation of the coated vesicle proton pump. *J. Biol. Chem.* 265:967–973.

Anderson, R.G., and L. Orci. 1988. A view of acidic intracellular compartments. *J. Cell Biol.* 106:539–543.

Arai, H., M. Berne, and M. Forgac. 1987a. Inhibition of the coated vesicle proton pump and labeling of a 17,000 dalton polypeptide by DCCD. *J. Biol. Chem.* 262:11006–11011.

Arai, H., M. Berne, G. Teres, H. Terres, K. Puopolo, and M. Forgac. 1987b. Subunit composition and ATP site labeling of the coated vesicle (H^+)-ATPase. *Biochemistry.* 26:6632–6638.

Arai, H., S. Pink, and M. Forgac. 1989. Interaction of anions and ATP with the coated vesicle proton pump. *Biochemistry.* 28:3075–3082.

Arai, H., G. Terres, S. Pink, and M. Forgac. 1988. Topography and subunit stoichiometry of the coated vesicle proton pump. *J. Biol. Chem.* 263:8796–8802.

Bae, H.R., and A. S. Verkman. 1990. Protein kinase A regulates chloride conductance in endocytic vesicles from proximal tubule. *Nature (Lond.)*. 348:637–639.

Bernasconi, P., T. Rausch, I. Struve, L. Morgan, and L. Taiz. 1990. An mRNA from human brain encodes an isoform of the B subunit of the vacuolar H^+-ATPase. *J. Biol. Chem.* 265:17428–17431.

Bowman, B.J., R. Allen, M.A. Wechser, and E.J. Bowman. 1988. Isolation of the genes encoding the *Neurospora* vacuolar ATPase: Analysis of vma-2 encoding the 57 kDa polypeptide and comparison to vma-1. *J. Biol. Chem.* 263:14002–14007.

Bowman, E.J., A. Siebers, and K. Altendorf. 1988a. Bafilomycins: A class of inhibitors of membrane ATPases from microorganisms, animal cells and plant cells. *Proc. Natl. Acad. Sci. USA.* 85:7972–7976.

Brown, D., S. Gluck, and J. Hartwig. 1987. Structure of the novel membrane coating material in proton-secreting epithelial cells and identification as an H^+ATPase. *J. Cell Biol.* 105:1637–1648.

Chatterjee, D., M. Chakraborty, M. Leit, L. Neff, S. Jamsa-Kellokumpu, R. Fuchs, and R. Baron. 1992. Sensitivity to vanadate and isoforms of subunits A and B distinguish the osteoclast proton pump from other vacuolar H^+ ATPases. *Proc. Natl. Acad. Sci. USA.* 89:6257–6261.

Clague, M.J., S. Urbe, F. Aniento, and J. Gruenberg. 1994. Vacuolar ATPase activity is required for endosomal carrier vesicle formation. *J. Biol. Chem.* 269:21–24.

Dscida, W.J., and B.J. Bowman. 1992. Structure of the vacuolar ATPase from *Neurospora crassa* as determined by electron microscopy. *J. Biol. Chem.* 267:18783–18789.

Feng, Y., and M. Forgac. 1992a. Cysteine 254 of the 73-kDa A subunit is responsible for inhibition of the coated vesicles (H$^+$)-ATPase upon modification by sulfhydryl reagents. *J. Biol. Chem.* 267:5817–5822.

Feng, Y., and M. Forgac. 1992b. A novel mechanism for regulation of vacuolar acidification. *J. Biol. Chem.* 267:19769–19772.

Feng, Y., and M. Forgac. 1994. Inhibition of vacuolar H$^+$-ATPase by disulfide bond formation between cysteine 254 and cysteine 532 in subunit A. *J. Biol. Chem.* 269:13224–13230.

Forgac, M. 1989. Structure and function of the vacuolar class of ATP-driven proton pumps. *Physiol. Rev.* 69:765–796.

Forgac, M. 1992. Structure and properties of the coated vesicle (H$^+$)ATPase. *J. Bioenerg. Biomembr.* 24:341–350.

Glickman, J., K. Croen, S. Kelly, and Q. Al-Awqati. 1983. Golgi membranes contain an electrogenic proton pump in parallel to a chloride conductance. *J. Cell Biol.* 97:1303–1308.

Gluck, S., C. Cannon, and Q. Al-Awqati. 1982. Exocytosis regulates urinary acidification in turtle bladder by rapid insertion of H$^+$ pumps into the luminal membrane. *Proc. Natl. Acad. Sci. USA.* 79:4327–4331.

Gogarten, J.P., J. Fichmann, Y. Braun, L. Morgan, P. Styles, S.L. Taiz, K. DeLapp, and L. Taiz. 1992. The use of antisense mRNA to inhibit the tonoplast H$^+$ATPase in carrot. *Plant Cell.* 4:851–864.

Kane, P.M. 1995. Disassembly and reassembly of the yeast vacuolar H$^+$-ATPase in vivo. *J. Biol. Chem.* 270:17025–17032.

Liu, Q., Y. Feng, and M. Forgac. 1994. Activity and *In Vitro* reassembly of the coated vesicle (H$^+$)-ATPase requires the 50-kDa subunit of the clathrin assembly complex AP-2. *J. Biol. Chem.* 269:31592–31597.

Mandel, M., Y. Moriyama, J.D. Hulmes, Y.C. Pan, H. Nelson, and N. Nelson. 1988. cDNA sequence encoding the 16-kDa proteolipid of chromaffin granules implies gene duplication in the evolution of H$^+$-ATPases. *Proc. Natl. Acad. Sci. USA.* 85:5521–5524.

Manolson, M.F., B. Wu, D. Proteau, B.E. Taillon, B.T. Roberts, M.A. Hoyt, and E.W. Jones. 1994. stv1 gene encodes functional homologue of 95-kDa yeast vacuolar H$^+$-ATPase subunit vph1p. *J. Biol. Chem.* 269:14064–14074.

Marquez-Sterling, N., I.M. Herman, T. Pesecreta, H. Arai, G. Terres, and M. Forgac. 1991. Immunolocalization of the vacuolar-type (H$^+$)-ATPase from clathrin-coated vesicles. *Eur. J. Cell Biol.* 56:19–33.

Martinez-Zaguilan, R., R. Lynch, G. Martinez, and R. Gillies. 1993. Vacuolar-type H$^+$-ATPases are functionally expressed in plasma membranes of human tumor cells. *Am. J. Physiol.* 265:C1015–C1029.

Mulberg, A.E., B.M. Tulk, and M. Forgac. 1991. Modulation of coated vesicle chloride channel activity and acidification by reversible protein kinase A-dependent phosphorylation. *J. Biol. Chem.* 266:20590–20593.

Myers, M., and M. Forgac. 1993a. Assembly of the peripheral domain of the bovine vacuolar

H$^+$-ATPase. *J. Cell. Physiol.* 156:35–42.

Myers, M., and M. Forgac. 1993b. The coated vesicle vacuolar (H$^+$)-ATPase associates with and is phosphorylated by the 50 kDa polypeptide of the clathrin assembly protein AP-2. *J. Biol. Chem.* 268:9184–9186.

Nelson, N. 1992. Structural conservation and functional diversity of V-ATPases. *J. Bioenerg. Biomembr.* 24:407–414.

Nelson, R.D., X.L. Guo, K. Masood, D. Brown, M. Kalkbrenner, and S. Gluck. 1992. Selectively amplified expression of an isoform of the V-ATPase 56 kDa subunit in renal intercalated cells. *Proc. Natl. Acad. Sci. USA.* 89:3541–3545.

Pearse, B.M., and M.S. Robinson. 1990. Clathrin, adaptors and sorting. *Annu. Rev. Cell Biol.* 6:151–171.

Pedersen, P.L., and L.M. Amzel. 1993. ATP synthases: Structure, reaction center, mechanism and regulation of one of nature's most unique machines. *J. Biol. Chem.* 268:9937–9940.

Penefsky, H.S., and R.L. Cross. 1991. Structure and mechanism of F_0F_1-type ATP synthases and ATPases. *Adv. Enzymol.* 64:173–214.

Perin, M.S., V.A. Fried, D.K. Stone, X.S. Xie, and T.C. Sudhof. 1991. Structure of the 116 kDa polypeptide of the clathrin-coated vesicle/synaptic vesicle proton pump. *J. Biol. Chem.* 266:3877–3881.

Puopolo, K., and M. Forgac. 1990. Functional reassembly of the coated vesicle proton pump. *J. Biol. Chem.* 265:14836–14841.

Puopolo, K., C. Kumamoto, I. Adachi, and M. Forgac. 1991. A single gene encodes the catalytic "A" subunit of the bovine vacuolar H$^+$-ATPase. *J. Biol. Chem.* 266:24564–24572.

Puopolo, K., C. Kumamoto, I. Adachi, R. Magner, and M. Forgac. 1992a. Differential expression of the "B" subunit of the vacuolar H$^+$-ATPase in bovine tissues. *J. Biol. Chem.* 267:3696–3706.

Puopolo, K., M. Sczekan, R. Magner, and M. Forgac. 1992b. The 40 kDa subunit enhances but is not required for activity of the coated vesicle proton pump. *J. Biol. Chem.* 267:5171–5176.

Senior, A.E. (1990). The proton-translocating ATPase of *E. coli. Annu. Rev. Biophys. Biophys. Chem.* 19:7–41.

Swallow, C.J., S. Grinstein, and O.D. Rotstein. 1990. A vacuolar type H$^+$ATPase regulates cytoplasmic pH in murine macrophages. *J. Biol. Chem.* 265:7645–7654.

Wang, S.Y., Y. Moriyama, M. Mandel, J.D. Hulmes, Y.C. Pan, W. Danho, H. Nelson, and N. Nelson. 1988. Cloning of cDNA encoding a 32-kDa protein; An accessory polypeptide of the H$^+$-ATPase from chromaffin granules. *J. Biol. Chem.* 263:17638–17642.

Xie, X.S., B.P. Crider, and D.K. Stone. 1993. Isolation of a protein activator of the clathrin-coated vesicle proton pump. *J. Biol. Chem.* 268:25063–25067.

Zhang, J., Y. Feng, and M. Forgac. 1994. Proton conduction and bafilomycin binding by the V_0 domain of the coated vesicle V-ATPase. *J. Biol. Chem.* 269:23518–23523.

Zhang, J., M. Myers, and M. Forgac. 1992. Characterization of the V_0 domain of the coated vesicle (H$^+$)-ATPase. *J. Biol. Chem.* 267:9773–9778.

Zhang, J., E. Vasilyeva, Y. Feng, and M. Forgac. 1995. Inhibition and labeling of the coated vesicle V-ATPase by 2-azido-[^{32}P]ATP. *J. Biol. Chem.* 270:15494–15500.

Zhang, K., Z.Q. Wang, and S. Gluck. 1992a. Identification and partial purification of a cytosolic activator of vacuolar H^+ATPases from mammalian kidney. *J. Biol. Chem.* 267:9701–9705.

Zhang, K., Z.Q. Wang, and S. Gluck. 1992b. A cytosolic inhibitor of vacuolar H^+ATPases from mammalian kidney. *J. Biol. Chem.* 267:14539–14542.

Zimniak, L., P. Dittrich, J.P. Gogarten, H. Kibak, and L.Taiz. 1988. The cDNA sequence of the 69 kDa subunit of the carrot vacuolar H^+-ATPase: Homology to the beta-chain of F_0F_1-ATPases. *J. Biol. Chem.* 263:9102–9112.

MscL: A Mechanosensitive Channel in *Escherichia coli*

Sergei I. Sukharev,* Paul Blount,* Boris Martinac,‡ H. Robert Guy,§ and Ching Kung*

*Laboratory of Molecular Biology and Department of Genetics, University of Wisconsin, Madison, Wisconsin 53706; ‡Department of Pharmacology, The University of Western Australia, Nedlands, Western Australia 6907; §Laboratory of Mathematical Biology, National Cancer Institute, National Institutes of Health, Bethesda, Maryland 20892

Force generation, motion, and perception of mechanical stimuli are inseparable features of living matter. Many of the molecular motors that convert chemical energy of ATP or electrochemical ion gradients into directed traffic of cellular components or body movements have been characterized in detail. At the same time the nature of molecules that do the opposite, i.e., convert mechanical stimuli into chemical or electrical signals in cells, remains largely unknown.

When protists stumble upon a solid surface, they change their swimming trajectories in a predictable manner; this suggests that mechanosensation evolved quite early in evolution. In multicellular organisms, the perception of mechanical stimuli has developed into highly specialized and critical functions such as hearing, balance, and proprioception. Although mechanosensation is ubiquitous, it is the least understood of all senses. There are several reasons for this. First, the specific sensing elements (touch neurons, for instance) are often dispersed throughout the body rather than localized in a specific organ, and second, the putative mechanoreceptor molecules within these elements are present in a relatively low abundance. Furthermore, mechanical stress is not a ligand, thus the established approach to identification of receptors by tagging them with their high-affinity agonists or blockers is not an option in many cases.

The first clues to where the mechanosensory responses may originate came in the early 1980s when the single-channel recording technique (patch-clamp) allowed the observation of a certain class of channels that increase their open probability when the membrane is mechanically stressed. Mechanosensitive (MS) or stretch-sensitive channels are believed to be primary mechanoreceptors in many cells.[1] Since their discovery in embryonic chick skeletal muscle cells (Guharay and Sachs, 1984) and frog muscle (Brehm et al., 1984), MS channels have been observed electrophysiologically in more than 30 cell types, including microbes. The biophysical and physiologic aspects of several diverse types of MS channels have been reviewed

---

[1]Besides ion channels, integrin complexes (Schwartz and Ingber, 1994) as well as some membrane-associated enzymes (Lehtonen and Kinnunen, 1995) may be involved in generation of primary mechanosensory signals in cells.

Organellar Ion Channels and Transporters © 1996 by The Rockefeller University Press

in detail by Sachs (1988 and 1992), Howard, et al. (1988), Morris (1990), Martinac (1993), Hamill and McBride (1994), and Sackin (1995). Unlike many voltage- or ligand-gated channels, none of the MS channels of higher organisms have been identified as molecular entities to date. Studies of mechanosensory mechanisms can be difficult in otherwise genetically amenable systems such as *Caenorhabditis elegans*, where not only channel-like proteins, but also specific elements of cytoskeleton and extracellular matrix were shown to be involved in such responses (Huang and Chalfie, 1994; Hong and Driscoll, 1994; reviewed by Bargmann, 1994).

Historically, microorganisms have often been used to begin the solving of many fundamental problems of contemporary biology. The complexity of multicellular organisms urged us to seek a more convenient system in which molecular participants of mechanosensory mechanisms could be identified biochemically or genetically. May bacteria help us again? Are they responsive to mechanical stimuli and do they possess appropriate molecular mechanisms?

In the present short review we will describe the approaches that led us to the identification of the mechano-sensitive channel of large conductance (MscL) from the *Escherichia coli* cell envelope and outline primary molecular data on this first cloned molecule that changes its functional state upon physiologically relevant mechanical stimuli.

Mechanosensitive Channels in *E. coli*

In 1987 bacteria became objects of single-channel recording techniques. (Martinac, et al., 1987). The presence of cephalexin, an antibiotic that blocks septation, induces filamentous forms of *E. coli*, which can be turned into round "giant" spheroplasts of 5–10 μm in diameter (Ruthe and Adler, 1985) amenable to patch-clamp experiments. Application of a ramp of negative pressure to a patch excised from an *E. coli* giant spheroplast reveals two types of mechanoactivated channel activities, a smaller conductance of 0.9–1 nS (in 400 mM salts) with a sustained open state (MscS) activated first, and a large ~2.5–3-nS conductance with faster kinetics (MscL) activated at a higher pressure. MscS exhibited a weak anionic preference, whereas MscL was found to be nonselective. Historically, MscS activity was discovered and characterized first and referred to as a "pressure-sensitive channel from *E. coli* cell envelope" (Martinac et al., 1987). Besides its mechanosensitivity, MscS exhibited voltage-dependence, tending to open upon depolarization. Activation of MscS by membrane-intercalating amphipathic compounds suggested that the channel is sensitive to mechanical perturbations in the lipid bilayer (Martinac et al., 1990). In addition to MscL and MscS, another channel that is activated at relatively low pressures and has yet a smaller, 0.3 nS (mini) conductance, called MscM, has recently been reported (Berrier et al., 1994; Cui et al., 1995).

Why does *E. coli* need these channels? Currently it is presumed that MS channels play a key role in fast osmoregulatory responses in bacteria. Osmotic force (turgor) is the major mechanical force acting on walled membranes of bacteria, protozoa, fungi, and plants. Enteric bacteria, cycling between intestines and the soil, are subject to drastic changes in their environment. *E. coli* possess a number of efficient defenses against both osmotic up- or down-shocks, thus they manage to maintain a practically constant osmotic gradient across their membrane in a wide range of external osmolarities (Csonka and Hanson, 1991). Upon a hypertonic challenge (dehydration), bacteria immediately activate their K^+ pumps and later synthesize osmoprotectants such as proline and glycine betaine. Upon a moderate hypotonic challenge, *E. coli* adjusts its porin ration (OmpF/OmpC) and synthesize membrane-derived oligosaccharides in the periplasm. However, abrupt placement of *E. coli* into distilled water causes the organism to immediately expel ions and small molecules while maintaining macromolecules and viability (Britten and Mc-Clure, 1962; Tsapis and Kepes, 1977, Csonka and Hanson, 1991). The mechanism of this solute exit is not completely understood, but mechanosensitive channels have been implicated in these fast adaptation responses (Berrier et al., 1992). Simple estimation shows that 20–30 mOsm difference between the cytoplasm and external medium should be sufficient to exert the tension in the bacterial envelope of $\sim$10–15 dynes/cm, equivalent to the activation threshold for MS channels in patch-clamp experiments. Recent results by Cui et al. (1995) obtained on *E. coli* protoplasts in the whole-cell configuration have demonstrated osmotic activation of MS channels in this system.

Reconstitution and Recording of Bacterial MS Channels in Liposomes

Reconstitution has proved to be a powerful approach in studies of a variety of channels (see Miller, 1986). It allows convenient recording of single channels at a desired density and usually indicates requirements for certain cellular components for proper channel functioning. In the present study, reconstitution techniques played a crucial role in functional assays of MS channel activity in chromatographic fractions.

In vitro patch-clamp recording on liposomes reconstituted with fragments of native *E. coli* membranes was performed according to the protocol initially proposed by Criado and Keller (1987) and then modified by Delcour et al., (1989). Native membranes isolated by differential centrifugation were mixed with phospholipid liposomes made of soybean azolectin and then subjected to a dehydration-rehydration cycle during which membranes fuse and form large multilayer proteoliposomes. Placement of several pieces of such lipid material in a bath containing 5–40 mM Mg^{2+} results in formation of large transparent blisters amenable to patch recording. (Delcour et al., 1989). We also have reconstituted detergent-solubilized membrane extracts or chromatographic fractions with exogenous lipids by use of a conventional dialysis protocol. Resultant proteoliposomes were subjected to a dehydration-rehydration cycle and examined by patch-clamp as above. Both types of preparations had activities of both MscS and MscL that were similar to those recorded in vivo. The activating pressure for both types of channels was lower in either of the liposome preparations when compared with spheroplasts (Sukharev et al., 1993).

Pilot separations of crude membrane extracts by size-exclusion chromatography indicated that MscS and MscL activities are associated with fractions of $\sim$300 and $\sim$70 kD, respectively, suggesting that they are distinct molecular entities (Sukharev et al., 1993). More robust and reproducible MscL activities in reconstituted fractions encouraged us to enrich and identify this channel protein by following its activity in vitro.

Identification of MscL Protein

The strategy of the experiment was as follows. Octylglucoside-solubilized membrane proteins were fractionated on several columns. Individual fractions were reconstituted with equal amounts of exogenous lipids and resultant proteoliposomes were examined by patch-clamp. The averaged numbers of MscL conducting units from several (7–20) patches sampled from each fraction reflect the specific MscL activity in the elution profile. Empty fractions were determined and discarded, whereas MscL-containing fractions were pooled for the next step of enrichment. Thereby, we were able to trace the characteristic MscL activity through several chromatographic steps and correlate it with the presence of a certain band on a SDS-polyacrylamide protein gel (Sukharev et al., 1994a,b).

The MscL activity was found to be retained most efficiently by hydroxyapatite and phenylsepharose columns. Starting with total *E. coli* membranes, we performed two different series of chromatographic enrichments based on these two core steps (see Sukharev et al., 1994b for details). Comparison of the two final fractions from these series of fractionations showed only one common component, a protein with an approximate molecular weight of 17,000 whose presence was apparently associated with the MscL activity.

Cloning of *mscL*

The identified protein was enriched, separated by SDS-PAGE, and microsequenced, revealing 37 NH_2-terminal residues. A database search matched this sequence to the partial sequence of a 17-kD protein of unknown function coded 3' of the *trkA* gene previously reported by Schlosser et al. (1993). By use of a λ clone in the Daniels-Blattner collection (Daniels and Blattner, 1987), the corresponding 3.1 kb *PstI* fragment was subcloned and the entire *mscL* was then sequenced (Sukharev et al., 1994a). The open reading frame (Fig. 1) predicts a 136-amino acid protein (15 kD) with a highly hydrophobic core comprising two putative transmembrane domains and a hydrophilic COOH terminus carrying multiple charges. The size of the functional channel complex estimated by gel-filtration under nondena-

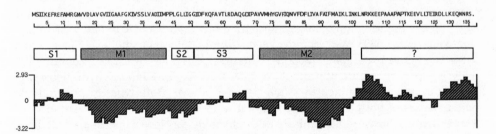

Figure 1. Structure of MscL. The predicted primary sequence, block-diagram for putative domains, and Kyte-Doolittle hydropathy profile for MscL protein. The two most hydrophobic regions, M1 and M2, likely represent α-helical membrane-spanning domains. The S2-S3 amphophilic region forms putative "hairpin," protruding into the pore of the open channel. S1 region may also be a part of pore lining. The hydrophilic region beyond M2 has not been modeled. The channel complex has been modeled as a pentamer or hexamer if identical 15-kD subunits (H.R. Guy, unpublished).

turing conditions was approximately 70 kD, suggesting either a multimer of several 15-kD subunits or a complex containing other kinds of subunits.

mscL Gene and Its Product Are Necessary for Mechanosensitive Channel Function

To prove that the cloned gene is indeed necessary for the MscL channel activity, we generated an *E. coli* strain with the *mscL* ORF disrupted by insertion of the Ω chloramphenicol (ΩCm) gene (knock-out strain). We also generated an overexpresser strain, i.e. knock-out strain bearing the wild-type *mscL* on a multicopy plasmid. Examination of membrane patches from giant spheroplasts derived from the wild-type parent showed 4–10 MscL conducting units per patch (standard diameter of pipettes 2 μm). No MscL channels were found in any of the 50 patches from the knock-out mutant, but more than 40 MscL units per patch were observed in every one of the 6 patches from the overexpresser strain after induction of the expression plasmid (Sukharev et al., 1994*a*).

Consistent with the electrophysiologic observations, protein patterns of the same chromatographically enriched fraction from these three strains showed that the 17-kD protein was missing in the knock-out mutant and was enriched in the rescued overexpresser strain. Such fractions were individually reconstituted into liposomes and examined by patch-clamp. The MscL occurrence in patches corresponded to the abundance of the 17-kD band in the fractions. No MscL activity was encountered in patches from liposomes with the knock-out fraction. (Sukharev et al., 1994*a*).

It should be mentioned that bacteria lacking MscL (knock-outs) grew normally and recovered after osmotic downshock at approximately the same rate as wild type (S. Sukharev, unpublished). Independent measurements of effluxes of some osmoprotectants (trehalose, glutamate, and glycine betaine) induced by strong hypotonic shocks indicated almost no difference between the wild-type and *mscL⁻* strains (A. Ghazi, personal communication). We assume that there might be functional redundancy and that the presence of MscS, as well as perhaps other mechanisms, may compensate for the absence of MscL.

The Product of the *mscL* Gene Is Sufficient for Mechanosensitive Channel Activity

We confirmed the direct relationship between the *mscL* product and the channel activity by heterologous expression of this gene in two different settings: in yeasts and in a cell-free system. The budding yeast (*Saccharomyces cerevisiae*) and a shuttle-type yeast expression vector containing a selectable marker and a strong inducible promoter were taken as a first system. The vector with a correctly oriented *mscL* ORF, or the control vector with no insert, was electroporated into yeast cells with subsequent selection. Since we could not be sure that the expressed MscL was transported into the plasma membrane, and not into some internal membranes, we reconstituted the total membrane fraction by the fusion method to ensure channel identification by patch-clamp in liposomes. Obvious MscL activities were recorded in all 20 patches of two independent preparations from *mscL*-expressing yeasts.

None of the 10 patches from the parallel empty-plasmid control preparations had any MscL activity (Sukharev et al., 1994*b*).

A cell-free expression system appears to be the cleanest, allowing controllable transcription and translation of channels or their subunits from a single template. The pSP64-polyA vector containing the *mscL* ORF was added to drive the reaction in the transcription-translation-coupled (TnT) reticulocyte lysate system supplemented with canine pancreatic microsomes. When [^{35}S]methionine was added to the reaction mixture, a single 17-kD protein was synthesized as indicated by gel autoradiography. In a parallel unlabeled preparation of microsomes reconstituted with azolectin liposomes, we encountered the typical 2.5-nS MscL activities in 4 patches out of 12 sampled. No such activities were found in 12 patches from the control preparation driven by the empty plasmid (Sukharev et al., 1994*a*). MscL activities recorded upon expression in two heterologous systems strongly suggest that the product of *mscL* gene is the only protein necessary for the channel to be formed.

What We Know

E. coli, a gram-negative bacterium, possesses at least two types of mechanoactivated channels, the 1-nS MscS and 2.5-nS MscL, which are evidently distinct molecular entities.

The channels survived solubilization in nondenaturing detergents and were functional upon reconstitution with exogenous lipids. Patch-sampling technique gave a reliable assessment of specific channel activity in reconstituted chromatographic fractions through several steps of enrichment, thus allowing us to identify the protein band associated with the MscL activity.

MscL, the large-conductance channel is formed by a relatively small (15 kD) mostly hydrophobic protein, the product of *mscL* gene, which is necessary as well as sufficient for the channel activity. The molecular weight of the functional complex as judged by size-exclusion chromatography suggests a multimer of several 15 kD subunits.

Functional reconstitution of purified MscL protein, as well as in vitro expression experiments indicated that virtually the only requirement for channel functionality is its placement in a lipid bilayer. Hence, the gating of MscL is driven directly by the tension transduced via the lipid bilayer. No other components, such as cell wall, submembrane cytoskeleton, or extracellular matrix, are required.

Problems and Future Perspectives
Structural Models for MscL

The *mscL* sequence is unique and has no homology to known voltage- or ligand-gated channels. The hydropathy plot for the predicted protein suggests that the first two-thirds of the molecule are relatively hydrophobic. Analysis of the MscL sequence by use of a number of computational approaches (Guy and Durell, 1995) predicted a tentative spatial model for MscL. In this model, each subunit has two α-helical hydrophobic membrane spanning domains, M1 and M2, and two domains that form amphipathic alpha helices (S1 and S3); the latter could either be helices at the bilayer surface, or possibly line the channel pore. If S3 is part of the pore lining, S2 and S3 may make a loop structure similar to the H5, or P domain, described for voltage-gated channels (H.R. Guy, unpublished). Similarly, in a recent review by Jan and Jan (1994), an M1-H5-M2 design was proposed for MscL, and MscL was considered to be a member of a family of very diverse but distantly related membrane transporters and channels sharing this structural motif. Note, however, that the putative H5 domain proposed by Jan and Jan is located in a slightly different location than the S2-S3 domains (Fig. 1). Although these models are tentative and currently have little experimental evidence to support them, they may prove to be very useful in that they give several testable predictions regarding the topology of the protein, the number of subunits, and possible domains and residues forming the pore lining.

MscL Protein: Antibodies, Location, and Stoichiometry of Assembly

A simple method of MscL purification by use of gene fusion with the glutathione *S*-transferase has recently been published by Häse et al., (1995). Using a similar approach utilizing COOH-terminal tagging with six sequential histidines and subsequent one-step purification on a Ni-NTA column, we have purified and reconstituted a functional 6xHis-tagged MscL protein. These rapid purification techniques have allowed the generation of antibodies (Häse et al., 1995; S. Sukharev, unpublished) that can now be used for localization and stoichiometric studies. For example, our preliminary studies have confirmed immunochemically previous studies by Berrier et al., (1989) suggesting that MS channels are primarily located in the inner membrane of *E. coli* (S. Sukharev, P. Blount, and C. Kung, unpublished). Finally, purified protein and antibodies will help facilitate studies of topology and stoichiometry of channel assembly. We are using antibodies generated against a COOH-terminal peptide to determine the protein orientation in the membrane. Finally, using crosslinking agents and detection of either purified protein, or native protein using the Western blot procedure, we hope to determine the subunit stoichiometry of the complex.

Identification and Analysis of Functional Domains

The activities of MscL-like channels have been observed in several other Gram-negative (P. Blount and P. Moe, unpublished), as well as Gram-positive species (Zoratti et al., 1990), an observation suggesting that MscL is likely a common component of bacterial membranes. The recent identification of very conserved MscL homologues in two diverse bacterial species, *Haemophilus influenza* (Gram-negative) (Fleischmann et al., 1995) and *Clostridium perfringens* (Gram-positive) (Matsushita et al., 1995), supports this hypothesis and suggests an important role for the MscL protein. Identification and electrophysiologic characterization of other potential homologues are in progress. By identifying and characterizing homologues, we hope to obtain insight into structural motifs important for channel activity. Finally, deletion and site-directed mutagenesis are beginning to provide information on whether or not domains are important for channel gating and function. The long-range goal of such experiments is to correlate structural features with functional characteristics.

References

Bargmann, C.I. 1994. Molecular mechanisms of mechanosensation? *Cell.* 78:729–731.

Berrier, C., A. Coulombe, C. Houssin, and A. Ghazi. 1989. A patch-clamp study of ion channels of inner and outer membranes and of contact zones of *E. coli*, fused into giant liposomes. *FEBS Lett.* 259:27–32.

Berrier, C., A. Coulombe, I. Szabo, M. Zoratti, and A. Ghazi. 1992. Gadolinium ion inhibits loss of metabolites induced by osmotic shock and large stretch-activated channels in bacteria. *Eur. J. Bio.* 206:559–565.

Berrier, C., M. Besnard, A. Coulombe, and A. Ghazi. 1994. Miltiplicity of mechanosensitive ion channels of the native plasma membrane of *E. coli*. *Biophys. J.* 66:A168.

Brehm, P., K. Kullberg, and F. Moody-Corbett. 1984. Properties of nonjunctional acetylcholine receptor channels on innervated muscle of *Xenopus laevis*. *J. Physiol. (Lond.).* 350:631–648.

Britten, R.J., and F.T. McClure. 1962. The amino acid pool of *Escherichia coli*. *Bact. Rev.* 26:292–335.

Criado, M., and B.U. Keller. 1987. A membrane fusion strategy for single-channel recordings of membranes usually non-accessible to patch-clamp electrodes. *FEBS Lett.* 224:172–176.

Csonka, L.M., and D.A. Hanson. 1991. Procaryotic osmoregulation: Genetics and physiology. *Annu. Rev. Microbiol.* 45:529–606.

Cui, C., D.O. Smith, and J. Adler. 1995. Characterization of Mechanosensitive channels in *Escherichia coli* cytoplasmic membrane by whole-cell patch clamp recording. *J. Membrane Biol.* 144:31–42.

Daniels, D.L., and F.R. Blattner. 1987. Mapping using gene encyclopedias. *Nature.* 325:831–832.

Delcour, A.H., B. Martinac, J. Adler, and C. Kung. 1989. Modified reconstitution method used in patch-clamp studies of *Escherichia coli* ion channels. *Biophys. J.* 56:631–636.

Fleischmann, R.D., M.D. Adams, O. White, R.A. Clayton, E.F. Kirkness, A.R. Kerlavage, C.J. Bult, J.F. Tomb, B.A. Dougherty, J.M. Merrick, et al. 1995. Whole-genome random sequencing and assembly of *Haemophilus influenzae* RD. *Science.* 269:496–512.

Guharay, F., and F. Sachs. 1984. Stretch-activated ion channel currents in tissue-cultured embryonic chick skeletal muscle. *J. Physiol. (Lond.).* 352:685–701.

Guy, H.R., and H.R. Durell. 1995. Structural models of Na$^+$, Ca^{2+}, and K$^+$ channels. *In* Ion Channels and Genetic Diseases. D. Dawson, editor. The Rockefeller University Press, New York. 1–16.

Hamill, O.P., and D.W. McBride, Jr. 1994. The cloning of a mechano-gated ion chanel. *Trends Neurosci.* 17:439–443.

Häse, C.C., A.C. Le Dain, and B. Martinac. 1995. Purification and functional reconstitution of the recombinant large mechanosensitive ion channel (MscL) of *Escherichia coli*. *J. Biol. Chem.* 270:18329–18334.

Hong K., and M. Driscoll. 1994. A transmembrane domain of the putative channel subunit MEC-4 influences mechanotransduction and neurodegeneration in *C. elegans*. *Nature.* 367:470–473.

Howard, J., W.M. Roberts, and A.J. Hudspeth. 1988. Mechanoelectrical transduction by hair cell. *Annu. Rev. Biophys. Biophys. Chem.* 17:99–124.

Huang, M., and M. Chalfie. 1994. Gene interactions affecting mechanosensory transduction in *Caenorhabditis elegans*. *Nature*. 367:467–470.

Jan, L.Y., and Y.N. Jan. 1994. Potassium channels and their evolving gates. *Nature*. 371:119–122.

Lehtonen, J.Y.A., and P.K.J. Kinnunen. 1995. Phospholipase A_2 as a mechanosensor. *Biophys. J.* 68:1888–1894.

Martinac, B. 1993. Mechanosensitive ion channels: Biophysics and physiology. *In* Thermodynamics of membrane receptors and channels. M.B. Jackson, editor. CRC Press, Boca Raton. 327–352.

Martinac, B., J. Adler, and C. Kung. 1990. Mechanosensitive channels of *E. coli* activated by amphipaths. *Nature*. 348:261–263.

Martinac, B., M. Buechner, A.H. Delcour, J. Adler, and C. Kung. 1987. Pressure-sensitive ion channel in *Escherichia coli*. *Proc. Natl. Acad. Sci. USA*. 84:2297–2301.

Matsushita, O., C.M. Jung, and A. Okabe. 1995. Identification of the gene encoding a mechanosensitive channel Mscl homologue in *Clostridium perfringens*. *Gene*. 165:147–148.

Miller, C., editor. 1986. Ion Channel Reconstitution. Plenum Press. New York.

Morris, C.E. 1990. Mechanosensitive ion channels. *J. Membrane Biol.* 113:93–107.

Ruthe, H.-J., and J. Adler. 1985. Fusion of bacterial spheroplasts by electric fields. *Biochim. Biophys. Acta*. 819:105–113.

Sachs, F. 1988. Mechanical transduction in biological systems. *CRC Crit. Rev. Biomed. Eng.* 16:141–169.

Sachs, F. 1992. Stretch-sensitive ion channels: An update. *In* Sensory Transduction. D. Corey, and S. Roper, editors. The Rockefeller University Press, New York 241–260.

Sackin, H. 1995. Mechanosensitive channels. *Annu. Rev. Physiol.* 57:333–353.

Schlosser, A., A. Hamann, D. Bossemeyer, E. Schnider, and E. Bakker. 1993. NAD^+ binding to the *Escherichia coli* K^+-uptake protein TrkA and sequence similarity between TrkA and domains of a family of dehydrogenases suggests a role for NAD^+ in bacterial transport. *Mol. Microbiol.* 9:533–543.

Schwartz, M.A., and D.E. Ingber. 1994. Integrating with integrins. *Mol. Biol. Cell.* 5:389–393.

Sukharev, S.I., P. Blount, B. Martinac, F.R. Blattner, and C. Kung. 1994*a*. A large-conductance mechanosensitive channel in *E. coli* encoded by *mscL* alone. *Nature*. 368:265–268.

Sukharev, S.I., B. Martinac, V.Y. Arshavsky, and C. Kung. 1993. Two types of mechanosensitive channels in the *Escherichia coli* cell envelope: Solubilization and functional reconstitution. *Biophys. J.* 65:177–183.

Sukharev, S.I., B. Martinac, P. Blount, and C. Kung. 1994*b*. Functional reconstitution as an assay for biochemical isolation of channel proteins: Application to the molecular identification of a bacterial mechanosensitive channel. *A Companion to Methods Enzymol.* 6:51–59.

Tsapis, A., and A. Kepes. 1977. Transient breakdown of the permeability barrier of the membrane of *Escherichia coli* upon hypoosmotic shock. *Biochim. Biophys. Acta*. 469:1–12.

Zoratti, M., V. Petronilli, and I. Szabo. 1990. Stretch-activated composite ion channels in *Bacillus subtilis*. *Biochem. Biophys. Res. Commun.* 168:443–450.

Chapter 3

Mitochondrial Channels and Transporters

Structure and Function of the Yeast Outer Mitochondrial Membrane Channel, VDAC

Michael Forte,* Elizabeth Blachly-Dyson,* and Marco Colombini‡

*Vollum Institute of Advanced Biomedical Research, Oregon Health Sciences University, Portland, Oregon 97201 and ‡Department of Zoology, University of Maryland, College Park, Maryland 27402

Introduction

The voltage-dependent anion channel (VDAC) of the outer mitochondrial membrane, also known as mitochondrial porin, is a small ($\sim$ 283 amino acids, 30–35 kD) abundant protein found in mitochondria from cells of all eukaryotes (Sorgato and Moran, 1993; Colombini, 1994). It was first identified in mitochondrial fractions of *Paramecium aurelia* by Schein et al. (1976) when these investigators were searching for voltage-dependent calcium channel activity. Subsequently, VDAC channel activity was identified in mitochondria by subcellular fractionation (Schein et al., 1976). Mitochondria from a wide variety of eukaryotes such as plants, humans, *Neurospora crassa*, and yeast have all been shown to have VDAC channels with properties that are evolutionarily conserved (for review, see Colombini et al., 1995). These channels share a similar single channel conductance (about 4–4.5 nS in 1 M KCl), ion selectivity (about 2:1 preference for Cl over K), and voltage dependence. Furthermore, all VDAC channels are symmetrical with respect to gating properties. When no voltage is applied, VDAC channels are in their high-conducting, open state. When voltage is increased to about 20–30 mV (both positive and negative potentials), channels switch to lower conducting, closed states. These properties characterize VDAC channels and distinguish them from all other channels observed after reconstitution into planar lipid bilayers.

Physiologically, VDAC is thought to function as the primary pathway for the movement of adenine nucleotides and other metabolites through the mitochondrial outer membrane, thus controlling the traffic of these essential compounds to and from this organelle as well as the entry of other substrates into a variety of metabolic pathways. These metabolites can reach a molecular weight of almost 1000, and therefore the permeability pathway must be large. Consistent with this function, VDAC has been demonstrated by both functional (Colombini, 1980) and electron microscopy (EM) studies (Thomas, et al., 1991) to form large (3-nm diameter) aqueous conduction pathways. VDAC has also been shown to be the site for binding of hexokinase and glycerol kinase to the mitochondrial outer membrane (for review, see Adams et al., 1991). The binding of these enzymes to the mitochondrion is dynamic; it varies between different tissues, during development, and with the metabolic state of the cell. It has been proposed that binding to the outer membrane allows these enzymes preferential access to mitochondrial ATP, thus regulating metabolism. Consistent with the notion that binding of these enzymes is an important

Organellar Ion Channels and Transporters © 1996 by The Rockefeller University Press

metabolic regulatory event, binding may occur specifically at contact sites between the inner and outer mitochondrial membranes, potentially linking cytoplasmic metabolism and ATP production, as regulated by hexokinase and glycerol kinase, to mitochondrial respiration and oxidative phosphorylation. Furthermore, malignant cells found in tumors have an increased percentage of mitochondrially bound hexokinase over normal cells, and it appears that VDAC is part of a complex forming the mitochondrial benzodiazepine receptor (McEnery et al., 1992), a distinct receptor that is similar to the central nervous system receptor in its affinity for diazepam but differs in its affinity for other drugs.

Over the past decade, VDAC has been exploited as a system in which to define the structure of a model ion channel and the conformational transitions associated with voltage gating in a somewhat simpler protein than those forming plasma membrane channels, such as K^+ or Na^+ channels. In addition, given the wide variety of proteins that are able to associate dynamically with VDAC, this protein is likely to represent a point at which mitochondrial function is regulated and thus offers an opportunity for the investigation of the coordination of mitochondrial function with the overall metabolic activity of the cell. To facilitate the analysis of this complex molecule, not only at the level of the voltage-driven conformational changes but also of the relevant cell biology associated with the function of this channel, we have turned to analysis of VDAC in the yeast *Saccharomyces cerevisae.* This experimental system offers a variety of advantages, among them the ability to analyze the function of this protein by both classical and molecular genetic approaches. These approaches have allowed the development of an experimental system in which to probe the structure of this channel and the topologic changes associated with voltage gating; they have recently resulted in the identification of a second yeast gene encoding a VDAC protein. In this chapter we will specifically deal with studies done over the past decade describing the VDAC system in yeast and will refer to the two yeast VDAC genes (YVDAC1 and YVDAC2) in the historical order of identification. For a more general synopsis, readers are referred to a recent, comprehensive review (Colombini et al., 1995).

Voltage-Driven Conformational Changes
The Basic System

The general experimental approach used in the analysis of the structure and conformational transitions of the YVDAC1 molecule points out the unique advantages afforded by the well-developed genetics of this experimental system (Blachly-Dyson et al., 1990) and is outlined in Fig. 1. Initially, haploid yeast strains in which the chromosomal copy of the YVDAC1 gene has been disrupted (YVDAC1$^-$) were created by standard gene transplacement methods. These strains are then used as recipients for the expression of a variety of YVDAC1 genes that have been modified by site-directed mutagenesis. Since these altered YVDAC1 genes on plasmids represent the only functional YVDAC1 genes in these organisms, only mutant YVDAC1 proteins are expressed in these cells. The plasmid vector used in these studies contains a *CEN* sequence so that transformants contain 1–2 copies of each mutant VDAC gene. Plasmid-encoded VDAC molecules were then purified from Triton X100–solubilized mitochondria by simple chromatographic procedures. For-

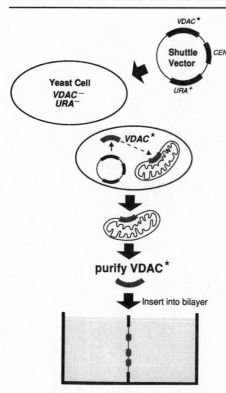

Figure 1. Scheme of the steps in the production of YVDAC1 molecules for electrophysiologic analysis. VDAC* refers to a YVDAC1 gene containing a site-directed mutation.

tunately, the protein encoded by the second yeast VDAC gene (YVDAC2, see below) does not elute from columns under these conditions. Resulting samples contain a single protein of appropriate molecular weight as judged by SDS-PAGE fractionation followed by silver staining. YVDAC1 molecules are then introduced into solvent-free, planar phospholipid bilayers for biophysical analysis. Typically, four channel characteristics are examined in detail. First, single-channel conductance measurements serve as a useful guide for the integrity of the channel. Second, reversal potential measurements are used to define the ion selectivity of individual channels. Selectivity measurements serve as an estimate of the interaction of the charges lining the pore with the charged ions as they pass. Finally, the voltage dependence of individual channels is described by two parameters, n and Vo. n is derived from the steepness of the voltage-dependent conductance changes and reflects the number of charges in the voltage sensor needed to account for the observed voltage dependence if these charges were able to respond to the entire applied potential. Thus, the larger the value of n, the steeper the voltage dependence. The second, V_o (also referred to as the midpoint of the switching region), is a measure of the potential at which the probability of any channel being in the open state is 50%.

The Structure of the YVDAC1 Channel as Probed by Site-Directed Mutagenesis

Fig. 2 outlines our current model of the structure of the YVDAC1 channel and the conformational changes that take place during the voltage-dependent transition

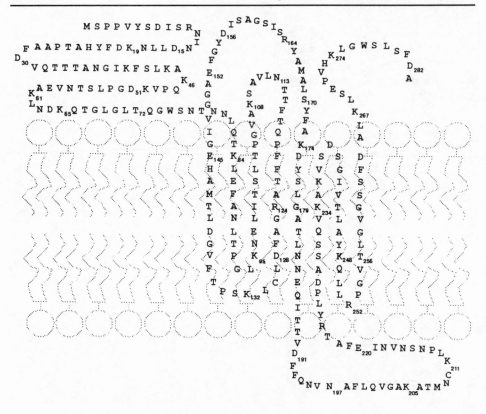

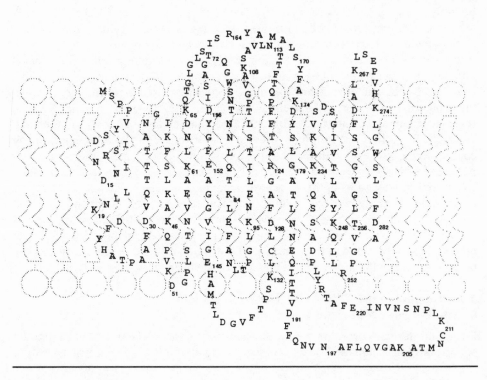

from the open to the closed state as revealed by analysis of over 40 different YVDAC1 molecules containing single or multiple site–directed changes. Structures of open and closed channels were developed on the basis of several assumptions. First, analysis of the sequence of a number of VDAC proteins has uncovered an overall protein motif that consists primarily of alternating hydrophilic and hydrophobic residues, generating transmembrane segments formed by sided β sheets with a hydrophobic side facing the lipid bilayer and a hydrophilic side facing the lumen of the aqueous pore. Circular dichroism (CD) spectra are also consistent with the view that VDAC is primarily composed of β sheets (Mangan and Colombini, unpublished; Shao et al., 1994). Second, the large pore radius of VDAC makes it likely that small ions such as K^+ and Cl^- probably cross the membrane without intimate interaction with the walls of the channel. In addition, genetic evidence (Peng et al., 1992*a*) and results obtained by EM analysis (Thomas et al., 1991) of frozen, hydrated samples strongly favor the conclusion that a single 282-residue polypeptide forms one channel. It is virtually certain, then, that the wall of the pore consists of a single layer of protein. The weak anion selectivity of the channel is thus likely to be controlled by charges lining the channel wall (i.e., the net charge in the pore of the channel is slightly positive), and most of the primary sequence of the molecule must be used to form the walls of the open channel pore. Replacement of some of the positive charges in the lining of the wall by negative charges should reduce, or even reverse, the selectivity of VDAC. However, changing the charge of residues located outside the lining of the pore should not affect selectivity and would therefore identify residues that cannot be close to the ion stream and reside in domains connecting transmembrane segments. The open channel properties of individual members of this collection of mutant YVDAC1 molecules are consistent with this interpretation and have led to a model in which the open channel is proposed to be composed of an NH_2 terminal, amphipathic α helix followed by 12 transmembrane β strands, each tilted at about 60° in order to form a pore 3 nm in diameter (Blachly-Dyson, et al., 1990; Colombini et al., 1992; Colombini et al., 1995). The severe tilting of transmembrane strands suggests that the lumen walls may not completely span the full 3–3.5 nm hydrophobic core of the membrane bilayer. Consistent with this prediction, channel openings in the membrane surface of freeze-dried/shadowed VDAC arrays are depressed relative to the surface of the membrane (Thomas et al., 1991).

Voltage-dependent closure of the VDAC channel is associated with dramatic conformational changes, as assessed by a number of different physical criteria (Colombini et al., 1995). Analysis of mutant molecules also indicates that some residues that affect selectivity in the open state no longer do so in the closed state (Peng et al., 1992*b*). The simplest interpretation is that these residues lie in protein segments that move out of the channel upon closure, resulting in a smaller pore diameter and pore volume and radical change in the net charge on the wall of the pore, consistent with previous experimental observations (Colombini et al., 1995). The movement of these strands out of the pore of the channel results in the net movement of charge through the membrane potential, a requirement of voltage gating, and pre-

Figure 2. Working model of the transmembrane topology of the YVDAC1 protein in the closed (*top*) and open channel states (*bottom*).

dicts that the strands that move out of the pore must be part of the voltage sensor. This prediction has been confirmed by the identification of residues in these strands that influence the voltage dependence of the channel in the expected manner when their charge is changed (Thomas et al., 1993). In our current working model for the molecular rearrangements associated with channel closure and voltage gating, the NH_2-terminal α helix and four adjacent β strands, as well as the extreme COOH-terminal β strand, move out of the channel during closure. As is the case with all models, these diagrams are simplified representations of structures and changes that are undoubtedly more complex. They are, however, valuable tools for understanding and summarizing results obtained in our functional studies and for designing future experiments that use tools like site-specific biotinlyation (Qiu et al., 1994; Slatin et al., 1994); these studies should allow a more direct assessment of the structure of this molecule in both the open and closed state.

An Additional VDAC Gene in Yeast
Phenotypes Associated with Elimination of the YVDAC1 Gene

If, as is generally held, VDAC functions as the primary pathway for the movement of essential metabolites through the mitochondrial outer membrane, and if there were a single YVDAC gene, elimination of the YVDAC1 gene should result in respiratory-deficient mitochondria. Since yeast are facultative anaerobes (can grow by fermentation as well as oxidative phosphorylation), yeast strains without functional mitochondria are unable to grow on nonfermentable carbon sources like glycerol but are able to grow, albeit more slowly, on fermentable carbon sources like glucose (the so called *petite* phenotype). Because a variety of early studies indicated that no other VDAC proteins were present in yeast that have a significant similarity to YVDAC1 at either nucleotide sequence or protein level, it was surprising to discover that strains in which the YVDAC1 had been eliminated were able to grow on nonfermentable carbon sources (e.g., glycerol) at 30° C (Dihanich et al., 1987; Blachly-Dyson et al., 1990). However, such mutant strains were determined to be conditional (temperature-sensitive) petites in that they were unable to grow on glycerol at elevated temperatures (37° C). Perhaps even more surprising, expression of any of a wide variety of VDAC molecules containing site-directed mutations that dramatically altered basic channel properties as determined in bilayers (changes from anion to cation selectivity, changes in voltage dependence) restored the ability of these mutant strains to grow on glycerol at 37° C, with several notable exceptions (Blachly-Dyson et al., 1990). Although there are many possible interpretations of these results, two seem most likely. First, it could be that many of the basic channel properties of this molecule defined in bilayers may be unrelated to the function of VDAC in vivo. Second, these results may be explained in part by the existence of a second YVDAC gene (YVDAC2) that can functionally replace YVDAC1 molecules at 30° C but not 37° C. In this latter case, it may be that the growth at 30° C on carbon sources like glycerol requires either YVDAC1 or YVDAC2 but that growth on these carbon sources requires a higher level of one of these molecules for reasons unrelated to channel activity. This last alternative would help explain why mutant YVDAC1 channels with vastly different biophysical properties can grow on glycerol at restrictive temperatures.

Identification of YVDAC2

To discriminate among these two general alternatives, we attempted to identify genes that, when overexpressed, can allow strains lacking YVDAC1 to grow on glycerol at 37°C. Genomic DNA was prepared from a strain missing the YVDAC1 gene, the DNA was partially digested with a restriction enzyme, and a library was created by insertion of the resulting fragments into a yeast shuttle vector. The vector chosen maintains plasmids in yeast at a relatively high copy number (50–100 copies per cell), effectively resulting in overexpression of proteins encoded by inserted genomic segments. Strains in which the YVDAC1 gene had been eliminated were transformed with this library, and transformants were selected for growth on glycerol at 37° C. Plasmids were then prepared from surviving transformants, and associated genomic sequences were characterized.

All of the surviving transformants contain vectors with overlapping segments of the same region of genomic DNA. This region contains a gene that encodes a protein which is roughly 50% identical to YVDAC1 that has been termed YVDAC2. Subdivision of this genomic region indicated that overexpression of the YVDAC2 gene alone was sufficient to allow growth of strains missing YVDAC1 on glycerol at the restrictive temperature and demonstrate that YVDAC2, and not associated genomic sequences, are responsible for allowing growth under these conditions. Analysis of the sequence of YVDAC2 indicates that despite the relatively low level of sequence conservation between YVDAC1 and YVDAC2, the overall pattern of alternating hydrophilic and hydrophobic residues is conserved as well as the position of putative transmembrane *sided* β strands. These results confirm conclusions reached in the analysis of human VDAC proteins, where expression of these distantly related human channels (~20% identical to YVDAC1) in yeast are also able to complement growth defects on glycerol at 37° C of strains missing YVDAC1 (Blachly-Dyson et al., 1993). These human proteins are also able to form channels with characteristics that are indistinguishable from those formed by yeast or Neurospora VDAC proteins. Thus, what appears to be important for VDAC channel structure and function is conservation of overall conformation, which is not constrained by high conservation of primary amino acid sequence. A more detailed description of the identification and characterization of the YVDAC2 gene and protein is being developed (Blachly-Dyson, E., M. Colombini, and M. Forte, manuscript in preparation).

Phenotypes Associated with Elimination of the YVDAC2 Gene

Standard gene-transplacement techniques similar to those used in the case of the YVDAC1 gene were used to create yeast strains in which the YVDAC2 gene is disrupted (YVDAC2⁻), as well as strains in which both the YVDAC1 and YVDAC2 genes are disrupted (YVDAC1⁻, YVDAC2⁻). As shown in Fig. 3, preliminary results suggest that at the EM level, the ultrastructure of mitochondria lacking both YVDAC1 and YVDAC2 is indistinguishable from mitochondria in wild-type strains. As shown in Fig. 4, initial experiments also suggest that there is no growth phenotype associated with elimination of the YVDAC2 gene; strains missing only the YVDAC2 gene grow as well as wild-type strains on both glucose or glycerol-based media at either 30° C or 37° C. Strains missing both YVDAC genes show rather pleiotropic growth defects, however. Growth of such strains on glucose-

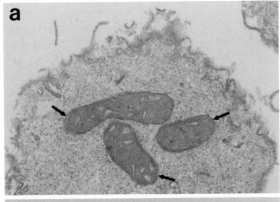

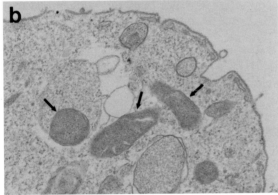

Figure 3. Electron microscopic analysis of mitochondria (*arrows*) present in a wild-type strains (*a*) and a strain in which both the YVDAC1 and YVDAC2 genes have been eliminated (*b*).

based media is significantly slowed relative to wild-type strains or strains missing YVDAC1 or YVDAC2 individually. It is surprising that these doubly mutant strains are still able to grow on glycerol-based media at 30° C, albeit at a much slower rate than either wild-type or single mutant strains and do not grow at all at 37° C on glycerol. This result suggests that although these YVDAC molecules may provide the primary pathway for the movement of metabolites between the cytoplasm and the mitochondria, transport of these molecules can occur, although much more inefficiently, by an alternate mechanism which remains to be identified.

Conclusions

VDAC clearly has advantages as a model system in which to study a variety of basic biologic processes. Over the past decade, this molecule has provided a useful system in which to examine the general phenomenon of voltage-gating of ion flow across membranes. While theoretical considerations may suggest how proteins could form such structures, it is only by the analysis of a variety of voltage-gated channels that we will begin to understand how the conformation of these molecules is modulated by transmembrane voltage. In this light, the study of the VDAC channels has clearly complemented and expanded our knowledge of this important class of molecules by providing us with a unique experimental system in which to understand how proteins can form voltage-gated pores. In addition, VDAC provides an

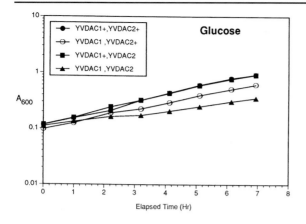

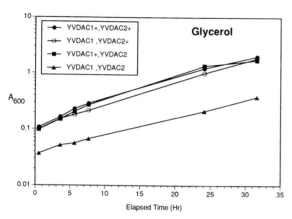

Figure 4. Growth of wild-type strains, strains missing either YVDAC1 or YVDAC2, and strains missing both YVDAC1 and YVDAC2 on either glucose- (*top*) or glycerol- (*bottom*) based media at 30° C.

opportunity to investigate the poorly understood mechanisms by which mitochondrial function is integrated with overall aspects of cell metabolism. In each instance, the unique advantages of the yeast system have allowed multidisciplinary approaches not possible in other experimental systems. Finally, the identification of a second yeast gene encoding a functional VDAC molecule demonstrates that multiple VDAC genes have evolved in even the simplest eukaryotic organisms, as had previously been observed in organisms from plants to humans (Colombini et al., 1995). At least in yeast, these proteins are functionally similar yet not completely redundant. Further analysis should help define the precise role of each protein in modulating mitochondrial function in response to constantly changing metabolic challenges.

References

Adams, V., L. Griffin, J. Towbin, B. Gelb, K. Worley, and E. McCabe. 1991. Porin interaction with hexokinase and glycerol kinase: Metabolic microcompartmentation at the outer mitochondrial membrane. *Biochem. Med. Metab. Biol.* 45:271–291.

Blachly-Dyson, E., S.-Z. Peng, M. Colombini, and M. Forte. 1990. Selectivity changes in site-directed mutants of the VDAC ion channel: Structural implications. *Science.* 247:1233–1236.

Blachly-Dyson, E., E. Zabronicz, W.-H. Yu, V. Adams, E. McCabe, J. Adelman, M. Colombini, and M. Forte. 1993. Cloning, heterologous expression in yeast and mapping of two human isoforms of the outer mitochondrial membrane channel, VDAC. *J. Biol. Chem.* 268:1835–1841.

Colombini, M. 1980. The pore size and properties of channels from mitochondria isolated from *N. crassa. J. Membrane. Biol.* 53:79–84.

Colombini, M. 1994. Anion channels in the mitochondrial outer membrane. *Curr. Top. Membr.* 42:73–101.

Colombini, M., E. Blachly-Dyson, and M. Forte. 1995. VDAC, a channel in the outer mitochondrial membrane. *In* Ion Channels. T. Narahashi, editor. Volume 4, Plenum Publishing Corp., New York.

Colombini, M., M. Forte, and M. Mannella. 1992. Toward the molecular structure of the mitochondria channel VDAC. *J. Bioenerg. Biomem.* 24:7–19.

Dihanich, M., K. Suda, and G. Schatz. 1987. A yeast mutant lacking mitochondrial porin is respiratory-deficient but can recover respiration with the simultaneous accumulation of an 86-kd extramitochondrial protein. *EMBO J.* 6:723–728.

McEnery, M., A. Snowman, R. Trifiletti, and S. Snyder. 1992. Isolation of the mitochondrial benzodiazepine receptor: Association with the voltage-dependent anion channel and the adenine nucleotide carrier. *Proc. Nat. Acad. Sci. USA.* 89:3170–3174.

Peng, S., E. Blachly-Dyson, M. Colombini, and M. Forte. 1992*a*. Determination of the number of polypeptide subunits in a functional VDAC channel from *Saccharomyces cerevisiae. J. Bioenerg. Biomem.* 24:27–33.

Peng, S., E. Blachly-Dyson, M. Forte, and M. Colombini. 1992*b*. Large scale rearrangement of protein domains is associated with voltage gating of the VDAC ion channel. *Biophysical J.* 62:123–135.

Qiu, X., K. Jakes, A. Finkelstein, and S. Slatin. 1994. Site-specific biotinylation of colicin 1a: A probe for protein confromation in the membrane. *J. Biol. Chem.* 269:7483–7488.

Schein, S., M. Colombini, and A. Finkelstein. 1991. Reconstitution in planar lipid bilayers of a voltage-dependent anion-selective channel obtained from *Paramecium* mitochondria. *J. Membrane Bio.* 30:99–120.

Shao, L., P. Van Roey, K. Kinnally, and C.A. Mannella. 1994. Circular dichroism of isolated mitochondrial channel protein, VDAC: First direct evidence for porin-like secondary structure. *Biophys. J.* 66:A21.

Slatin, S., X. Qiu, K. Jakes, and A. Finkelstein. 1994. Identification of a translocated protein segment in a voltage-dependent channel. *Nature.* 371:158–161.

Sorgato, M., and O. Moran. 1993. Channels in mitochondrial membranes: Knowns, unknowns and prospects for the future. *Crit. Rev. Biochem. Mol. Biol.* 18:127–171.

Thomas, L., E. Blachly-Dyson, M. Colombini, and M. Forte. 1993. Identification of gating charges within the VDAC ion channel. *Proc. Nat. Acad. Sci. USA.* 90:5446–5449.

Thomas, L., E. Kocsis, M. Colombini, E. Erbe, B. Trus, and A. Steven. 1991. Surface topography and molecular stoichiometry of the mitochondrial channel, VDAC. *J. Struct. Biol.* 106:161–171.

Mitochondrial Inner Membrane Channels in Yeast and Mammals

Cristina Ballarin, Alessandro Bertoli, Grazyna Wojcik, and M. Catia Sorgato

Dipartimento di Chimica Biologica, Università di Padova, and Centro CNR di Studio delle Biomembrane, 35121 Padova, Italy

In recent years, the presence of ion channels has been established in all intracellular membranes subjected to electrophysiologic analysis. If structure-function relationships are already under scrutiny for some channels (e.g., the ryanodine and IP$_3$ receptors), our current knowledge of those belonging to other organelles, including the inner membrane of mitochondria, is largely phenomenological. In this paper a brief excursus on what has emerged so far from the electrophysiologic research of the inner mitochondrial membrane will be presented, with particular emphasis on channels transporting anions, as these were best studied in our laboratory.

Inner Membrane Channels

The mammalian inner membrane (IM) was the first of the two mitochondrial membranes studied with the patch-clamp technique (Sorgato et al., 1987). It is important to remember that for the direct analysis of this membrane, mitochondria must be manipulated further after their isolation to remove the external (outer) membrane (OM) enclosing the organelle. Disruption of the OM is generally accomplished by imposing mechanical forces generated by either a French press or by subjecting mitochondria to hyposmotic-hyperosmotic transitions. The main difference between the two methods is that the IM is probably stretched during the osmotic shock; this, however, seems to have no consequence on the function of the channels (Kinnally et al., 1989; Lohret and Kinnally, 1995*a*). With either procedure, the membrane, becoming exposed, is set free to unfold the cristae present in the integral organelle. The resulting large vesicles, called *mitoplasts*, (with a diameter of 1–5 µm) are amenable to the patch clamp electrode and, in parallel, number of accessible channels is increased. Vesicles with even larger diameters have been obtained by inducing fusion of swollen mitoplasts at low pH and in the presence of Ca^{2+} (Inoue et al., 1991). The majority of studies concerning the inner mitochondrial membrane (IMM) have been carried out by use of the patch clamp technique. As an alternative approach to uncover other high conductance pathways (possibly present at low densities or physically inaccessible to the patch clamp electrode), the membrane has been fused to planar lipid bilayers (Hayman et al., 1993; Hayman and Ashley, 1993; Szabò et al., 1995) or membrane fractions have been reconstituted in giant liposomes (Moran et al., 1990; Sorgato et al., 1989).

Mitoplasts isolated from several mammalian tissues have been examined. These include rat and mouse liver (Inoue et al., 1991; Kinnally et al., 1989; Petronilli et al., 1989; Sorgato et al., 1987; Sorgato et al., 1989); rat, mouse, and sheep heart

Organellar Ion Channels and Transporters © 1996 by The Rockefeller University Press

(Hayman et al., 1993; Kinnally et al., 1993; Sorgato et al., 1989; Zorov et al., 1992*b*); rat brown adipose tissue (Klitsch and Siemen, 1991), and human cultured cell lines (Murphy et al., 1995). Ion channels were unequivocally detected in all cases; thus they are not specific for a particular tissue or species.

Results of recent electrophysiologic studies of yeast mitoplasts have demonstrated the presence of high-conductance pathways in this simpler eukaryotic organism as well (Ballarin and Sorgato, 1995*a*; Lohret and Kinnally, 1995*a*; Szabò et al., 1995). These results complement those obtained in mammals and strongly support the notion that mitochondrial channels, being constitutive elements of all eukaryotic cells, must play an essential role in cell physiology.

Before describing the details of the functional properties, we must point out that because of the small dimensions of mitoplasts, in particular of those obtained from yeast, application of a patch-clamp electrode to the IM is technically rather challenging. Generally, the percentage of successful patches is very low. Nevertheless, as it is widely accepted that the potential risk of artifacts is less with the patch clamp than with other methods, our efforts with this method are ongoing.

Mammalian Inner Membrane Channels
Studies In Situ with a Patch Clamp Electrode

On the basis of their electric features and response to pharmacologic agents, a minimum of five types of channels have been identified in the inner membrane of mammalian mitochondria (Table I). Their main features are now summarized. (Unless otherwise stated, reported values were obtained with symmetrical 150 mM KCl salt conditions.)

The Mitochondrial Centum Pico-Siemens (mCS) Channel

Electric features. In 1987, the first electrophysiologic study of the IM demonstrated the presence of a channel with a conductance of 107 pS (from which the acronym mCS: mitochondrial Centum pico-Siemens) and with a slight preference for translocating anions over cations ($P_{Cl}/P_K = 4.5$) (Sorgato et al., 1987). It was also found

TABLE I
Channels Identified in the Inner Membrane of Mammalian Mitochondria

Conductance (pS in 0.15 M salt)	Voltage dependence	Selectivity	Physiologic effectors	Function
9.7* (K_{ATP})	No	K^+	ATP (blocks)	Volume regulation?
15 (ACA)	No	Cationic	pH, Mg^{2+}	?
45 (AAA)	No	Anionic	pH, Mg^{2+}	IMAC (volume regulation)?
107 (mCS)	Yes	Anionic	Nucleotides? Ca^{2+}?	Safeguard-valve?
>1000 (MCC)	Yes	Unselective (substates cationic)	Mg^{2+}, ADP, H^+, Ca^{2+}	PTP (mBzR)? Protein import?

* in 0.1 M salt. All data were obtained by use of the patch-clamp technique. For details see Sorgato and Moran (1993), Antonenko et al., (1994), and Lohret and Kinnally (1995*b*).

that the gating mechanism was sensitive to voltage so that the channel was inoperative at physiologic (negative) membrane potentials (Fig. 1). These features, first observed in mitoplasts isolated from the liver of mice treated with the liver-mitochondria–enlarging agent, cuprizone, were then confirmed in the IMM of untreated animals (Inoue et al., 1991; Kinnally et al., 1991; Klitsch and Siemen, 1991; Petronilli et al., 1989; Sorgato et al., 1989) as well as, more recently, in mitoplasts of human cultured osteosarcoma cells (Murphy et al., 1995). In some instances slight variations in the single-channel conductance were observed (Antonenko et al., 1991*a*; Campo et al., 1992; Inoue et al., 1991; Klitsch and Siemen, 1991; Petronilli et al., 1989), possibly as a result of current rectification at positive potentials; this also can be seen in the traces of Fig. 1. Subconductance states, ranging between 30 and 60 pS, were reported (Campo et al., 1992; Kinnally et al., 1992; Klitsch and Siemen, 1991; Sorgato et al., 1987, 1989), apparently where the kinetic, permeability, and voltage-sensitive properties of the parent 107 pS transition were conserved (Kinnally and Tedeschi, 1994).

On the basis of several determinations of the distribution of the open and closed times at opposite values of the applied potential difference (Antonenko et al., 1991*a*; Ballarin et al., 1994; Campo et al., 1992; Klitsch and Siemen, 1991; Sorgato et al., 1987), at least two open (fast and slow) and two closed (fast and slow)

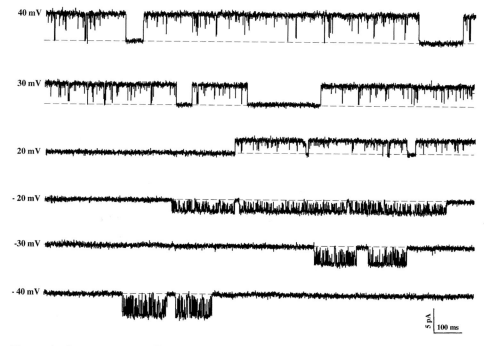

Figure 1. Current traces at different voltages of the mammalian mCS channel recorded from a mitoplast-attached patch. Note the higher open probability and the slight current rectification at positive voltages. *Dashed lines* indicate the closed state. Mouse liver mitoplasts were obtained as described in Ballarin and Sorgato (1995*c*). Symmetrical solutions of 150 mM KCl, 0.1 mM $CaCl_2$, 20 mM Hepes-KOH (pH 7.4) were used. Gain: 10 mV/pA. Filter: 1 kHz. The sign of the voltage refers to the interior (matrix side) of the vesicle.

time constants have been identified for the channel. In either case, however, the slow component was the one that was crucial for voltage dependence: upon membrane polarization the (slow) open time constant (in the millisecond range) decreased at least six-fold, whilst the (slow) closed time constant increased from milliseconds to several seconds. These observations, combined with the need for long periods of time (up to minutes) to activate fully the channel when passing from a negative to a positive potential and the almost immediate cessation of activity when the opposite voltage protocol is used, have led to the construction of the minimal kinetic model shown in Fig. 2 (Ballarin et al., 1994).

It is of interest that the current-voltage relationship of the entire IM analyzed in whole-mitoplast patches was found to vary in the same fashion as for mCS channels (Ballarin et al., 1994; Klitsch and Siemens, 1991; Sorgato et al., 1987). Therefore, in face of the several pieces of evidence supporting the existence of other channels of even higher conductance (see below), there are conditions whereby mCS channels are apparently the major, if not the only, contributors to the macroscopic current of native inner membranes.

$$Q \longleftrightarrow \overset{*}{C_2} \longleftrightarrow \overset{*}{C_1} \longleftrightarrow O$$

Figure 2. A minimal kinetic model of the mCS channel. *Asterisks* indicate voltage dependence. Equilibrium between the open state of the channel (*O*) and the C_1 closed state is very rapid (the fast closed time constant being less than 1 ms) and voltage independent. On the contrary, the slow closed time constant is voltage dependent (much higher at negative potentials) and accounts for the transition C_1-C_2. Finally, the third (quiescent) closed state, *Q*, has been postulated to justify latencies of long (minutes) duration observed for inducing channel openings when passing from high negative to positive voltages. For other details see the text. (From Ballarin et al., 1994, with permission.)

Pharmacology. As detailed in Sorgato and Moran (1993), a variety of drugs have been tested with the hope of finding a specific ligand for the channel. Several compounds had no effect while others affected other conductances as well, although in a different manner. Of interest is the very similar effect, at nanomolar concentrations, that specific ligands of the mitochondrial benzodiazepine receptor (mBzR) exerted on the mCS and MCC (see below) activities; this has led to the conclusion that both channels are associated with the benzodiazepine receptor (Kinnally et al., 1993). The mBzR is thought to be a complex of proteins belonging to the outer (the voltage-dependent anion channel (VDAC) and an 18-kD protein) and inner (the adenine nucleotide translocator) membrane (McEnery et al., 1992).

We believe, however, that by showing the different mode of action of certain drugs on mitochondrial channels, an important conclusion of this type of study is the physical independence of each type of channel listed in Table I. Likewise, similar studies enabled us to discriminate channels from other known mitochondrial translocating systems. In the case of mCS channels, for example, it was possible to show a lack of correlation with the adenine nucleotide translocator (no effect of specific inhibitors); the alkaline-activated, Mg^{2+}-inhibited putative anion channel (IMAC; inner membrane anion channel; no effect of pH, Mg^{2+}, and quinine); the proton-conducting membrane-embedded part of the ATP synthase (no effect of specific inhibitors); and the uncoupling protein implicated in nonshivering thermogenesis (different K_D for nucleotides) (Sorgato and Moran, 1993).

Physiology. From what we have reported above, it is clear that we lack experimental grounds for suggesting a role for the mCS channel, in particular if and how the response to voltage is regulated in vivo. On the basis of different, although not entirely mutually exclusive, assumptions, two hypotheses for the role of mCS channels can be proposed.

In the first hypothesis (Moran et al., 1990), it is assumed that the electric features routinely disclosed in patch-clamp experiments are representative of the behavior of altered channels. That is, they have lost the ability to operate in connection with other proteins and/or in a different lipid milieu, and thus their functional properties (including the voltage gating) are different. Under these circumstances, the peculiar voltage dependence, which allows activity only at depolarized and/or low negative voltages, is thought to represent the necessary autoinhibitory mechanism to guarantee unwanted waste of energy. This hypothesis stems from the overwhelming evidence that, by juxtaposing the two membranes in specific regions (called *adhesion*, or *contact*, sites), mitochondria create particular microenvironments which provide a direct junction between the matrix and the cytoplasm (Hackenbrock, 1968) or a connecting device for contiguous mitochondria (Skulachev, 1990). Intense metabolic activity has been proposed to take place at these sites. Examples are the translocation of preproteins from the cytoplasm into the matrix through the independent machineries of the outer and the inner membrane (Glick et al., 1991; Pfanner et al., 1992), and the flow of ions and metabolites between adjacent mitochondria in the power-transmitting cable hypothesis of Skulachev (1990). In either case water-filled pores have been implicated. Were mCS channels part of these devices, it would be necessary to guarantee inactivation at physiologic voltages whenever the connections become displaced. This possibility is certainly met in the case of mitochondria deprived of the OM, as with the membrane vesicles (mitoplasts) where channels are studied. On the other hand, physiologic conditions per se could trigger autoinhibition. In line with this hypothesis, Glick et al. (1991) and Pfanner et al. (1992) have suggested that dynamic and reversible, rather than fixed, associations occur between the import machineries of the two mitochondrial membranes. Thus, when dissociation takes place (e.g., when the import apparatus is not engaged in protein translocation), mCS channels are inactivated. Incidentally, the same argument can hold true in the case of association of mCS channels with other protein complexes thought to span mitochondrial membranes at contact sites, as suggested by Kinnally et al. (1993) for the mBzR. Regardless of the situation, an important conclusion of this hypothesis is that the channel activity detected in vitro pertains to the "inoperative" state of the channel. The features of the channel operating in vivo are presently not known.

An alternative hypothesis, in which the operational mode of the voltage gating mechanism is physiologically relevant, can also be proposed (Ballarin and Sorgato, 1995*b*). Even if rapid flux of anions such as Cl^- through mCS channels were impeded by the high negative potential sustained by mitochondria (-180 mV), one can nevertheless imagine that (a quasi-) electrochemical equilibrium of Cl^- is reached by slow ion permeation. Now, if a transient drop of the membrane potential occurs, depolarization would automatically open the channels allowing Cl^- to flow into the matrix to reestablish the original equilibrium potential. The substantial diffusion potential arising from the increased anion conductivity could then help to restore normal energetic conditions. In conclusion, in this hypothesis the channels may be regarded as a mechanism protecting against a complete collapse of the mitochondrial membrane potential. The essential features of this hypothesis are depicted in Fig. 3.

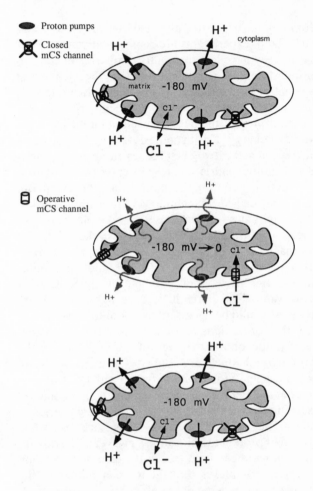

Figure 3. A hypothesis for the physiologic role of mCS channels. *Top panel.* The voltage sensitivity of mCS channels is responsible for inactivation at the high negative potentials generated in mitochondria by the proton ejection activity of the respiratory chains. It is assumed, however, that Cl$^-$ can approach electrochemical equilibrium through leak pathways. *Middle panel.* Were proton pumps transiently less efficient (*squiggled arrows*), the collapse of the membrane potential would open the channels thus allowing Cl$^-$ influx to regenerate a negative potential. *Lower panel.* The Cl$^-$ diffusion potential is thus envisaged to restore the function of the respiratory chains. In turn, the re-established high negative potential again closes mCS channels.

The Mitochondrial Megachannel/Multiconductance Channel (MMC/MCC)

Electric features. The functional properties of this channel have been studied primarily in the laboratories of the authors of two recent reviews on this subject (Kinnally and Tedeschi, 1994; Zoratti and Szabò, 1994). Here, we will only briefly summarize the most prominent characteristics of this channel, which is readily distinguishable from the other IM channels by its huge single-channel current (the conductance can reach values up to 1.3–1.5 nS; hence the acronym MMC: mitochondrial megachannel) and for the presence of an array of sublevels from pico- to nano-Siemens transitions (hence the acronym MCC: multiconductance channel).

According to Szabò and Zoratti (1992), this channel is essentially unselective, although a slight cationic selectivity has been attributed to some substates (Kinnally et al., 1989). MMC/MCC can be activated only under specific conditions: by the application of voltages higher than ± 60 mV (Zorov et al., 1992a), or by high levels of Ca^{2+} (in the micromolar range) present either during the preparation of mitochondria (Kinnally et al., 1991) or in the patch-clamp experimental medium (Szabò and Zoratti, 1992). The kinetics of this channel are complicated, and the voltage dependence is not entirely clear. According to Zorov et al. (1992b), the MMC/MCC opens fully at physiologic voltages and closes to lower conductance levels at positive potentials. Szabò and Zoratti (1993) found a different voltage dependence when using different experimental protocols. With short voltage pulses (1–2 sec) of opposite polarity, the behavior was essentially as described above. However, with longer pulses, the maximal open conducting state—predominant around zero—shuts off at negative voltages, with a time course of seconds. At positive potentials, they found that the MMC/MCC flickers rapidly from the maximal to subconductance levels.

Pharmacology and physiology. Comparative studies, carried out on mitochondrial patches and mitochondrial suspensions with a wide range of agents (including divalent ions, metabolites, protons, and drugs such as cyclosporin A; see Zoratti and Szabò, 1994, for a detailed list), have led to the suggestion that MMC/MCC is the permeability transition pore (PTP), which, when open, is thought to be the basis of irreversible cell damage (Gunter and Pfeiffer, 1990).

On the other hand, as mentioned above (Kinnally et al., 1993), inhibition of the MMC/MCC by the binding of benzodiazepines to the high affinity (cytoplasmic) sites, was interpreted as indicative of an association of MMC/MCC (together with the 107-pS channel) to the receptor supramolecular structure thought to reside at contact sites. The functional requirement of the receptor for the involvement of both membranes implies a similar requirement for MMC/MCC. According to Kinnally and Tedeschi (1994), several lines of evidence support this expectation, an important one being that Ca^{2+}, heavily involved in conferring assembling integrity to contact sites, is also essential for creating the necessary conditions to activate MMC/MCC activity (Kinnally et al., 1991).

Recently, on the basis of several independent observations (Szabò et al., 1993; Szabò and Zoratti, 1993; Zoratti et al., 1994), the two different sites of action attributed to MMC/MCC have been integrated into a single scheme in which the mBzR is part of the PTP (Szabò and Zoratti, 1993). Moreover, upon reinvestigation of the electrophysiologic behavior of voltage-dependent anion channel (VDAC), the most abundant OM channel, some investigators (Szabò et al., 1993; Zoratti et al., 1994) have used planar bilayers and proteoliposomes to refine further the above model. They have proposed that MMC/MCC comprises two cooperating VDAC molecules, possibly residing in the IM. This latter conclusion, however, is in conflict with some results obtained with yeast (see below).

The K_{ATP} Channel

Electric features and pharmacology. The only mitochondrial channel highly selective for an ion (K^+) is the channel described by Inoue et al. (1991) by patch clamping fused giant liver mitoplasts. Another important feature of this channel is that it almost certainly has a counterpart in a protein studied biochemically (see below), a feature still missing for many intracellular channels. In a patch, the channel has a conductance of 9.5 pS (bath: 33.3 mM KCl, 66.7 mM NaCl; pipette: 100 mM KCl), is not voltage dependent, and is reversibly inhibited by ATP ($k_{1/2} \approx 0.8$ mM) in the absence of Mg^{2+}, but is not inhibited by ADP or GTP. These properties, together with inhibition by 4-aminopyridine and glibenclamide (a sulphonylurea drug blocking most plasma membrane K_{ATP} channels) have prompted the suggestion that the mitochondrial channel may belong to the family of K_{ATP} channels.

The same conclusion was reached with biochemical studies of light-scattering measurements on suspensions of respiring mitochondria (Beavis et al., 1993) and by the use of a K^+-sensitive fluorescent probe to test the ability of proteoliposomes containing IM components to mediate K^+ fluxes (Paucek et al., 1992). These reports confirmed the existence of a uniport in the IMM that is highly selective for K^+ and inhibited by ATP, although the regulation by adenine nucleotides (and adenine analogs) was more complex. For example, at variance with patch-clamp studies, ATP acted more efficiently, and ADP was more potent than ATP (in mitochondria), but only in the presence of Mg^{2+}. Most interesting, the channel was activated by K^+-channel openers and by low amounts of GDP or GTP (Garlid, 1994; Paucek et al., 1995).

Physiology. It has long been recognized that mitochondria are under the continuous threat of excessive swelling and lysis due to the influx of K^+ through leak pathways (accompanied by anions and water) driven by the high (negative) membrane potential. Therefore, to fine-tune mitochondrial volume, nature has provided the IM with special transporters assigned to export K^+ against an electric gradient. One of these is the K^+/H^+ antiporter, an 82-kD protein that has been purified and reconstituted (Garlid, 1994). However, as just described, another means of K^+ translocation across the IM is the K_{ATP} channel. The function of this protein is yet to be established, although Beavis et al. (1993) and Garlid (1994) have proposed several circumstances in which it could operate. For example, it could serve as an additional mechanism for regulation of mitochondrial volume, or it could allow uncompensated influx of K^+ to ensure the expansion of the matrix and/or energy dissipation required for metabolic needs. The possibility that inhibition is relieved by ATP is, of course, central to these hypotheses, as is the observation that guanine nucleotides play an important role in the regulation of the channel (Garlid, 1994; Paucek et al., 1995).

Alkaline-induced Cation Selective Activity (ACA) and Alkaline-induced Anion Selective Activity (AAA)

Electric features, pharmacology and physiology. According to Antonenko et al. (1991*b*), if, under depletion of magnesium ions, the pH of the medium bathing the matrix side of a mitoplast excised patch is changed from 6.8 to 8.2, then reversible currents are activated. Additional experiments have shown that one current (cationic) was mediated by a 15-pS channel (ACA: alkaline-induced cation selective activity) while another channel of approximately 45 pS (AAA: alkaline-induced anion selective activity) was responsible for the other (anionic) current (Antonenko et al., 1994). The AAA was inhibited by Mg^{2+} addition, by a shift back in the pH, and by amphiphilic inhibitors (Antonenko et al., 1991*b*). Similar evidence has been reported for the regulation in mitochondrial suspension of the inner membrane anion channel (IMAC), a channel implicated in mitochondrial volume regulation during stressed mitochondrial conditions (for a review, see Beavis, 1992). Therefore, a tentative correspondence has been made between AAA and IMAC.

The 15-pS cation channel has an increased probability of opening with Mg^{2+} depletion; this suggests that it may be similar to the so called K^+-uniport, the activation of which occurs under similar conditions in mitochondrial suspensions (Bernardi et al., 1989; Nicolli et al., 1991).

Studies in Reconstituted Systems

In planar bilayers. Incorporation, at alkaline pH, of IM vesicles of cardiac cells in planar bilayers resulted in electric activity that Hayman et al. (1993) and Hayman and Ashley (1993) have ascribed to two distinct anion channels, one of $\sim$100-pS conductance (with multiple substates) and one of $\sim$50-pS conductance (with only two substates of a quarter and a half of the main state, respectively), for which a mechanistic model has also been proposed (Hayman and Ashley, 1993). Some of the features displayed resemble those of mCS and AAA channels. However, the lack of effect of various drugs and physiologic effectors and the insensitivity to voltage exclude the superimposition of data obtained with the different electrophysiologic tools or in mitochondrial suspensions. It is plausible that either the channels studied in planar membranes represent distinct molecules or incorporation in bilayers distorts the behavior of the proteins.

In proteoliposomes. Moran et al. (1990, 1992) and Sorgato et al. (1989) carried out a study, using the patch clamp technique, of the electric properties of giant liposomes containing the OM, or fractions of the IM, isolated in the absence of detergents. Some of the conductances found were similar in value and voltage dependence to conductances (other than VDAC) detected by patch clamping intact mitochondria (Moran et al., 1992) or with the mCS channel of mitoplasts. These studies demonstrated that reconstitution is not harmful, at least to some mitochondrial channel proteins. On the other hand, by incorporating a fraction enriched in contact sites as defined by morphologic and biochemical criteria, Moran et al. (1990) could not find a proper correspondence for all of the large number of voltage-insensitive conductances—ranging from few pS to nS values—with those observed in situ. Frequently, the high conductances of these proteoliposomes have been attributed to MMC/MCC activity, and hence were taken as further proof that this channel is located at contact sites (Kinnally and Tedeschi, 1994; Zoratti and Szabò, 1994). Some uncertainties, however, apply to these conclusions, as little consideration is given to the fact that we do not know whether, following the reconstitution procedure, the entire contact-site junction (i.e., the inner plus the outer membrane parts), or the two independent halves, are present in the patch under scrutiny. The corresponding conductances could be, of course, quite different.

Molecular identity. Attempts have been made to isolate the proteins responsible for the various IM channels, although these studies have not been as extensive as those of the functional analysis of the membrane. The major difficulty of the biochemical approach to this goal probably lies in the fact that no channel-specific ligand is available, thus hampering the possibility of quickly obtaining a pure protein fraction from which to start tracing the corresponding gene.

With these problems at hand, and also in the absence of much comparative (structural) information on the majority of intracellular channels, the search for mitochondrial channel proteins has been started by fractionation of the IM with classical biochemical tools: ethanol extraction (Mironova et al., 1981); solubilization with detergents and affinity chromatography (Costa et al., 1991; Paliwal et al., 1992); or precipitation with ammonium sulphate (Sorgato et al., 1989). After separation by these techniques, the fractions were tested for channel activity in reconstituted systems (Sorgato and Moran, 1993). A 57-kD protein of rat liver submitochondrial particles, obtained from a quinine-affinity column eluate, was shown to have a voltage-independent, cation unselective, 40-pS conductance (Costa et al., 1991; Paliwal et al., 1992), but it was not easily referable to one of the in situ channels.

In some cases, the corresponding cDNA clones of some proteins present in the fractions have also been examined (Chiaramonte, S., C. Ballarin, M.C. Sorgato, and J.E. Walker, unpublished results). Yet, perhaps as expected from the paucity of expression of channel proteins, molecular identification has failed so far, even when activity could be attributed to a presumed single band (Mironova et al., 1981; Paliwal et al., 1992).

As mentioned, K_{ATP} function also has been followed in reconstituted systems with biochemical tools (Garlid, 1994; Paucek et al., 1992). Through these studies K_{ATP} activity has been attributed to a 54-kD protein, which was partially purified from rat-liver and beef-heart mitochondria and is probably the same protein tested electrophysiologically by Mironova et al. (1981). The validity of this result is strengthened by the findings that the reconstituted channel is inhibited by antibodies raised against the protein and that some positive cDNA clones have been found to these same antibodies (Paucek et al., 1992; Garlid, 1994).

Yeast Inner Membrane Channels

Because of the slow progress of the molecular identification of mammalian channels, several laboratories have turned to yeast cells. Yeast cells may not be the best choice for the electrophysiologic analysis of the IMM because yeast mitoplasts are smaller than mammalian ones and some difficulty can be encountered in their preparation (Ballarin and Sorgato, 1995c); nevertheless, they offer the obvious advantage of genetic manipulation.

Ion channels in yeast mitoplasts have been found by three different laboratories through the study of membrane in situ (Ballarin and Sorgato, 1995a; Lohret and Kinnally, 1995a; Szabò et al., 1995) or reconstituted in planar lipid bilayers (Szabò et al., 1995) and proteoliposomes (Lohret and Kinnally, 1995a). A uniform functional picture has not yet emerged in spite of some common results. One of these has been the failure to detect mCS channels, which are considered the marker conductances of the mammalian IM.

Wild type *Saccharomyces cerevisiae* strains have generally been the system of choice. However, for purpose of comparison but also for the wider diameter of mitochondria (Szabò et al., 1995), mutants lacking the VDAC gene were also used. (Values reported here refer to symmetrical 150-mM salt conditions.)

The Large Conductance Channel (Large Cl_{ATP} Channel)

Electric features. If one assumes that the same protein is responsible for the high conductance found by all laboratories, the simplest behavioral picture for this channel, obtained exclusively with the patch-clamp technique, is that described by Ballarin and Sorgato (1995*a*) in both wild type and mutant yeast mitoplasts. Briefly, these authors found that, independent of the patch configuration, the slightly anionic ($P_{Cl}/P_K = 4$) channel rectified at positive potentials (approximately 400 pS conductance at -40 mV increasing up to $\sim$800 pS at 40 mV), almost entirely lacked subconductance levels and possessed a strong voltage sensitivity ensuring closure at physiologic potentials (Fig. 4, upper trace). Inactivation, which resulted in closures of longer duration as the negative potential was increased, was very rapid, in contrast to the slow activation process occurring at positive voltages.

Were it not for the opposite selectivity and for the presence of multiple subconductance levels, these results would largely agree with those obtained in the

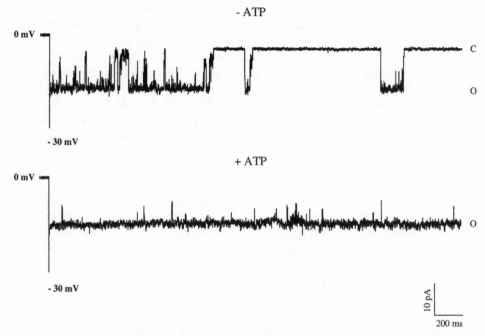

Figure 4. Current traces of a single yeast large Cl_{ATP} channel, recorded from a mitoplast excised patch in the absence (*upper trace*) or in the presence (*lower trace*) of ATP (0.8 mM). In either case, -30 mV were imposed starting from 0 mV. The nucleotide addition kept the channel mainly in the open state and reduced the conductance (Ballarin and Sorgato, 1995*a*). Mitoplasts of the wild type yeast strain HR125-2B were prepared as described in Ballarin and Sorgato (1995*c*). Gain: 10 mV/pA. Filter: 1kHz. Other conditions were as in the legend to Fig. 1. *O*, open state; *C*, closed state.

VDAC-less strain by Szabò et al. (1995), but only when activity was followed in whole mitoplast patches. In fact, results with IM-containing planar bilayers or mitoplast-attached patches were dissimilar in several aspects. Undoubtedly, however, results of these two studies appear close when comparisons are made between the kinetic and voltage-dependent profiles detected by Lohret and Kinnally (1995*a*) in the native or reconstituted IMM from wild type and mutant yeast (see next paragraph).

Pharmacology and physiology. In view of the lack of modification by Ca^{2+}, Mg^{2+}, or bongkrekic acid found by Ballarin and Sorgato (1995a), the yeast high conductance should be a protein other than that responsible for MMC/MCC, IMAC, or the adenine nucleotide translocator.

On the other hand, matrix ATP (with a $k_{1/2}$ of around 0.5 mM) was found to affect the gating mechanism of the channel in such a way as to remove inactivation at negative potentials (see Fig. 4, lower trace). However, this concentration is close to the endogenous mitochondrial ATP concentration for stimulation of channel activity at physiologic voltages. This situation requires us to hypothesize another regulatory device to counterbalance the effect of ATP. Indeed, only with a fine on-off switch mechanism would mitochondrial (and cell) survival not be threatened by the presence of such a high conductance.

In contrast, Lohret and Kinnally (1995a) provided evidence for an almost coincidental behavior of the yeast high-conductance pathway with the MMC/MCC of mammalian tissues. Szabò et al. (1995) denied such identification for kinetic reasons but particularly because of the inefficacy of several agents known to interact with the mammalian megachannel. In their opinion, the properties displayed could best be attributed to the peptide-sensitive channel (PSC). This is a mammalian and yeast conductance, believed to reside in the OM (Chich et al., 1991), that has been thoroughly studied in reconstituted systems (with the tip-dip and planar bilayers methods and in giant liposomes). Several experiments, demonstrating a voltage-dependent decrease of the mean open time upon addition of presequences of mitochondrial proteins, have been interpreted to support a possible involvement of PSC in mitochondrial biogenesis (Fevre et al., 1994; Thieffry et al., 1992; Vallette et al., 1994). Indeed, Szabò et al. (1995) followed a similar procedure by using the leader peptide of an IM protein (pCOx-IV), and this result reinforced their conclusion. At any rate, it remains to be seen if PSC can also reside in the IM (Zoratti and Szabò, 1994; Szabò et al., 1995), or if Szabò et al. (1995) were routinely patching residuals of the OM instead of the IM.

Of course, having been obtained in yeast lacking VDAC, the data of Szabò et al. (1995) argue in favor of the proposal that VDAC molecules constitute MMC/MCC (Zoratti et al., 1993 and above). These results, however, impinge heavily on MMC/MCC activity detected by Lohret and Kinnally (1995a) in the same mutant strain. On the other hand, modification, at $V > \pm 40$ mV, of the voltage sensitivity of MMC/MCC activity in VDAC-less mitoplasts (Lohret and Kinnally, 1995a), follow the expectations of Kinnally et al. (1993) and Kinnally and Tedeschi (1994) for a regulatory role, at high transmembrane potentials, of VDAC on MMC/MCC. It should be mentioned, however, that in other laboratories, MMC/MCC activities cannot be detected either in yeast (see above) or in mammalian membranes (see Sorgato and Moran, 1993, for this topic).

This unusual situation is further complicated by another recent report in which, under similar conditions to those used by Szabò et al. (1995) to demonstrate the involvement of the yeast high-conductance (PSC) in protein translocation, Lohret and Kinnally (1995b) showed that the same activity can be attributed to yeast (and mammalian) MMC/MCC. It should be pointed out, however, that if MMC/MCC belongs to the benzodiazepine receptor as proposed (Kinnally et al., 1993), then, in principle, the receptor itself should be part of the machinery of protein transport across mitochondrial membranes. To our knowledge, no such evidence is present in the literature for the intact receptor or for its other elements (VDAC, the 18-kD protein, and the adenine nucleotide translocator).

As a general comment to what is presented above, it is clear that more information is needed to explain the different results and to achieve full comprehension.

The Small Cl$_{ATP}$ Channel

Electric features. Yeast inner membranes from wild type and VDAC-less strains harbor at least one more channel, which was defined as *small* by Ballarin and Sorgato (1995*a*) to distinguish it from the large conductance discussed above. The conductance of this channel, around 40 pS at positive voltages (the value varied marginally depending on the strain), decreased at physiologic voltages. The channel

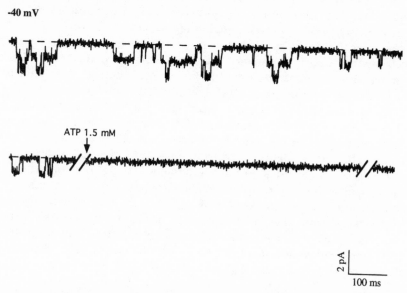

Figure 5. Current traces of yeast small Cl$_{ATP}$ channels, recorded from a mitoplast excised patch. After addition of ATP (*arrow*) activity disappeared. Gain: 50 mV/pA. Filter: 1kHz. The first interruption indicates few seconds, the second 4 min. All other conditions were as described in the legends to Figs. 1 and 4. *Dashed lines* indicate the closed state.

showed preference for anions (P$_{Cl}$/P$_K$ around 3), no strong voltage dependence (although a slightly higher open probability was present at negative voltages), and activated in bursts (Fig. 5). Patches with only one channel are extremely rare; in fact, the higher frequency of silent patches or of patches containing more than one channel, alone or together with the large conductance, lends support to the idea of a clustering of yeast IM channels.

Pharmacology and physiology. The presence of either Ca^{2+} or Mg^{2+} has no effect on the small Cl$_{ATP}$ channel. In contrast, matrix ATP interacts with the channel by drastically diminishing the open probability at potentials of either sign (Ballarin and Sorgato, 1995*a*) (Fig. 5). As in the case of the high conductance, another regulatory mechanism must be envisaged, otherwise, endogenous concentrations of matrix ATP are such that channels would remain permanently closed ($k_{1/2}$ for ATP being approximately 0.3 mM). This presupposition led us to test other nucleotides such as ADP, AMP, and cAMP. If added alone, only ADP decreased the open probability of the channel, even if at a lower extent than ATP at the same concentration. However, recovery of activity from an ATP-inhibited patch was observed only in the presence of cAMP (the percent inhibition decreasing around 50% at a cAMP/ATP of 0.5, unpublished results). The presence of cAMP per se in the mitochondrial matrix is still under debate; therefore, the effect of cAMP may be taken to indicate that the molecule mimics an (unknown) matrix factor able to contrast and/or to minimize the in vivo effect of ATP.

It is of interest that at concentrations insufficient to provoke complete closure of the channel, it can be shown that ATP reduces the channel conductance by ~30%. Alteration of the conductance size occurred with all nucleotides tested, an observation that may account for at least two binding sites whose occupancy regulates the protein in different ways (unpublished results).

In spite of the similar conductance value, other properties of the yeast small Cl_{ATP} channel are clearly at variance with the AAA or IMAC described in mammals, primarily because the latter are blocked by Mg^{2+} and are insensitive to ATP (Antonenko et al., 1991b; Beavis, 1992; Powers et al., 1994). Conversely, the close correspondence between Cl_{ATP} and K_{ATP} channel properties (low conductance, insensitivity to voltage and inactivation by ATP) seems to agree with the contention that either channel, under the control of adenosine nucleotides (and of other molecules), may act in the regulation of the volume of mitochondria. In fact, mitochondria must possess mechanisms for volume homeostasis, not only because they are under the continuous threat of volume changes by the high concentration of cytoplasmic K^+ (see above: physiology of the K_{ATP} channel), but also because they must respond to changes in extracellular osmolality. Thus, just as cells such as those in the kidney, activate a subtle network of osmolyte transporters and ion channels for electrolyte and solutes movement, mitochondrial K_{ATP} and Cl_{ATP} channels could mediate salt movements across the IM of the organelle.

Acknowledgments

This work was supported by grants from the Consiglio Nazionale delle Ricerche and from the Ministero dell'Università e della Ricerca Scientifica e Tecnologica of Italy.

References

Antonenko, Y.N., K.W. Kinnally, S. Perini, and H. Tedeschi. 1991a. Selective effect of inhibitors on inner mitochondrial membrane channels. *Fed. Eur. Biochem. Soc. Lett.* 285:89–93.

Antonenko, Y.N., K.W. Kinnally, and H. Tedeschi. 1991b. Identification of anion and cation pathways in the inner mitochondrial membrane by patch clamping of mouse liver mitoplasts. *J. Membr. Biol.* 124:151–158.

Antonenko, Y.N., D. Smith, K.W. Kinnally, and H. Tedeschi. 1994. Single-channel activity induced in mitoplasts by alkaline pH. *Biochim. Biophys. Acta.* 1194:247–254.

Ballarin, C., and M.C. Sorgato. 1995*a*. An electrophysiological study of yeast mitochondria. Evidence for two inner membrane anion channels sensitive to ATP. *J. Biol. Chem.* 270:19262–19268.

Ballarin, C., and M.C. Sorgato. 1995*b*. Anion channels of the inner membrane of mammalian and yeast mitochondria. *J. Bioenerget. Biomembr.* 28:123–128.

Ballarin, C., and M.C. Sorgato. 1995*c*. Patch clamping of mitochondrial membranes and of proteoliposomes. *In* Bioenergetics: A Practical Approach. C. Cooper, and G.E. Brown, editors. Oxford University Press, Oxford, New York, Tokyo. 133–157.

Ballarin, C., M.C. Sorgato, and O. Moran. 1994. A minimal kinetic model of the activity of the 107 pS channel of the inner membrane of mitochondria. *In* Molecular Biology of Mitochondrial Transport Systems. M. Forte and M. Colombini, editors. Springer-Verlag, Berlin, Heidelberg. 131–136.

Beavis, A.D. 1992. Properties of the inner membrane anion channel in intact mitochondria. *J. Bioenerget. Biomembr.* 24:77–90.

Beavis, A.D., Y. Lu, and K.D. Garlid. 1993. On the regulation of K^+ uniport in intact mitochondria by adenine nucleotides and nucleotide analogs. *J. Biol. Chem.* 268:997–1004.

Bernardi, P., A. Angrilli, V. Ambrosin, and G.F. Azzone. 1989. Activation of latent K^+ uniport in mitochondria treated with the ionophore A23187. *J. Biol. Chem.* 264:18902–18906.

Campo, M.L., K.W. Kinnally, and H. Tedeschi. 1992. The effect of antimycin A on mouse liver inner mitochondrial membrane channel activity. *J. Biol. Chem.* 267:8123–8127.

Chich, J.F., D. Goldschmidt, J.-P. Henry, and M. Thieffry. 1991. A peptide sensitive channel of large conductance is localised on the mitochondrial outer membrane. *Eur. J. Biochem.* 196:29–35.

Costa, G., K.W. Kinnally, and J.J. Diwan. 1991. Patch clamp analysis of a partially purified ion channel from rat liver mitochondria. *Biochem. Biophys. Res. Commun.* 175:305–310.

Fevre, F., J.-P. Henry, and M. Thieffry. 1994. Reversible and irreversible effects of basic peptides on the mitochondrial cationic channel. *Biophys. J.* 66:1887–1894.

Garlid, K.D. 1994. Mitochondrial cation transport: A progress report. *J. Bioenerget. Biomembr.* 26:537–542.

Glick, B., C. Wachter, and G. Schatz. 1991. Protein import into mitochondria: Two systems acting in tandem? *Trends Cell Biol.* 1:99–103.

Gunter, T.E., and D.R. Pfeiffer. 1990. Mechanisms by which mitochondria transport calcium. *Am. J. Physiol.* 258:C755–C786.

Hackenbrock, C.R. 1968. Chemical and physical fixation of isolated mitochondria in low and high energy states. *Proc. Natl. Acad. Sci. USA.* 61:598–605.

Hayman, K.A., and R.H. Ashley. 1993. Structural features of a multisubstate cardiac mitoplast anion channel: inferences from single channel recording. *J. Membr. Biol.* 136:191–197.

Hayman, K.A., T.D. Spurway, and R.H. Ashley. 1993. Single anion channels reconstituted from cardiac mitoplasts. *J. Membr. Biol.* 136:181–190.

Inoue, I., H. Nagase, K. Kishi, and T. Higuti. 1991. ATP-sensitive K^+ channel in the mitochondrial inner membrane. *Nature (Lond.).* 352:244–247.

Kinnally, K.W., Y.N. Antonenko, and D.B. Zorov 1992. Modulation of inner mitochondrial membrane channel activity. *J. Bioenerget. Biomembr.* 24:99–110.

Kinnally, K.W., M.L. Campo, and H. Tedeschi. 1989. Mitochondrial channel activity studied by patch-clamping mitoplasts. *J. Bioenerget. Biomembr.* 21:497–506.

Kinnally, K.W., and H. Tedeschi. 1994. Mitochondrial channels: An integrated view. *In* Molecular Biology of Mitochondrial Transport Systems. M. Forte and M. Colombini, editors. Springer-Verlag, Berlin, Heidelberg. 169–198.

Kinnally, K.W., D.B. Zorov, Y.N. Antonenko, and S. Perini. 1991. Calcium modulation of mitochondrial inner membrane channel activity. *Biochem. Biophys. Res. Commun.* 176:1183–1188.

Kinnally, K.W., D.B. Zorov, Y.N. Antonenko, S.H. Snyder, M.W. McEnery, and H. Tedeschi. 1993. Mitochondrial benzodiazepine receptor linked to inner membrane ion channels by nanomolar actions of ligands. *Proc. Natl. Acad. Sci. USA.* 90:1374–1378.

Klitsch, T., and D. Siemen. 1991. Inner mitochondrial membrane anion channel is present in brown adipocytes but is not identical with the uncoupling protein. *J. Membr. Biol.* 122:69–75.

Lohret, T.A., and K.W. Kinnally. 1995*a*. Multiple conductance channel activity of wild-type and voltage-dependent anion-selective channel (VDAC)-less yeast mitochondria. *Biophys. J.* 68:2299–2309.

Lohret, T.A., and K.W. Kinnally. 1995*b*. Targeting peptides transiently block a mitochondrial channel. *J. Biol. Chem.* 270:15950–15953.

McEnery, M.W., A.M. Snowman, R.R. Trifiletti, and S.H. Snyder. 1992. Isolation of the mitochondrial benzodiazepine receptor: Association with the voltage-dependent anion channel and the adenine nucleotide carrier. *Proc. Natl. Acad. Sci. USA.* 89:3170–3174.

Mironova, G.D., N.I. Fedotcheva, P.R. Makarov, L.A. Pronevich, and G.P. Mironov. 1981. A protein of the bovine heart mitochondria inducing channel potassium conductivity in bilayer lipid membranes. *Biofizika.* 26:458–465.

Moran, O., G. Sandri, E. Panfili, W. Stühmer, and M.C. Sorgato. 1990. Electrophysiological characterisation of contact sites in brain mitochondria. *J. Biol. Chem.* 265:908–913.

Moran, O., M. Sciancalepore, G. Sandri, E. Panfili, R. Bassi, C. Ballarin, and M.C. Sorgato. 1992. Ionic permeability of the mitochondrial outer membrane. *Eur. Biophys. J.* 20:311–319.

Murphy, R.C., M.P. King, J.J. Diwan, and K.W. Kinnally. 1995. Patch clamp analysis of human mitoplasts from cultured osteosarcoma cell lines. *Abstr. 49th Annu. Meet. Soc. Gen. Physiol.* 24a.

Nicolli, A., A. Redetti, and P. Bernardi. 1991. The K^+ conductance of the inner mitochondrial membrane. *J. Biol. Chem.* 266:9465–9470.

Paliwal, R., G. Costa, and J.J. Diwan. 1992. Purification and patch clamp analysis of a 40-pS channel from rat liver mitochondria. *Biochemistry.* 31:2223–2229.

Paucek, P., G. Mironova, F. Mahdi, A.D. Beavis, G. Woldegiorgis, and K.D. Garlid. 1992. Reconstitution and partial purification of the glibenclamide-sensitive, ATP-dependent K^+ channel from rat liver and beef heart mitochondria. *J. Biol. Chem.* 267:26062–26069.

Paucek, P., V. Yarov-Yarovoi, X. Sun, and K.D. Garlid. 1995. Physiological and pharmacological activators of the mitochondrial K_{ATP} channel. *Biophys. J.* 68:A145.

Petronilli, V., I. Szabò, and M. Zoratti. 1989. The inner mitochondrial membrane contains ion-conducting channels similar to those found in bacteria. *Fed. Eur. Biochem. Soc. Lett.* 259:137–143.

Pfanner, N., J. Rassow, I.J. van der Klei, and W. Neupert. 1992. A dynamic model of the mitochondrial protein import machinery. *Cell.* 68:999–1002.

Powers, M.F., L.L. Smith, and A.D. Beavis. 1994. On the relationship between the mitochondrial inner membrane anion channel and the adenine nucleotide translocase. *J. Biol. Chem.* 269:10614–10620.

Skulachev, V.P. 1990. Power transmission along biological membranes. *J. Membr. Biol.* 114:97–112.

Sorgato, M.C., B.U. Keller, and W. Stühmer. 1987. Patch-clamping of the inner mitochondrial membrane reveals a voltage-dependent ion channel. *Nature (Lond.).* 330:498–500.

Sorgato, M.C., and O. Moran. 1993. Channels in mitochondrial membranes: Knowns, unknowns, and prospects for the future. *Crit. Rev. Biochem. Mol. Biol.* 18:127–171.

Sorgato, M.C., O. Moran, V. De Pinto, B.U. Keller, and W. Stühmer. 1989. Further investigation on the high-conductance ion channel of the inner membrane of mitochondria. *J. Bioenerget. Biomembr.* 21:485–496.

Szabò, I., G. Bàthori, D. Wolff, T. Starc, C. Cola, and M. Zoratti. 1995. The high-conductance channel of porin-less yeast mitochondria. *Biochim. Biophys. Acta.* 1235:115–125.

Szabò, I., and M. Zoratti. 1992. The mitochondrial megachannel is the permeability transition pore. *J. Bioenerget. Biomembr.* 24:111–117.

Szabò, I., and M. Zoratti. 1993. The mitochondrial permeability transition pore may comprise VDAC molecules. I. Binary structure and voltage dependence of the pore. *Fed. Eur. Biochem. Soc. Lett.* 330:201–205.

Szabò, I., V. De Pinto, and M. Zoratti. 1993. The mitochondrial permeability transition pore may comprise VDAC molecules. II. The electrophysiological properties of VDAC are compatible with those of the mitochondrial megachannel. *Fed. Eur. Biochem. Soc. Lett.* 330:205–210.

Thieffry, M., J. Neyton, M. Pelleschi, F. Fevre, and J.-P. Henry. 1992. Properties of the mitochondrial peptide-sensitive cationic channel studied in planar bilayers and patches of giant liposomes. *Biophys. J.* 63:333–339.

Vallette, F.M., P. Juin, M. Pelleschi and J.-P. Henry. 1994. Basic peptides can be imported into yeast mitochondria by two distinct targeting pathways. *J. Biol. Chem.* 269:13367–13374.

Zoratti, M., and I. Szabò. 1994. Electrophysiology of the inner mitochondrial membrane. *J. Bioenerget. Biomembr.* 26:543–553.

Zoratti, M., I. Szabò, and V. De Pinto. 1994. The mitochondrial permeabilization pore. *In* Molecular Biology of Mitochondrial Transport Systems. M. Forte and M. Colombini, editors. Springer-Verlag, Berlin, Heidelberg. 153–168.

Zorov, D.B., K.W. Kinnally, S. Perini, and H. Tedeschi. 1992*a*. Multiple conductance levels in rat heart inner mitochondrial membranes studied by patch clamping. *Biochim. Biophys. Acta.* 1105:263–270.

Zorov, D.B., K.W. Kinnally, and H. Tedeschi. 1992*b*. Voltage activation of heart inner mitochondrial membrane channels. *J. Bioenerget. Biomembr.* 24:119–124.

The ADP/ATP Transport System: A Paradigm of Metabolite Transport in Mitochondria

G. Brandolin,* A. Le Saux,‡ P. Roux,* V. Trezeguet,‡ C. Fiore,* C. Schwimmer,‡ A.C. Dianoux,* G.J.M. Lauquin,‡ and P.V. Vignais*

*Laboratoire de Biochimie, Unité de Recherche Associée 1130 du Centre National de la Recherche Scientifique, Département de Biologie Moléculaire et Structurale, CEA/ Grenoble, France, and ‡Laboratoire de Physiologie Moléculaire et Cellulaire, Institut de Biochimie et Génétique Cellulaires, Unité Propre de Recherche 9026 du Centre National de la Recherche Scientifique, Bordeaux, France

Introduction

Mitochondria provide most of the energy usable by aerobic eukaryotic cells in the form of ATP generated by conversion of respiratory energy through oxidative phosphorylation. For mitochondria to perform this function, electron-rich substrates, phosphate, oxygen, and ADP are taken up, and products, i.e., CO_2, water, and ATP, are released to the cytosol. Though both mitochondrial membranes are freely permeable to water, CO_2, and oxygen, only hydrophilic metabolites can easily penetrate the outer membrane, mainly because of the presence of non-specific pores consisting of porin (for review, see Benz, 1994). In contrast, the inner mitochondrial membrane displays highly selective permeability, since carrier proteins present in this membrane catalyze the specific transport of metabolites across the lipid bilayer. Mitochondrial carrier proteins not only provide mitochondria with the required metabolites, but they also allow regulation of the phosphate potential and the redox potential inside and outside the mitochondrial compartment. In some tissues or organisms, the carriers are involved in specialized metabolic pathways, as in gluconeogenesis and urea synthesis in liver or thermogenesis in the brown adipose tissue (for review see Lanoue and Schoolwerth, 1984; Krämer and Palmieri, 1992).

To date, thirteen mitochondrial transport systems have been identified on the basis of their activity, measured either in intact mitochondria or after functional reconstitution of purified carriers in liposomes (Fig. 1). At physiologic pH, most of the transported metabolites are anions; only a few of them—carnitine, ornithine, and glutamine—are cationic species. The uncoupling protein (UCP), specifically synthesized in brown adipose tissue from mammals, has been demonstrated to be a proton carrier.

The ADP/ATP carrier was the first mitochondrial transport system to be discovered, and because of its unique properties it has been the most extensively studied. Two families of inhibitors, characterized by their high specificity and affinity, have aided in the identification and characterization of the ADP/ATP transport system (Vignais et al., 1985; Klingenberg, 1985). The first one includes atractyloside (ATR) and carboxyatractyloside (CATR), two toxic compounds isolated from the thistle *Atractylis gummifera*. These two inhibitors interact with sites of the ADP/ATP carrier exposed to the cytosol. The other family comprises bongkrekic acid

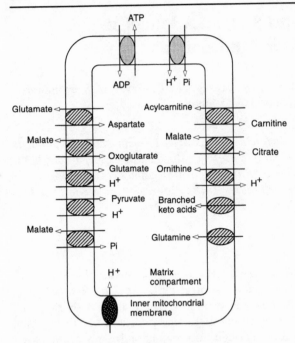

Figure 1. Schematic representation of the major metabolite carriers in the inner mitochondrial membrane. ▨, carriers directly involved in ATP synthesis and export; ▨, carriers participating in general metabolic processes; ■, uncoupling protein (UCP) from brown adipose tissue mitochondria, involved in thermogenesis.

(BA) and its isomer isobongkrekic acid (isoBA), two other toxic compounds secreted by the bacteria *Pseudomonas cocovenenans*. BA and isoBA bind to sites of the ADP/ATP carrier accessible from the matrix compartment of mitochondria; therefore they have to penetrate the inner mitochondrial membrane. Asymmetrical binding of atractylosides and bongkrekic acid to the ADP/ATP carrier made it possible to demonstrate and characterize two conformational states of the carrier protein that are probably involved in the transport process. This peculiar feature has rendered the carrier especially advantageous for the study of the transport mechanism at a molecular level.

Physiological Aspects of Mitochondrial ADP/ATP Transport

The ADP/ATP carrier is present in mitochondria of all eukaryotic cells and displays high specificity for ADP and ATP, with AMP excluded from the transport. Under physiologic conditions, the ADP/ATP carrier catalyzes the exchange between cytosolic ADP and mitochondrial ATP generated by oxidative phosphorylation. The stoichiometry of one-to-one maintains the mitochondrial pool of adenine nucleotides at a constant level. This feature distinguishes the ADP/ATP transport system from the mitochondrial ATP-Mg/Pi transport system, the function of which is believed to regulate the size of the matrix adenine nucleotide pool in catalyzing the net uptake of adenine nucleotides in a counter-exchange with phosphate (for review see Aprille, 1993). ATP-Mg/Pi exchange also differs from ADP/ATP exchange in that it is much slower and virtually insensitive to atractylosides. In addition, the ATP-Mg/Pi carrier transport activity is dependent on the presence of divalent cations, whereas the ADP/ATP exchanger transports only the free forms of nucleotides (for review, see Vignais et al., 1985).

The electrical imbalance that results from the transmembrane exchange between ADP^{3-} and ATP^{4-} is not charge-compensated by proton movement. For this reason, the transport is electrogenic and has to be driven by the membrane potential of the mitochondrial membrane. As a consequence, ATP export is an energy-consuming process that requires about 30% of the energy generated by mitochondrial respiration in the course of oxidative phosphorylation. In keeping with its strategic task of providing ATP for multiple endergonic functions in the cell, the capacity of the ADP/ATP carrier is very high, despite a turnover rate of 1000–2000 min^{-1}, which is relatively modest in comparison to that of the Pi carrier at 20–25°C: 50000–60000 min^{-1} (Vignais et al., 1985; Ligeti et al., 1985). Every day, 60 kg of ADP and ATP are transported across the mitochondrial membranes in an adult human body. In fact, the high concentration of the ADP/ATP carrier in the mitochondrial membrane compensates for the moderate intrinsic activity of the carrier. For instance, in heart mitochondria the ADP/ATP carrier protein amounts to 10% of the protein content of the mitochondrial inner membrane.

The key physiologic function of the ADP/ATP transport system has led different groups to evaluate the control strength exerted by this transport in the overall ADP/ATP cycle in cells from different tissues (see Vignais et al., 1985). The rate-limiting function of the ADP/ATP carrier has been demonstrated to depend on the nature of the tissue and on metabolic conditions (Lanoue and Schoolwerth, 1984; Vignais et al., 1985).

Detailed studies of the kinetics of ADP/ATP transport have provided evidence for the existence of a compartmentation of the adenine nucleotides in the matrix space of mitochondria. ADP has been shown to enter the matrix space where, instead of mixing with internal nucleotides, it was preferentially phosphorylated into ATP, which was then exported outside mitochondria (see Vignais, 1976; Vignais et al., 1985). Corroboration of this finding occurs in results of experiments in which the ADP/ATP exchange in rat heart mitochondria was assayed by a rapid filtration technique in the millisecond time-range, without requirement of inhibitors (Brandolin et al., 1990). Biphasic kinetics of exchange were demonstrated and interpreted as a reflection of the occurrence of a rapidly exchangeable pool of mitochondrial nucleotides distinct from, but in equilibrium with, the total pool of mitochondrial nucleotides. It is important to note that the entire pool of mitochondrial nucleotides is exchangeable over a sufficient period of time, a fact that points to the kinetic nature of the compartmentation. Mitochondrial nucleotide compartmentation most likely increases the efficiency of delivery of ATP to the cell.

Because of its central role in the cell energy metabolism, ADP/ATP transport defects are expected to result in severe disorders. Indeed ADP/ATP carrier deficiencies in muscle have been reported to result in myopathy (Bakker et al., 1993). To quantify the ADP/ATP carrier in muscle homogenates, we set up a sensitive fluorometric method based on the use of fluorescent derivatives of atractyloside (Roux et al., 1996).

Common Features to the Mitochondrial Carriers

Though mitochondrial carriers differ from each other with respect to nature, size, and polarity of the transported metabolites, ranging from the small cation H_3O^+, which is transported by UCP, to the large anions ADP^{3-} and ATP^{4-}, they display common features that justify their classification as members of the same family. All are encoded by nuclear genes and expressed as mature proteins with molecular masses in the range of 30 kD, under the monomeric form. These carrier proteins are directed to the mitochondrial inner membrane by a common general import pathway (Pfanner and Neupert, 1990). However, a number of mitochondrial carriers, including the mammalian phosphate and citrate carriers and the ADP/ATP carrier from plant mitochondria, are synthesized with a cleavable targeting presequence, whereas the yeast phosphate carrier, the ADP/ATP and oxoglutarate carriers, and UCP are synthesized without any presequence. In contrast to UCP and to the oxoglutarate and the phosphate carriers, for which only one gene per carrier has been identified, several isoforms of the ADP/ATP carrier encoded by specific genes have been identified. In humans, expression of the ADP/ATP carrier is tissue-specific (see references in Brandolin et al., 1993; Walker and Runswick, 1993). In the yeast *Saccharomyces cerevisiae* three genes, *ANC1*, *ANC2* and *ANC3*, encoding the mitochondrial ADP/ATP carrier have been characterized. Only one of them, *ANC2*, is required for the cells to grow on a nonfermentable source of carbon, whereas expression of *ANC3* is paradoxically essential for growth under anaerobic conditions (Kolarov et al., 1990; Drgon et al., 1991).

Analysis of protein sequences of the mitochondrial ADP/ATP carrier, phosphate carrier, oxoglutarate carrier, and UCP, led to the proposal that the mitochondrial carriers have a triplicate structure, consisting of domains 100 amino acids long (Walker and Runswick, 1993). Similarities among these domains suggest that the mitochondrial carriers originated from a common ancestor and have evolved by gene duplication and subsequent diversification.

Most of the mitochondrial transport systems operate by a counterexchange mechanism (see Lanoue and Schoolwerth, 1984). A number of kinetic data obtained either with intact mitochondria or with reconstituted systems argue in favor of a sequential mechanism of transport (see Krämer and Palmieri, 1992), which requires simultaneous binding of two substrates, one on the cytosolic face of the carrier and the other one on the matrix face, at a given time during the transport cycle. This requirement is fulfilled in the case of the ADP/ATP carrier, since the existence of two nucleotide binding sites on each face of the carrier unit has been demonstrated (see below).

Dynamics of the ADP/ATP Carrier

The ADP/ATP carrier can adopt two conformations, known as CATR and BA conformations because they are recognized by CATR and BA, respectively (Vignais et al., 1985). Reversible conversion from one form to the other is facilitated considerably by catalytic amounts of ADP and ATP and therefore is probably involved in the transport process. Binding of CATR and BA results in trapping of the carrier into the form of stable inactive CATR- or BA-carrier complexes. On the basis of its different reactivities to chemical and immunochemical probes and its different susceptibilities to specific proteases, the carrier adopts distinct conformations when bound to CATR and BA (for review see Brandolin et al., 1993).

Spectrofluorometric experiments carried out with naphthoyl-ADP (N-ADP), a fluorescent derivative of ADP, used as a probe of the membrane-bound carrier, demonstrated that the CATR and the BA conformers of the beef heart mitochondria ADP/ATP carrier co-exist in equilibrium (Vignais et al., 1985). Furthermore, both the CATR and BA conformers were found to bind externally added ADP or ATP, a result that is not explainable by the *single reorienting site* mechanism of ADP/ATP transport. According to this mechanism, a single binding site for nucleotides and inhibitors may be alternatively open to the inside (*m* state of the carrier) and to the cytosol (*c* state) during the transport process (Klingenberg, 1985). As a consequence, the CATR conformation and the BA conformation are not equivalent to the postulated *c* state and *m* state of the single-site mechanism.

Even solubilized in the presence of detergent, the ADP/ATP carrier protein is able to undergo a transition between CATR and BA conformations. This was shown by the following of ADP- or ATP-induced intrinsic fluorescence changes of the beef heart carrier protein isolated in presence of the detergent laurylamidodimethylpropylaminoxide (LAPAO) (Brandolin et al., 1985). Addition of ADP or ATP resulted in an increase in fluorescence that was preventable by adding CATR before ADP (ATP) and reversable by adding CATR after ADP (ATP). Surprisingly, BA further enhanced the ADP- or ATP-induced fluorescence increase. These results suggest the transition of the carrier initially in the CATR conformation, in the absence of any ligand, to the BA conformation. Only in the presence of transportable nucleotides does this transition become possible.

The fluorometric approach combined to the genetic approach has been recently applied to the ADP/ATP carrier from the yeast *S. cerevisiae*. A yeast strain expressing exclusively the Anc2 isoform of the ADP/ATP carrier was first constructed by reintroduction of the *ANC2* gene in a strain whose genome had been previously disrupted for the three *ANC1*, *ANC2* and *ANC3* carrier-encoding genes (Brandolin et al., 1993). Assessment of the efficient expression of the Anc2 carrier occurred by titration of the atractyloside binding sites of the carrier in mitochondria. Similar to the beef heart carrier, the isolated yeast carrier underwent ADP- or ATP-induced conformational changes that were assessed by fluorescence measure-

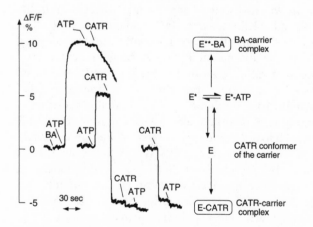

Figure 2. Time-course of substrate- and inhibitor-induced fluorescence changes of the isolated yeast Anc2 carrier. Fluorescence excitation was at 296 nm and fluorescence emission at 350 nm. Fluorescence states of the isolated yeast Anc2 carrier protein are correlated with the postulated conformational states of the carrier. Transition between the CATR and the BA conformers is triggered exclusively by transportable nucleotides. CATR and BA bind to the respective conformers of the carrier; this results in stabilization of either the low-fluorescence CATR-carrier complex or the high-fluorescence BA-carrier complex.

ments and could be prevented or reversed by CATR (Fig. 2). Upon addition of ADP or ATP, fluorescence was increased, and a further increase was observed upon addition of BA. Titration experiments revealed that both CATR and BA interacted with very high affinity to binding sites in the carrier. Fig. 2 summarizes the transitions between the CATR and BA conformations of the Anc2 carrier. Under our experimental conditions, the isolated carrier was present in the basal state E, which can be trapped as a low fluorescence CATR-carrier complex. Upon addition of ADP or ATP, the carrier shifted to the E*-ATP state, E* denoting a high-fluorescence state of the carrier. BA was able to bind to E* or to E*-ATP; this resulted in the stabilization of the highly fluorescent BA-carrier complex. Addition of ADP or ATP in micromolar amounts was necessary for the transition from E to E* to occur. Nontransportable nucleotides proved inefficient. On the whole, a striking parallel occurs between the conformational changes that occur in the mammalian and the yeast ADP/ATP carriers during the transport process.

The Anc2 protein contains three tryptophanyl residues—W87, W126, and W235—that are responsible for the fluorescence changes. Fluorometric study of the isolated Anc2 carrier in which the tryptophanyl residues were substituted by tyrosyl residues, either individually or in combination, showed that conformational changes of the carrier are probed differently by each of the three tryptophanyl residues: the conformational changes of the carrier induced by CATR affected mainly the COOH-terminal half of the carrier, whereas those induced by ADP or ATP were essentially detected by tryptophanyl residues located in the NH_2-terminal half of the polypeptide chain of the carrier (Le Saux et al., submitted).

Are Functional Carriers Dimeric or Tetrameric?

Evidence for a dimeric structure of mitochondrial carriers was obtained from cross-linking experiments for membrane-bound UCP and the oxoglutarate carrier (for review see Krämer and Palmieri, 1992) and from analytical centrifugation experiments for isolated UCP (see Klingenberg, 1993). The state of oligomerization of the ADP/ATP carrier from beef heart was assessed by analytical centrifugation in the case of the CATR-carrier complex (see Klingenberg, 1993) and by neutron scattering for the BA-carrier complex (see Vignais et al., 1985). In both cases the inhibited carrier was found to be dimeric. In the absence of inhibitor, the ADP/ATP carrier assumed a higher degree of oligomerization than that in the inhibited state. From binding experiments carried out by different approaches, with either the membrane-bound carrier or the isolated carrier in detergent, an equal number of high- and low-affinity nucleotide binding sites emerged, along with a number of CATR binding sites, equal to that of the nucleotide binding sites (see Vignais et al., 1985). It turned out that the minimal number of sites for CATR is two. Since one CATR binds per carrier dimer (see Klingenberg, 1985; Block et al., 1986), it was concluded that the functional ADP/ATP carrier is organized as a tetramer. Each membrane-bound tetrameric carrier might thus contain two nucleotide binding sites on each face of the membrane and, in addition, two CATR binding sites exposed to the cytosol and two BA binding sites facing the matrix. The presence of two CATR-binding sites and two BA-binding sites per functional carrier unit is consistent with the positive cooperative binding of CATR and BA to the membrane-bound carrier and

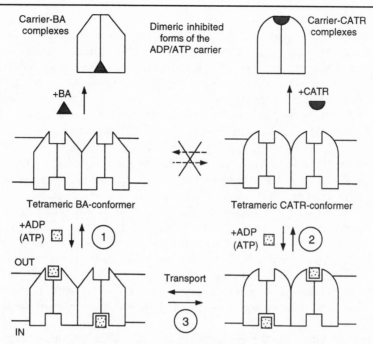

Figure 3. Model illustrating the postulated conformational changes of the ADP/ATP carrier occurring during the transport process. The figure represents the tetrameric CATR and BA conformers of the functional ADP/ATP carrier. Each tetrameric conformer contains two paths for translocation of ADP or ATP. Simultaneous binding of ADP(ATP) on inward- and outward-facing sites (*steps 1 and 2*) results in the formation of a ternary complex, which triggers interconversion between the two conformers and allows transport to proceed (*step 3*). Binding of CATR and BA to the respective tetrameric conformers appears to induce splitting of the ADP/ATP carrier into stable inactive dimers. The scheme illustrates the overall asymmetry of the carrier relative to the plane of the membrane. The model is consistent with the sequential mechanism of ADP/ATP transport and with binding data obtained with either the substrates ADP and ATP or the inhibitors CATR and BA.

the isolated carrier in detergent (see Vignais et al., 1985; Brandolin et al., 1985). Binding of CATR or BA to the ADP/ATP carrier might thus result in the splitting of the functional tetramer to an inactivated stable dimeric CATR-carrier complex or BA-carrier complex, as illustrated in Fig. 3.

Topography of the ADP/ATP Carrier in the Mitochondrial Membrane

Since the ADP/ATP carrier can adopt stable CATR and BA conformations, the transmembrane arrangement of its polypeptide chain could be investigated in these two conformations by classical methods based on the use of chemical reagents, site-directed antibodies, and proteases. An immunochemical approach demonstrated the orientation of the NH_2-terminal region of the ADP/ATP carrier to the cytosol by use of antibodies raised against a synthetic peptide whose sequence was identical to the NH_2-terminal region of the carrier. In addition, the conformation of the carrier demonstrably influenced accessibility of the NH_2-terminal region to specific antibodies, illustrated by a decrease of reactivity when mitoplasts were incubated with BA. The converse occurred, however, by an enhancement of reactivity when CATR was used instead of BA (Brandolin et al., 1989). In the presence of BA, the lower accessibility of the NH_2-terminal region of the carrier to antibodies from the cytosol was accompanied by unfolding of the corresponding region of the peptide chain exposed to the matrix, resulting in a marked increase in the reactivity of the C56 residue to NEM (Vignais et al., 1985) and in the susceptibility of the peptide bonds R30-V31, R59-I60, and K42-E43 to endo-Arg– and endo-Lys–specific proteases (Brandolin et al., 1989; Marty et al., 1992). These results pointed to the ability of sequences of the NH_2-terminal region exposed to both the cytosol and the matrix to report conformational changes. These changes were not directly involved in the binding of substrates and inhibitors since these ligands bind to sequences located in the COOH-terminal half of the polypeptide chain. Upon binding, conformational changes are likely to be propagated towards the NH_2-terminal extremity along the polypeptide chain of individual monomers, or transmitted through interactions between mobile regions belonging to adjacent monomers in the tetrameric functional carrier.

Proteolysis experiments were carried out with trypsin and with a lysine-specific endoprotease, either on mitoplasts or on inside-out submitochondrial particles (SMP), in the presence of CATR or BA. The membrane-bound carrier in the CATR state was remarkably resistant to proteolysis: only in SMP pretreated by BA could it be cleaved, at bonds K42-E43, K146-G147, and K244-G245 (Marty et al., 1992). These bonds probably belong to flexible regions of the carrier that become exposed to proteases during the transition from the CATR conformation to the BA conformation.

Chemical and photochemical labeling experiments have produced additional information about the topography of the ADP/ATP carrier in the mitochondrial membrane. Mapping of the nucleotide and inhibitor binding sites of the beef heart ADP/ATP carrier were carried out with non-permeant radiolabeled photoactivable derivatives of atractyloside (Boulay et al., 1983) and ADP (Dalbon et al., 1988), respectively. Photoirradiation of beef heart mitochondria in the presence of 2-azido(α^{32}P)ADP led to covalent labeling of two peptide segments, spanning residues F153 to M200 and Y250 to M281, with residues K162, K165, I183, V254, and K259 predominantly labeled. The region F153–M200 was also photolabeled by azido-atractyloside. It corresponds to the segment spanning residues G172–M210 that was labeled by 2-azido(α^{32}P)ADP in the yeast ADP/ATP carrier, whereas in UCP, a region equivalent to the sequence Y250-M281 in the beef carrier was photolabeled by the same probe (see Klingenberg, 1993). These results indicate the propensity of the COOH-terminal region of the UCP and of the ADP/ATP carrier to bind nucleotides either for regulation or for transport. The two nucleotide binding regions of the ADP/ATP carrier are presumably located within a translocation pathway, but the question remains whether they belong to the same carrier monomer or to different monomers juxtaposed to form the path.

Chemical labeling of the membrane carrier with reagents modifying specific amino acids allowed further insights in structural dynamics of the carrier. For example, iodination of tyrosyl groups and alkylation of cysteine 56 (for review see Vignais, 1985) have brought out convincing evidence of topographical differences in the ADP/ATP carrier in the CATR conformation and in the BA conformation. However, use of chemical reagents carries problems relating to their membrane penetration, making the sidedness of the reactions difficult to assess. This problem was illustrated in the case of pyridoxal phosphate that labeled a high number of lysine groups, obviously located on both sides of the membrane (Klingenberg, 1989).

The membrane topography of other mitochondrial carriers including the phosphate and the oxoglutarate carrier (Palmieri et al., 1993), the citrate carrier (Capobianco et al., 1995) and UCP (Klingenberg, 1993; Miroux et al., 1993) was also explored with immunochemical methods and by a controlled proteolysis approach similar to that developed for the study of the topography of the ADP/ATP carrier. However, in those cases, no data were available on the conformational states of the carriers and thus on the influence of these conformations on the carrier topography.

The Mutagenesis Approach

Site-directed mutagenesis has been applied to the yeast ADP/ATP carrier with the aim of locating strategic amino acid residues expected to play a role in the transport mechanism. Although promising, this technique has not often afforded a clear-cut interpretation of data in terms of mechanism. The site-directed mutagenesis approach has been extended with the search of intragenic second-site revertants, but in some cases the number of revertants was unexpectedly high, as illustrated in the case of the R254-I primary mutation (Klingenberg, 1993).

The mutation R96-H in the yeast ADP/ATP carrier prevents yeast cells from growing on non-fermentable substrates such as glycerol (Kolarov et al., 1990; Klingenberg, 1993). However in this case the transport capacity of the ADP/ATP carrier, assessed with a reconstituted system, was only partially impeded. Other substitutions, including those of residue R96 by aspartyl, histidyl, leucyl, or prolyl residues (Klingenberg, 1993) or by lysyl, asparagyl, or glutamyl residues (Lauquin et al., unpublished data), were incompatible with the growth of yeast cells on a glycerol medium. Similarly, the mutations R204-L and R294-L as well as the mutations R252-I, R253-I, and R254-I made the yeast cells unable to grow on glycerol. Whether these arginine residues are directly involved in functioning of the carrier, for example in binding of nucleotides, or contribute to the proper folding of the carrier, remains undetermined. Similar interpretations might be proposed to explain inactivation of the carrier function by mutation of K39, which is postulated to be localized within a transmembrane helix. Surprisingly, the substitutions of K179 and K182, which are in the neighborhood of the identified nucleotide binding site, do not significantly affect the transport activity of the carrier (Klingenberg, 1993). In contrast to positively charged residues, C73 of the yeast carrier corresponding to C56 of the beef heart carrier was found to be nonessential for transport (Klingenberg, 1993). In fact, in contrast to alkylation by thiol-specific reagents such as NEM (Boulay et al., 1983), substitution of C73 by serine did not impair the ADP/ATP transport, an observation suggesting that the inhibitory effect of alkylation was due to steric hindrance. Similar results have been reported for a NEM-sensitive cysteine residue in the mitochondrial phosphate carrier (Phelps et al., 1991) and UCP (Arechaga et al., 1993).

In addition to the approach that consists of inactivating transport by site-directed mutagenesis, we have addressed a fluorometic approach based on the use of tryptophan-directed mutants that were selected for their ability to keep full activity of transport, as briefly reported in the section "Dynamics of the ADP/ATP Carrier."

Models

Analysis of the distribution of hydrophilic and hydrophobic residues along the sequence of membrane proteins allows detection of membrane spanning segments, usually predicted as α-helices, even though this type of folding has been recently questioned (Fischbarg et al., 1994). Hydrophobic profiles obtained for a number of mitochondrial ADP/ATP carriers of known sequence indicated the presence of essentially five hydrophobic segments long enough to cross the membrane as α helices. An alternative model for the ADP/ATP carrier took the triplicated structure of the mitochondrial carriers into account, with each of the three domains of this structure consisting in two membrane-spanning α helices connected by hydrophilic loops. This model included a sixth transmembrane segment in the first repeat, although this additional segment contained a number of polar residues (Walker and Runswick, 1993; see also Brandolin et al., 1993). The six-α-helix model is consistent with the orientation of both the NH_2- and the COOH-terminal ends of the phosphate carrier, the oxoglutarate carrier, the citrate carrier, and UCP to the cytosolic side. A similar arrangement of the ADP/ATP carrier has been suggested according to the homology principle (Klingenberg, 1989), but other models not conforming to this scheme have been proposed on the basis of topographic data (see Brandolin et al., 1993).

The alternative exposure of the two amphipathic sequences 137–170 and 234–266 of the beef ADP/ATP carrier to cytosol and to the mitochondrial matrix may be considered a typical feature of the dynamics of transport of ADP and ATP in mitochondria. These amphipathic sequences appear to belong to the path through which the nucleotides are transported and to be inserted within the mitochondrial membrane as hairpin structures, consisting of either short α helices or β sheets, with the hydrophobic residues clustered on one face of the α helix or the β sheet and the hydrophilic residues on the other face (Marty et al., 1992; Brandolin et al., 1993). A hydrophilic channel might be delineated by association of the monomers with juxtaposition of these amphipathic segments to shield polar residues from the hydrophobic core of the bilayer. In addition, this structure would significantly shorten the transmembrane path because of the locally reduced thickness of the membrane, thus facilitating transport of bulky molecules such as nucleotides. The gating of the channel and the transport itself might proceed through conformational changes triggered by the binding of ADP or ATP and undergone by the amphipathic mobile segments. It is noteworthy that a nucleotide binding region of the UCP polypeptide chain, which has a regulatory function and is equivalent to the sequence 234–266 of the beef carrier, is accessible from both sides of the mitochondrial membrane and is probably deeply embedded in the membrane (Miroux et al., 1993).

Despite the fact that the detailed mechanism of the ADP(ATP) transport across the mitochondrial membrane is little understood, and that the topology of the ADP/ATP carrier in the membrane remains largely unknown, significant progress has been accomplished with identification of the sequences, whose secondary structures are sensitive to conformational changes brought about by the binding of specific ligands, and which are postulated to belong to the translocation pathway for ADP and ATP. Ligand binding and kinetic data are consistent with the tetrameric organization of the carrier and the occurrence of two translocation channels. A striking peculiarity of the ADP/ATP carrier protein is its relatively high hydrophilic character, not typical of a membrane protein. This feature contrasts with the low sensitivity of the membrane-bound carrier to proteases. Thus, the structure of the ADP/ATP carrier in the mitochondrial membrane is probably very compact, with hydrophilic loops not expanding in the extra-membrane aqueous medium, but rather penetrating the membrane within the carrier itself.

References

Aprille, J.R. 1993. Mechanism and regulation of the mitochondrial ATP-Mg/Pi carrier. *J. Bioenergetics Biomembr.* 25:473–481.

Arechaga, I., S. Raimbault, S. Prieto, C. Levi-Meyrueis, P. Zaragoza, B. Miroux, D. Ricquier, F. Bouillaud, and E. Rial. 1993. Cysteine residues are not essential for uncoupling protein function. *Biochem. J.* 296:693–700.

Bakker, H.D., H.S. Scholte, C. van der Bogert, W. Ruitenbeek, J.A.L. Jeneson, R. Wanders, N.G.G. Abeling, B. Dorland, R.C.A. Sengers, and H. van Gennip. 1993. Deficiency of the adenine nucleotide translocator in muscle of a patient with myopathy and lactic acidosis: A new mitochondrial defect. *Ped. Res.* 33:412–417.

Benz, R. 1994. Permeation of hydrophilic solutes through mitochondrial outer membranes: review on mitochondrial porins. *Biochim. Biophys. Acta.* 1197:167–196.

Block, M.R., F. Boulay, G. Brandolin, G.J.M. Lauquin, and P.V. Vignais. 1986. Chemical modification and active site labeling of the mitochondrial ADP/ATP carrier. *Meth. Enzymol.* 125:658–670.

Boulay, F., G.J.M. Lauquin, A. Tsugita, and P.V. Vignais. 1983. Photolabeling approach to the study of the atractyloside binding site in mitochondrial adenosine 5'-diphosphate/adenosine 5'-triphosphate carrier protein. *Biochem.* 22:477–484.

Brandolin, G., Y. Dupont, and P.V. Vignais. 1985. Substrate-induced modifications of the intrinsic fluorescence of the isolated adenine nucleotide carrier protein: Demonstration of distinct conformational states. *Biochem.* 24:1991–1997.

Brandolin, G., F. Boulay, P. Dalbon, and P.V. Vignais. 1989. Orientation of the N-terminal region of the membrane-bound ADP/ATP carrier protein explored by antipeptide antibodies and an arginine-specific endoprotease. Evidence that the accessibility of the N-terminal residues depends on the conformational state of the carrier. *Biochem.* 28:1093–1100.

Brandolin, G., I. Marty, and P.V. Vignais. 1990. Kinetics of nucleotide transport in rat heart mitochondria studied by a rapid filtration technique. *Biochem.* 29:9720–9727.

Brandolin, G., A. Le Saux, V. Trezeguet, G.J.-M. Lauquin, and P.V. Vignais. 1993. Chemical, immunological, enzymatic, and genetic approaches to studying the arrangement of the peptide chain of the ADP/ATP carrier in the mitochondrial membrane. *J. Bioenergetics Biomemb.* 25:459–472.

Capobianco, L., F. Bisaccia, A. Michel, F.E. Sluse, and F. Palmieri. 1995. The N- and C-termini of the tricarboxylate carrier are exposed to the cytoplasmic side of the inner mitochondrial membrane. *FEBS Lett.* 357:297–300.

Dalbon, P., G. Brandolin, F. Boulay, J. Hoppe, and P.V. Vignais. 1988. Mapping of the nucleotide binding sites in the ADP/ATP carrier of beef heart mitochondria by photolabeling with 2-azido-(α^{32}P)-adenosine triphosphate. *Biochem.* 27:5141–5149.

Drgon, T., L. Sabova, N. Nelson, and J. Kolarov. 1991. Yeast ADP/ATP carrier (AAC) proteins exhibit similar enzymatic properties but their deletion produces different phenotypes. *FEBS Lett.* 289:159–162.

Fischbarg, J., M. Cheung, J. Li, P. Iserovich, F. Czegledy, K. Kuang, and M. Garner. 1994. Are most transporters and channels beta barrels? *Mol. Cell. Biochem.* 140:147–162.

Klingenberg, M. 1985. The ADP/ATP carrier in the mitochondrial membrane. *In* The Enzymes of Mitochondrial Membrane: Membrane Transport. Vol 4. A. Martonosi, editor. John Wiley, New York. 511–553.

Klingenberg, M. 1989. Molecular aspects of the adenine nucleotide carrier from mitochondria. *Arch. Biochem. Biophys.* 270:1–14.

Klingenberg, M. 1993. Dialectics in carrier research: the ADP/ATP carrier and the uncoupling protein. *J. Bioenergetics Biomembr.* 25:447–457.

Kolarov, J., N. Kolarova, and N. Nelson. 1990. A third ADP/ATP translocator gene in yeast. *J. Biol. Chem.* 265:12711–12716.

Krämer, R., and F. Palmieri. 1992. Metabolite carriers in mitochondria. *In* Molecular Mechanisms in Bioenergetics. L. Ernster, editor. Elsevier, Amsterdam. 359–384.

Lanoue, K.F., and A.C. Schoolwerth. 1984. Metabolite transport in mammalian mitochondria. *In* Bioenergetics. L. Ernster, editor. Elsevier, Amsterdam. 221–268.

Ligeti, E., G. Brandolin, Y. Dupont, and P.V. Vignais. 1985. Kinetics of Pi-Pi exchange in rat liver mitochondria. Rapid filtration experiments in the millisecond time range. *Biochem.* 24:4423–4428.

Marty, I., G. Brandolin, and P.V. Vignais. 1992. Topography of the membrane-bound ADP/ATP carrier assessed by enzymatic proteolysis. *Biochem.* 31:4058–4065.

Miroux, B., V. Froscard, S. Raimbault, D. Ricquier, and F. Bouillaud. 1993. The topology of the brown adipose tissue mitochondrial uncoupling protein determined with antibodies against its antigenic sites revealed by a library of fusion proteins. *EMBO J.* 12:3739–3745.

Palmieri, F., F. Bisaccia, L. Capobianco, V. Dolce, G. Fiermonte, V. Iacobazzi, and V. Zara. 1993. Transmembrane topology, genes, and biogenesis of the mitochondrial phosphate and oxoglutarate carriers. *J. Bioenergetics Biomemb.* 25:493–501.

Pfanner, N., and W. Neupert. 1990. The mitochondrial protein import apparatus. *Annu. Rev. Biochem.* 59:331–353.

Phelps, A., C. Schobert, and H. Wohlrab. 1991. Cloning and characterization of the phosphate transport protein gene from the yeast *Saccharomyces cerevisiae*. *Biochem.* 30:248–252.

Roux, P., A. Le Saux, C. Fiore, C. Schwimmer, A.-C. Dianoux, V. Trézéguet, P.V. Vignais, G.J.-M. Lauquin, G. Brandolin. 1996. Fluorometric titration of the mitochondrial ADP/ATP carrier protein in muscle homogenate with atractyloside derivatives. *Anal. Biochem.* 234:31–37.

Vignais, P.V. 1976. Molecular and physiological aspects of adenine nucleotide transport in mitochondria. *Biochim. Biophys. Acta.* 456:1–38.

Vignais, P.V., M.R. Block, F. Boulay, G. Brandolin, and G.J.M. Lauquin. 1985. Molecular aspects of structure-function relationships in mitochondrial adenine nucleotide carrier. *In* Structure and Properties of Cell Membranes. Vol. II. G. Bengha, editor. CRC Press, Boca Raton, 139–179.

Walker, J.E., and M.J. Runswick. 1993. The mitochondrial transport protein superfamily. *J. Bioenergetics Biomembr.* 25:435–446.

Chapter 4

Nuclear Pores, Channels, and Transporters

Inositol 1,4,5-Trisphosphate Receptor Activation and Nuclear Envelope Assembly

Katherine L. Wilson, Kathleen M.C. Sullivan, and Christiane Wiese

Department of Cell Biology and Anatomy, The Johns Hopkins University School of Medicine, Baltimore, Maryland 21205

We tested the hypothesis that inositol 1,4,5-trisphosphate (IP$_3$) receptor activation is required for nuclear envelope assembly. Vesicles were pretreated with polyclonal antibodies to different domains of the type-1 IP$_3$ receptor and then tested for their ability to release Ca^{2+} when challenged with exogenous IP$_3$. The antibody-treated vesicles were also tested for their ability to assemble nuclear envelopes in vitro. Two different sera that inhibited IP$_3$-stimulated Ca^{2+} release also inhibited nuclear envelope assembly. On the basis of these results and other recent discoveries, we concluded that IP$_3$ receptor activation and Ca^{2+} release are required for two aspects of nuclear envelope assembly: nuclear pore complex assembly and membrane fusion.

Nuclear Structural Dynamics

The nucleus is a complex three-dimensional structure bounded by the inner and outer nuclear membranes (reviewed by Wiese and Wilson, 1993; Goldberg and Allen, 1995). Underlying the inner membrane is a polymer of intermediate filament proteins named *lamins*, which anchor the inner nuclear membrane, chromatin, and nuclear pore complexes (NPCs) (reviewed by Moir and Goldman, 1993). To enter or exit the nucleus, molecules larger than ~40 kD must be actively transported through the nuclear envelope via the pore complexes (reviewed by Melchior and Gerace, 1995). In higher eukaryotes the nucleus disassembles entirely during mitosis—all major structural components are converted into smaller subunits. The nuclear membranes and their enclosed lumenal space are fragmented into small vesicles and membrane cisternae. During anaphase and telophase, these membranes somehow recognize the chromosomes, bind to their surface, and fuse with each other to begin reforming the nuclear envelope. Nuclear pore complexes also assemble. We think that structures inside the nucleus begin to reassemble only after chromatin is enclosed by membranes. The complete assembly of a functional nucleus therefore involves the convergence of a dizzying array of structural components, including membranes, chromatin, and many different soluble proteins.

Kathleen M.C. Sullivan's current address is Department of Molecular/Cell Biology, University of California, Box 539/LSA Building, Berkeley, CA 94720-3200.

Organellar Ion Channels and Transporters © 1996 by The Rockefeller University Press

An In Vitro System for the Study of Nuclear Assembly

Our goal is to understand the mechanisms and regulation of nuclear envelope assembly, one step at a time. We use a crude but versatile in vitro system derived from *Xenopus* egg extracts (Lohka and Masui, 1983; Newmeyer and Wilson, 1991). The eggs are arrested in metaphase and contain large stockpiles of disassembled subunits of the nuclear envelope, endoplasmic reticulum, and Golgi complex. The membranes and soluble components can be separated from each other by centrifugation at 200,000 *g*, frozen, and reconstituted with chromatin to assemble nuclei in vitro. In addition, the cytosolic fraction can be biochemically manipulated to assemble nuclei (S-phase extract) or disassemble them (M-phase extract). A typical nuclear assembly reaction consists of S-phase cytosol (with an ATP-regeneration system), membranes, and demembranated *Xenopus* sperm chromatin; an enclosed nuclear envelope with nuclear pore complexes usually forms within 30 min at room temperature, and nuclear growth proceeds for 4–5 h.

Assays for Nuclear Vesicle Fusion

We have been particularly interested in the mechanisms of vesicle fusion during nuclear envelope assembly. Using light microscopy, we can assay the binding of vesicles to chromatin and the formation of an enclosed nuclear envelope. However,

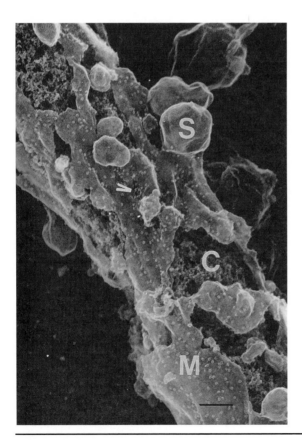

Figure 1. Scanning electron micrograph of an early stage in nuclear envelope assembly, before enclosure of the chromatin. Demembranated sperm chromatin was incubated with fractionated *Xenopus* egg cytosol and membranes in the presence of an ATP-regenerating system (Newmeyer and Wilson, 1991). Aliquots were fixed and processed for scanning electron microscopy at various times (Wiese, C., M.W. Goldberg, T.D. Allen, and K.C. Wilson, manuscript submitted for publication). This micrograph shows patches of ribosome-studded membranes (*M*) bound to chromatin (*C*), at a stage preceding full enclosure of the chromatin. A subset of smooth vesicles (*S*) also associates with chromatin and ribosome-studded membranes. One nuclear pore complex (*arrowhead*) is visible at this stage, but most NPCs appear later. *Scale bar*: 333 nm. (After Wiese et al., manuscript submitted for publication.)

many individual vesicle fusion events are required to reach the enclosed state, and single fusion events cannot be detected by light microscopy. After enclosure, the rate of fusion can be quantitated by light microscopy as the time-dependent increase in nuclear membrane surface area. To improve our assay for early fusion, and other structural events, we recently began using high-resolution scanning electron microscopy (Fig. 1; C. Wiese, M.W. Goldberg, T.D. Allen, and K.L. Wilson, manuscript submitted for publication).

Ca^{2+} Mobilization from Internal Vesicle Stores Is Required for Nuclear Envelope Assembly

We previously found that nuclear envelope assembly appears to require Ca^{2+} release via IP₃ receptors, which are ligand-gated Ca^{2+} channels located on ER membranes and the outer nuclear membrane. The evidence was as follows (Sullivan et al., 1993). BAPTA, a fast Ca^{2+} buffer that suppresses local increases in cytosolic free $[Ca^{2+}]$ but does not change the resting $[Ca^{2+}]$, inhibits fusion and delays the time of enclosure. In contrast EGTA, a slow Ca^{2+} buffer, has no effect. The BAPTA results suggested that a localized and transient Ca^{2+}-release event was required. The only possible source of mobilizable Ca^{2+} in these extracts is the lumen of the ER- and nuclear envelope–derived vesicles. Because *Xenopus* eggs contain only one class of intracellular Ca^{2+} channels, namely IP₃ receptors, these results suggested that IP₃ receptors mediate Ca^{2+} release during nuclear assembly. This hypothesis was supported by the finding that heparin, a potent but nonselective antagonist of Ca^{2+} release via IP₃ receptors, inhibits nuclear envelope assembly in an IP₃-reversible manner (Sullivan et al., 1993). On the basis of the light microscope assay and electron microscopic analysis at early timepoints, we interpreted these findings as an effect on vesicle fusion: Enclosure was delayed, and the eventually enclosed nuclei failed to increase their membrane surface area.

IP₃ Receptor Antibodies That Block Ca^{2+} Release Also Block Nuclear Envelope Assembly

To test the role of IP₃ receptors in nuclear assembly using selective reagents, we obtained antisera against two different bacterially expressed domains of the mouse IP₃ receptor (type 1), which is 90% identical to (Kume et al., 1993), and crossreacts with, the *Xenopus* type 1 receptors in the egg extracts. The experimental design was simple: Vesicles were preincubated with the antibodies, washed, and then tested for their ability to release Ca^{2+} in response to exogenous IP₃. Alternatively, the antibody-treated vesicles were incubated with cytosol and chromatin to determine if they were competent for nuclear assembly. Two antibodies that inhibited IP₃-stimulated Ca^{2+} flux also blocked nuclear envelope assembly (Sullivan et al., 1995). One inhibitory serum recognized a 44-kD region that is part of the "regulatory" domain of the IP₃ receptor, which includes potential sites for phosphorylation and ATP-binding (Berridge, 1993; Mikoshiba, 1993). Two independent polyclonal sera were raised against a 10–kD region near the COOH-terminus; these COOH-terminal antibodies bound equally well to vesicles, but only the one that inhibited Ca^{2+} flux also inhibited nuclear assembly. None of the bound antibodies had any effect on receptor affinity for IP_3. We have not yet identified the epitopes for these inhibitory sera.

BAPTA, the Fast Ca^{2+} Buffer, Inhibits Nuclear Pore Complex Assembly

In a surprise discovery, Forbes and colleagues recently found that enclosed, BAPTA-arrested nuclei have no nuclear pore complexes (Macaulay and Forbes, 1996). We have confirmed their finding and are now using the improved resolution of scanning EM to characterize in structural detail the phenotype of BAPTA-arrested nuclear envelopes. Our goal is to understand if Ca^{2+} release independently mediates two disparate events of nuclear envelope assembly (vesicle fusion and NPC assembly) and if these two events might be coupled (Wiese et al., manuscript submitted for publication).

More Questions Than Answers

We conclude that IP_3 receptor activation is required for nuclear assembly, but we are left with three big questions. First, exactly which event(s) in assembly require Ca^{2+} mobilization—vesicle fusion and NPC assembly, or just NPC assembly? Second, we do not understand how the channel is activated in the context of nuclear assembly. Are IP_3 receptors activated via the hydrolysis of phosphatidylinositol-bisphosphate (PIP_2), or is channel activity regulated by mechanisms that do not involve IP_3 production, such as phosphorylation? We originally speculated that channel activation may be coupled to the local assembly of fusion complexes between nuclear vesicles (Sullivan and Wilson, 1994). This speculation is based on the proposed mechanism of synaptic vesicle fusion in which an action potential opens voltage-gated Ca^{2+} channels at the synaptic plasma membrane and the influx of free Ca^{2+} then activates one or more Ca^{2+}-sensitive proteins associated with the docked vesicles, triggering fusion (Augustine et al., 1991). However, given the effect of BAPTA on NPC assembly, we must determine if antibodies to IP_3 receptors also block NPC assembly. The final big question—if the involvement of IP_3 receptors and Ca^{2+} release in nuclear assembly is a signal transduction event, what is being monitored?

Acknowledgments

We thank Martin Goldberg and Terry Allen, with whom we collaborated to obtain the scanning electron micrograph shown in Fig. 1.

This work was supported by National Institutes of Health grant RO1-GM48646 to K.L. Wilson.

References

Augustine, G.J., E.M. Adler, and M.P. Charlton. 1991. The calcium signal for transmitter secretion from presynaptic nerve terminals. *Ann. NY Acad. Sci.* 635:365–381.

Berridge, M.J. 1993. Inositol trisphosphate and calcium signalling. *Nature (Lond.).* 361:315–325.

Goldberg, M.W., and T.D. Allen. 1995. Structural and functional organization of the nuclear envelope. *Curr. Opin. Cell Biol.* 7:301–309.

Kume, S., A. Muto, J. Aruga, T. Nakagawa, T. Michikawa, T. Furuichi, S. Nakade, H. Okano, and K. Mikoshiba. 1993. The *Xenopus* IP₃ receptor: Structure, function, and localization in oocytes and eggs. *Cell.* 73:555–570.

Lohka, M.J., and Y. Masui. 1983. Formation in vitro of sperm pronuclei and mitotic chromosomes induced by amphibian ooplasmic components. *Science.* 220:719–721.

Macaulay, C., and D.J. Forbes. 1996. Assembly of the nuclear pore: Biochemically distinct steps revealed with NEM, GTPαS, and BAPTA. *J. Cell Biol.* 132:5–20.

Melchior, F., and L. Gerace. 1995. Mechanisms of nuclear protein import. *Curr. Opin. Cell Biol.* 7:310–318.

Mikoshiba, K. 1993. Inositol 1,4,5-trisphosphate receptor. *Trends Pharmacol. Sci.* 14:86–89.

Moir, R.D., and R.D. Goldman. 1993. Lamin dynamics. *Curr. Opin. Cell Biol.* 5:408–411.

Newmeyer, D.D., and K.L. Wilson. 1991. Egg extracts for nuclear import and nuclear assembly reactions. *Meth. Cell Biol.* 36:607–634.

Sullivan, K.M.C., W.B. Busa, and K.L. Wilson. 1993. Calcium mobilization is required for nuclear vesicle fusion in vitro: Implications for membrane traffic and IP₃ receptor function. *Cell.* 73:1411–1422.

Sullivan, K.M.C., D.D. Lin, W. Agnew, and K.L. Wilson. 1995. Inhibition of nuclear vesicle fusion by antibodies that block activation of inositol 1,4,5-trisphosphate receptors. *Proc. Natl. Acad. Sci. USA.* 92:8611–8615.

Sullivan, K.M.C., and K.L. Wilson. 1994. A new role for IP₃ receptors: Ca²⁺ release during nuclear vesicle fusion. *Cell Calcium.* 16:314–321.

Wiese, C., and K.L. Wilson. 1993. Nuclear membrane dynamics. *Curr. Opin. Cell Biol.* 5:387–394.

Nuclear Ion Channels and Regulation of the Nuclear Pore

Lisa Stehno-Bittel,* Carmen Perez-Terzic,‡ Andreas Luckhoff,§
and David E. Clapham‡

*Department of Physical Therapy, University of Kansas Medical Center, Kansas
City, Kansas 66160-7601; ‡Department of Pharmacology, Mayo Foundation,
Rochester, Minnesota 55905; and §Institute of Pharmacology, Berlin D-14195,
Germany

Introduction

The nucleus is surrounded by a concentric doublet of membranes separating the
nuclear contents from the cytosol. The outer nuclear membrane is in contact with
the cytoplasm and is continuous with the endoplasmic reticulum (ER). The inner
nuclear membrane interacts with the nuclear lamina. The space between the inner
and outer nuclear membranes (the nuclear cisterna) is continuous with the lumen
of the ER and, as does the rest of the ER, sequesters Ca^{2+}. At regular intervals the
two membranes fuse around a superstructure of proteins called the nuclear pore
complex (NPC, Fig. 1). The NPC has a diameter of 0.13 μm with a relative molecular mass of over 100 MD (Hinshaw et al., 1992). The NPC has two known primary
functions: first, to control active nuclear/cytoplasmic transport of macromolecules
through the large opening located in the center of the complex (Silver, 1991), and,
second, to permit diffusion of small molecules and ions. The nuclear envelope has
been considered freely permeable to solutes of less than 40–70 kD lacking nuclear
localization sequences (Lange et al., 1986). The latter function has been questioned
because of mounting evidence of ionic gradients (especially Ca^{2+}) between the nucleoplasm and the cytoplasm (Bachs et al., 1992; Dale et al., 1994; Williams et al.,
1985).

Over the last five years ion channels have been identified and characterized by
patch-clamp methods applied to the isolated nuclei. In addition, specific binding
sites for members of the phosphoinositide pathway have been identified on the nuclear membrane; these point to the possibility of ligand-gated nuclear channels.
This paper reviews the nuclear ion channels presently identified and describes the
inositol trisphosphate ($InsP_3$)-dependent current that releases nuclear Ca^{2+}. Also,
we provide an overview of data establishing that $InsP_3$-dependent Ca^{2+} release inhibits diffusion of intermediate-sized molecules across the nuclear envelope.

As shown in Fig. 1, receptor activation at the plasma membrane of cells may
produce second messengers that diffuse to the nucleus to initiate nuclear-specific
events. While cells process the components of the pathway required for this signaling scheme, a direct link between plasma membrane receptors and nuclear ion
channels has not been established *in vivo*. In fact, very little is known about the gating and function of the ionic currents identified on nuclear membranes. Most currents discovered to date are spontaneously active; upon gigaohm seal formation,
channel activity is observed.

Organellar Ion Channels and Transporters © 1996 by The Rockefeller University Press

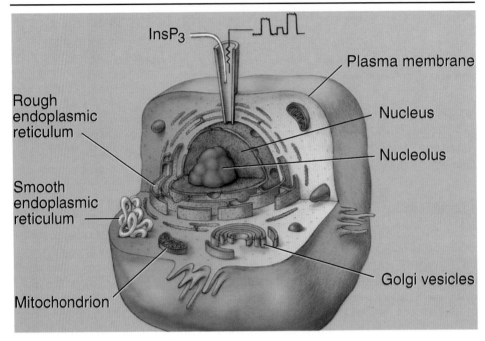

Figure 1. Possible signaling mechanisms between plasma membrane receptors and ion channels in the nuclear membrane. The nuclear envelope is a double membrane organelle with an apparent Ca^{2+} store located between the two membranes. Activated plasma membrane receptors (*R*) may stimulate production of second messengers that diffuse to the nuclear envelope and activate nuclear channels. The nuclear pore complex (*NPC*) is a macromolecular structure that crosses both nuclear membranes and is thought to allow free diffusion of small molecules and ions.

Spontaneously Active Nuclear Channels
Nuclear Membrane Potential

The nuclear membrane maintains an electrical potential, which varies in magnitude depending on the technique and cell type assayed. By use of patch-clamp techniques, an average membrane potential of 10 mV in 120 mM $[K^+]$ was measured across mouse pronuclei, germinal vesicles, two-cell embryo nuclei, and nuclei from adult mouse hepatocytes (Mazzanti et al., 1991). Conventional intracellular microelectrode recordings across the starfish germinal vesicles ranged from +4 to +30 mV with respect to the cytoplasm (Dale et al., 1994). In *Xenopus laevis* oocyte nuclei we have seen little evidence of a significant membrane potential across the outer nuclear membrane. Similar to Mazzanti et al. (1994), we have found no difference in the reversal potential of K^+ and Cl^- channels in the nuclear-attached mode when compared with excised patches (n = 55). No resting membrane potential was recorded across nuclei from cardiac myocytes (Bustamante, 1992).

Cation Channels

Channels have been reported in sufficient density in nuclei to be recorded in nearly every patch of membrane. The most prominent channel type was K^+-selective, with a maximum conductance of 200 pS (Mazzanti et al., 1990). A smaller conductance of 55 pS was thought to be a substate of the larger current (Mazzanti et al., 1990). The 200 pS current was identified in murine pronuclei, germinal vesicles, two-cell embryos and adult liver nuclei (Mazzanti et al., 1991). Thus, maturity and developmental stage of the cell did not drastically alter the single channel characteristics. In mouse cardiac myocyte nuclei, a K^+-selective current of approximately the same amplitude (198 pS in 150 mM symmetrical KCl) was measured (Table I; Bustamante, 1992). The inactivation of the channel was voltage-dependent with an e-fold

TABLE I
Channels Identified in Nuclear Membrane

Charge carrier	Conductance (pS)	Blockers	Source	Reference
K^+	200 55	——	murine pronuclei, germinal vesicles, rat liver	Mazzanti et al., 1991
K^+	198	Zn^{2+} and La^{3+} modulated by PKA	mouse cardiac myocytes	Bustamante, 1992
K^+	125	TEA-insensitive	*Xenopus laevis* oocytes	Stehno-Bittel et al., 1996
Cation	800	Cs^+-insensitive	avian erythrocyte nuclear liposomes	Matzke et al., 1990
K^+	1000	——	mouse pronuclei	Mazzanti et al., 1991
Cation	1000	Cs^+-insensitive	coconut endosperm	Matzke et al., 1992
Cation	1000–1200	——	*Xenopus laevis* oocytes	Stehno-Bittel et al., 1994; Mazzanti et al., 1994
Cl^-	150 58	ATP, DIDS, and niflumic acid	rat hepatocytes	Tabares et al., 1991
Cl^-	25	——	*Xenopus laevis* oocytes	Stehno-Bittel et al., 1996

decrease in the inactivation time constant for a 20-mV change in the membrane potential (Bustamante, 1992).

We identified $\sim$125 pS spontaneously opening K^+-selective currents in oocyte nuclei (Fig. 2, n = 55). The channel mean open time was > 150 ms. The open probability of the channel did not vary significantly with changes in the membrane potential. The oocyte nuclear K^+ channel was not sensitive to TEA (0.5 to 10 mM, n = 15), $InsP_3$, or $InsP_4$ (n = 42). We also measured a large current of 1000 pS at positive membrane potentials in *Xenopus* oocyte nuclei, but the current was seen too infrequently to determine a meaningful mean open time. Such large currents have been described previously in other nuclei. Recent work demonstrated that a single channel conductance of > 1200 pS from *Xenopus* oocyte nuclei was sensitive to cytoplasmic ATP (Mazzanti et al., 1994). Mazzanti et al., also observed a 1000-pS conductance in mouse pronuclei, probably due to the superposition of smaller substates. A large K^+-conducting current was identified in the nuclear membrane from

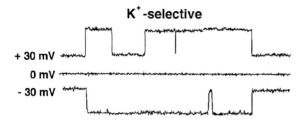

Figure 2. Spontaneous nuclear currents. Oocyte nuclei were patch-clamped as previously described (Stehno-Bittel et al., 1995a). Bath and pipette solutions were: 140 mM KCl, 10 mM HEPES, 3 mM $MgCl_2$, and 10 mM EGTA resulting in low free $[Ca^{2+}]$. Upon formation of a GOhm seal, spontaneous channel activity was measured. Current recordings from two different excised patches of nuclear membrane show typical examples of the spontaneously activating K^+ and Cl^--conducting channels. Membrane potential was recorded relative to the cytoplasm.

mature avian erythrocytes by use of giant liposomes composed of phosphatidylcholine and nuclear envelope membranes (Matzke et al., 1990). This preparation contained several subconductance states in multiples of 50 pS with the maximum conductance of $\sim$ 800 pS (Matzke et al., 1990). Similarly, giant liposomes from the nuclear envelope of coconut endosperm cells possess 1000-pS currents and a less frequent 450-pS conductance level (Matzke et al., 1992). The current was present in KCl or CsCl, an observation leading to the suggestion that the current represents the non-selective movement of ions through the NPC (Matzke et al., 1992). Table I summarizes nuclear ion channels currently described in the literature.

Anion Channels

Cl^--selective outer nuclear membrane currents have also been recorded. Two chloride channel subtypes were described on the outer nuclear membrane from hepatocytes on the basis of their unique conductances and sensitivity to ATP (Tabares et al., 1991). Both channels (150 and 58 pS) were voltage-sensitive at potentials ranging from +30 to −50 mV in symmetrical 140 mM KCl. The channels were inhibited by anion transport inhibitors including DIDS (4,4 diisothiocyanotostilbene, 2.2′ disulfonic acid) and niflumic acid. The ATP block was dose-dependent and induced a rapid flicker with complete suppression of channel activity at 5 mM ATP (Tabares et al., 1991). The nuclear Cl^- channels were not affected by Ca^{2+} on either side of the membrane within a range of 10 nM to 3.5 mM. TEA and Mg^{2+} did not alter the channel activity (Tabares et al., 1991). In addition to the Cl^- currents measured in rat liver nuclei, we identified a small, Cl^--selective channel in *Xenopus* oocyte nuclei with a single channel conductance of 25 pS and a mean open time of $\sim$ 10 ms. This channel was observed most commonly in the nuclear-attached mode with rundown apparent following excision of the patch. The Cl^- current did not rectify within a range of membrane potentials from −40 to +60 mV (n = 9).

As summarized in Table I numerous cation and anion channels have been described in the nuclear envelope from cell types ranging from coconut endosperm to mouse cardiac myocytes. Most of these channels are minimally sensitive to changes in membrane potential and are classified as *spontaneously activated* simply because they are observed under steady-state conditions. In the future it is likely that receptors and second messengers will be discovered that activate nuclear channels, a discovery that will allow us to reclassify some of these channels as *ligand-gated channels*.

Ligand-gated Nuclear Channels

The nuclear envelope contains receptors for angiotensin (Eggena et al., 1993), Ah (Jain et al., 1994), insulin (Goldfine and Smith, 1976), and inositol tetraphosphate (Malviya, 1994), but the only direct measurement of a ligand-gated channel on the nuclear envelope is the inositol trisphosphate receptor (InsP$_3$R). High-affinity [^{32}P]InsP$_3$ binding sites were identified on isolated rat liver nuclei devoid of microsomal, mitochondrial, or plasma membrane components (Malviya et al., 1990). Heparin (100 µg/ml) completely abolished the nuclear InsP$_3$ binding. Furthermore, application of InsP$_3$ caused release of ^{45}Ca from intact isolated liver nuclei (Malviya et al., 1990). These results suggested that the nucleus, or a portion of it, acted as a Ca^{2+} store that released Ca^{2+} when stimulated.

InsP$_3$-dependent Nuclear Ca^{2+} Release

Both the nucleoplasm and the lumen of the nuclear envelope (nuclear cisterna) have the potential to regulate Ca^{2+} independently (Bachs et al., 1992). Membrane-permeant forms of Ca^{2+}-sensitive dyes have been used to load the cisterna preferentially, while membrane-impermeant dyes have been used to monitor [Ca^{2+}] within the nucleoplasm of isolated nuclei (Stehno-Bittel et al., 1995a; Stehno-Bittel et al., 1995b; Lin et al., 1994; Gerasimenko et al., 1995). Images obtained with the membrane-permeant dyes and isolated nuclei revealed a ring of fluorescent dye surrounding the nucleus, as expected if the dye fills the nuclear cisterna. We previously showed that the release of Ca^{2+} from isolated nuclei was dependent on the InsP$_3$ concentration by measuring the percentage of Ca^{2+} released within two minutes after InsP$_3$ application (Stehno-Bittel et al., 1995a). In time, oocyte nuclei release nearly all of the detectable Ca^{2+}, an observation suggesting that the rate of Ca^{2+} release may be a more important parameter in determining the InsP$_3$ sensitivity. The dose-response relationship of the relative rate of Ca^{2+} release and the applied InsP$_3$ concentration show high sensitivity of the receptor for InsP$_3$ (Fig. 3). The dose of InsP$_3$ required for half maximal Ca^{2+} release was the same whether calculated as the percentage or the rate of Ca^{2+} release, although the shapes of the curves differed [compare Fig. 3 with Stehno-Bittel et al., (1995a)].

Single Channel Characteristics of the Nuclear InsP$_3$ Receptor

Convincing functional data established that InsP$_3$-dependent Ca^{2+} release occurred within isolated nuclei, but the single channel characteristics of the current had not been described. We employed both nuclear-attached and excised–patch-clamp techniques to identify single-channel activity dependent on InsP$_3$. Perfusion of the recording pipette with InsP$_3$ activated the channels in a dose-dependent manner (Stehno-Bittel et al., 1995a). Furthermore, channels that were already activated by InsP$_3$ were inhibited when the recording pipette was perfused with heparin (10 µg/ml), a blocker of the InsP$_3$ receptor (Fig. 4). The single-channel activity in equimolar 140 mM KCl displayed four subconductance levels, with the third level (172 pS) being most common. Two smaller substates had single-channel conductances of 90 and 126 pS while a large 244-pS subconductance was rare. The current-voltage relation was linear for all substates (Stehno-Bittel et al., 1995a).

The four conductance levels observed are similar to the four levels reported

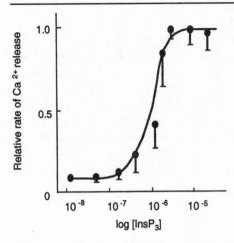

Figure 3. Rate of Ca^{2+} release depends on the InsP$_3$ concentration. Intact, isolated nuclei were loaded with the Ca^{2+}-permeant form of indo-1, a dual wavelength Ca^{2+}-sensitive dye, in the bath solution (Fig. 2 legend). InsP$_3$ was added to the bath at the concentrations stated, and the nuclear Ca^{2+} concentration monitored over a period of 5 min. The maximal rate of [Ca^{2+}] decrease was observed within the first two minutes of InsP$_3$ application. Data were normalized so that a relative rate of 1 is the maximum rate measured for any of the preparations (Iino and Endo, 1992).

previously for the cerebellar InsP$_3$R isolated from ER vesicles and reconstituted in lipid bilayers. Table II describes the similarities and differences between the nuclear InsP$_3$R channel from *Xenopus* oocytes (Stehno-Bittel et al., 1995*a*), and the cerebellar ER InsP$_3$R channel studied following reconstitution in lipid bilayers (Bezprozvanny et al., 1991, 1993*a*, and 1994). Both the ER cerebellar InsP$_3$ channel and the nuclear InsP$_3$R channel were sensitive to cytoplasmic [Ca^{2+}], displaying a bell-shaped dependence of channel activity on free Ca^{2+}. For the nuclear InsP$_3$-dependent channel, the optimal cytoplasmic [Ca^{2+}] was approximately 1 μM, while the cerebellar channel in the lipid bilayer was 200–300 nM. We used K$^+$ as the charge carrier in contrast to the work in bilayers, which measured the Ca^{2+}-sensitivity with Ca^{2+} as the charge carrier. Since it is not possible to clamp [Ca^{2+}] at the mouth of the pore of a Ca^{2+}-conducting channel, Ca^{2+} is higher at its binding site near the mouth of the pore than that measured in the bath or bulk cytoplasm. Thus, the optimal [Ca^{2+}] for the probability of channel opening may be close to 1 μM for the cerebellar ER InsP$_3$R as it is for the oocyte nuclear InsP$_3$R.

The nuclear and ER InsP$_3$ channels have different sensitivities to ATP (Table II). While the ER channel was sensitive to ATP, the nuclear channel was not affected by the addition of ATP under optimal Ca^{2+} and InsP$_3$ concentrations (Stehno-Bittel et al., 1995*a*). Only in cases in which the initial channel activity was low did the addition of ATP enhance channel opening. The maximum channel activity we attained with nuclear-attached or excised patches was 0.3, in contrast to 0.7 reported in a similar preparation (Mak and Foskett, 1994). In reconstituted lipid bilayers the maximum channel activity reported for the ER InsP$_3$R under optimal conditions was 0.15 (Bezprozvanny et al., 1993*a*). Both oocyte nuclear and ER InsP$_3$-dependent channel activity had a short mean open time, which varied from 1.3 to 5 ms (Stehno-Bittel et al., 1995*a*; Mak and Foskett, 1994; Watras et al., 1991).

It is not surprising that few differences were found between the InsP$_3$-dependent current from canine cerebellum (Bezprozvanny et al., 1991, 1993*a*, and 1994; Watras et al., 1991) and *Xenopus* oocyte nuclei (Stehno-Bittel et al., 1995*a*; Mak and Foskett, 1994) since both contain type I InsP$_3$Rs (Kume et al., 1993). Antibodies raised against the mouse brain InsP$_3$R cross-react with *Xenopus* oocyte InsP$_3$Rs (Stehno-Bittel et al., 1995*a*; Parys et al., 1992). The *Xenopus* oocyte InsP$_3$R has a

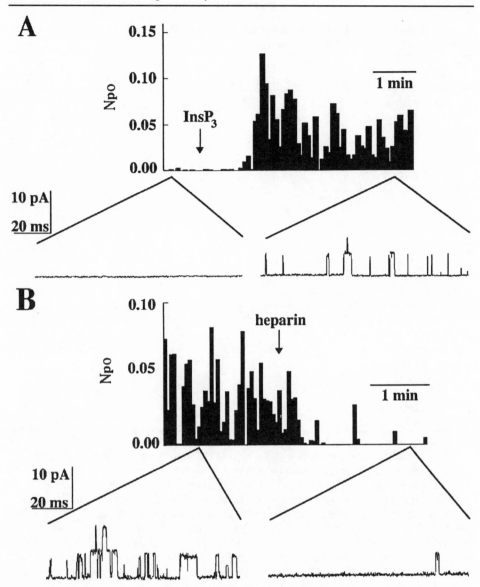

Figure 4. Channel activity dependent on InsP$_3$ in nuclear membrane. Isolated oocyte nuceli were patch clamped as described (Stehno-Bittel et al., 1995a). (*A*) After formation of a GOhm seal, the interior of the recording pipette was perfused with a solution containing 10 μM InsP$_3$ (*arrow*), initiating channel activity. (*B*) Perfusion of 10 μg/ml of heparin blocked channel activity. InsP$_3$ was present in the patch-clamp pipette during seal formation and in the heparin-containing solution. During these experiments the voltage was clamped at +30 mV. (From Stehno-Bittel et al., 1995a).

monomeric molecular mass of 256 kD, and that of the brain receptor is 273 kD (Parys et al., 1992). Slight differences in the amino acid sequence could account for the different sensitivities to ATP and Ca^{2+}. However, *Xenopus* InsP$_3$ receptors have 90% amino acid identity with the mouse type I receptor, with complete con-

Table II
Characteristics of the InsP$_3$-dependent Current in Oocyte Nuclei and
Reconstituted, Cerebellar ER Membrances

		Cerebellar InsP$_3$R (lipid bilayer)	Oocyte nuclear InsP$_3$R (inside-out patch)
Ca^{2+} conductance		[Ca^{2+}]= 50 mM	[Ca^{2+}]= 80 mM
4 substates	1	20 pS	85 pS
	2	40	
	3	60	
	4	80	
K$^+$ conductance			
4 substates	1		90 pS
	2		126
	3		172
	4		244
Ba^{2+} conductance		85 pS (55 mM Ba^{2+})	130 pS (75 mM Ba^{2+})
Mean open time (τ_o) (main conductance substate)		2.7 ms	1–6 ms
Voltage sensitivity (e-fold change in P$_o$)		43 mV	12 mV
Maximum NP$_o$		0.15	0.32
Ca^{2+}- sensitivity (Max NP$_o$)		0.2 µM free Ca^{2+}	1.0 µM free Ca^{2+}
ATP-sensitivity		Increased to τ_o 2.5-fold	Increased τ_o only for low initial NP$_o$
Half-max [InsP$_3$] for Ca^{2+} release		0.15 µM	0.05 µM

Four substates were measured in the oocyte nuclear channel with K$^+$ as the charge carrier, and four substates were also seen with Ca^{2+} as the charge carrier for the ER preparation. (Unfortunately, the ER preparation contains InsP$_3$-independent K$^+$ channels, which make it risky to measure the InsP$_3$ receptor in K$^+$ solution). With Ca^{2+} as the charge carrier in the nuclear preparation, channel activity increased dramatically so that four substate levels could not be discerned. Canine cerebellar vesicles were incorporated in a planar lipid bilayer with final solutions of (*cis*) 250 mM HEPES-Tris, 1 mM EGTA, 0.5 mM CaCl$_2$, pH 7.3; (*trans*) 250 mM HEPES, 53 mM Ca(OH)$_2$ or Ba(OH)$_2$, pH 7.3. Free Ca^{2+} was clamped at 200 nM Ca^{2+} with 4.43 mM CaK$_2$EGTA and 5.57 mM H$_2$K$_2$EGTA. All experiments at 22±2°C. Results are summarized from (Stehno-Bittel et al., 1995a; Watras et al., 1991; Bezprozvanny et al., 1991; Bezprozvanny et al., 1993; Bezprozvanny et al., 1994).

servation of the amino acid sequence in the putative pore region between the fifth and sixth transmembrane regions (Kume et al., 1993).

Nuclear InsP$_3$-dependent Ca^{2+} Release Blocks Pore Diffusion

The presence of functional InsP$_3$Rs in the nuclear membrane may simply reflect the fact that the outer nuclear and ER membranes are continuous. If this is the case, the nuclear InsP$_3$Rs may not possess any unique, nuclear-specific functions. However, recent work by Sullivan and Wilson illustrated that nuclear InsP$_3$ receptor activation was essential for nuclear vesicle fusion (Sullivan et al., 1993). Fusion of nuclear vesicles to *Xenopus*-egg–extract chromatin was inhibited by low [Ca^{2+}], but could be overcome with exogenous $InsP_3$, (Sullivan et al., 1993). The authors proposed that release of Ca^{2+} by $InsP_3$ created a microdomain of high cytosolic Ca^{2+} that was required for nuclear vesicle fusion (Sullivan and Wilson, 1994).

Greber and Gerace have shown that release of intracellular Ca^{2+} blocked transport of intermediate-sized molecules (10 kD) across the nuclear envelope in intact cells (Greber and Gerace, 1995). However, intracellular Ca^{2+} release initiates a cascade of events making it difficult to identify the components responsible for blocking transport across the nuclear pore in vivo. An optimal preparation for the study of nuclear transport is the nuclear ghost we recently have described (Stehno-Bittel et al., 1995*b*). Nuclear ghosts contain intact nuclear membranes without the nucleoplasmic contents. Nuclear ghosts have been used previously to study transport and accumulation of proteins across nuclear envelopes (Riedel and Fasold, 1987; Prochnow et al., 1994). The resealed nuclear ghosts retained all the components of the nuclear envelope (both membranes, the Triton-resistant lamina, and the pore complexes), but little of the nuclear DNA content (1.5% of the total DNA). They appeared to retain specific uptake and export properties of the nuclear envelope in situ (Riedel and Fasold, 1987).

In the determination of whether the Ca^{2+} store within nuclear ghosts was functional and whether $InsP_3$ could release Ca^{2+} from the ghosts, Mn^{2+} quench of Ca^{2+}-sensitive dyes was employed. The addition of 1 μM Ins(1,4,5)P_3 to ghosts loaded with indo-1 AM in the presence of Mn^{2+} resulted in immediate quench of the signal, a result indicating that the $InsP_3$ channels opened, allowing Mn^{2+} to enter the nuclear envelope in a manner similar to the intact nuclei (Stehno-Bittel et al., 1995*a*). Neither Ins(1,3,4)P_3 nor Ins(1,3,4,5)P_4, initiated Mn^{2+} entry into the nuclear envelope. Thus, the inner and outer membrane of nuclear ghosts resealed after ghost formation, and the resulting preparation released Ca^{2+} in a manner similar to that described for intact, isolated nuclei (Stehno-Bittel et al., 1995*b*).

Consistent with earlier reports (Schlenstedt et al., 1993), we found that 70–500 kD dextran-bound dyes (calcium green and lucifer yellow) were unable to diffuse into the *Xenopus* oocyte nucleoplasm. However, calcium green and lucifer yellow conjugated to 10-kD dextrans passed into intact, isolated nuclei when added to the bath. Nuclear ghosts also excluded 70–500 kD molecules, but allowed 10-kD-dextran–bound dyes to pass into the core of the ghost (Stehno-Bittel et al., 1995*b*). We exposed intact nuclei and nuclear ghosts to 1 μM $InsP_3$ for 2–5 min to deplete the nuclear Ca^{2+} store, then added the 10-kD form of calcium green to the bath. Incubation in $InsP_3$ resulted in exclusion of 10-kD dextrans from the nucleoplasmic region in isolated intact nuclei as well as in nuclear ghost (Stehno-Bittel et al., 1995*b*). $InsP_3$ release of Ca^{2+} from the nuclear store was specific because related inositol polyphosphates that did not release Ca^{2+} at similar concentration ranges (Stehno-Bittel et al., 1995*a*) also failed to block diffusion of the 10-kD-dextran calcium green into the nucleoplasm (Fig. 5). Alternative methods of depleting the nuclear Ca^{2+} store (incubation in low Ca^{2+} and BAPTA-AM) resulted in prevention of the 10-kD dextrans from crossing the nuclear envelope. Diffusion block was reversed by the addition of 2 μM Ca^{2+} and 1 mM ATP (Fig. 5). We concluded that store depletion blocks the transport of intermediate-sized molecules across the nuclear membrane and ATP in the presence of Ca^{2+} was necessary to replenish the intracisternal Ca^{2+} supply.

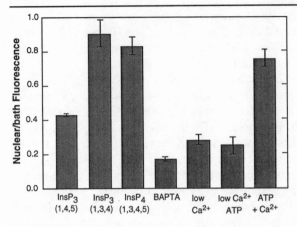

Intermediate-sized molecules of approximately 10 kD were excluded from passing across the nuclear envelope when the Ca^{2+} store was emptied, but smaller molecules were not blocked. Intact nuclei were Ca^{2+}-depleted by incubation in 10 nM Ca^{2+} solution with 1 μM $InsP_3$ for 3 min. Nuclei were then exposed to a low–molecular-weight form of lucifer yellow (470 D). Within two minutes after the addition of lucifer yellow, all nuclei had roughly the same fluorescence intensity as the bath (Stehno-Bittel et al., 1995*b*). To determine whether ions were excluded from nuclei, intact nuclei were loaded with the salt form of indo-1, and the nuclear Ca^{2+} store was depleted as described above. After store depletion, 100 μM Mn^{2+} was added to the bath and the fluorescence within the nucleoplasm was monitored. All fluorescence in the nucleoplasm was quenched with the addition of Mn^{2+}, regardless of the amount of Ca^{2+} within the store. Taken together, the results suggest that the nuclear Ca^{2+} store regulates the movement of molecules of approximately 10 kD in size, but the level of Ca^{2+} within the cisterna does not regulate the diffusion of smaller molecules or ions.

The most interesting questions related to our finding are how store depletion is sensed and the nature of its communication with the nuclear pore. The nuclear pore protein, gp210, contains multiple Ca^{2+}-binding domains predicted to reside within the nuclear cisterna that could act as Ca^{2+} sensors (Greber et al., 1990). Nuclear Ca^{2+} store depletion might then induce a conformational change in gp210 to alter diffusion through the nuclear pore complex. We suggest that Ca^{2+} sensors within the nuclear cisterna initiate an alteration in the NPC, resulting in block of diffusion of intermediate-sized molecules (10–70 kD).

Summary

Multiple K^+, Cl^-, and nonselective cationic nuclear channels have been identified in a variety of cell types from coconut endosperm to cardiac myocytes. To date, only one ligand-gated nuclear channel has been characterized—the $InsP_3R$—but it is likely that others are also present. The $InsP_3R$ channel has been implicated in two important nuclear events: (1) nuclear vesicle fusion (Sullivan et al., 1993) and (2) regulation of molecular transport through the nuclear pore (Stehno-Bittel et al., 1995*b*). Regulation of passive diffusion across the nuclear envelope by the nuclear Ca^{2+} store may play an important role in nuclear events ranging from apoptosis to cell division.

References

Bachs, O., N. Agell, and E. Carafoli. 1992. Calcium and calmodulin function in the cell nucleus. *Biochimica et Biophysica Acta.* 1113:259–270.

Bezprozvanny, I., and B.E. Ehrlich. 1993*a*. ATP-modulates the function of inositol 1,4,5-trisphosphate-gated channels at two sites. *Neuron.* 10:1175–1184.

Bezprozvanny, I., and B.E. Ehrlich. 1994. Inositol (1,4,5)-trisphosphate ($InsP_3$)-gated Ca channels from cerebellum: conduction properties for divalent cations and regulation by intraluminal calcium. *J. Gen. Physiol.* 104:821–856.

Bezprozvanny, I.B., K. Ondrias, E. Kaftan, E.A. Stoyanovsky, and B.E. Ehrlich. 1993*b*. Activation of the calcium release channel (ryanodine receptor) by heparin and other polyanions is calcium dependent. *Mol. Biol. Cell.* 4:347–352.

Bezprozvanny, I., J. Watras, and B.E. Ehrlich. 1991. Bell-shaped calcium-response curves of $Ins(1,4,5)P_3$- and calcium-gated channels from endoplasmic reticulum of cerebellum. *Nature.* 351:751–753.

Bustamante, J.O. 1992. Nuclear ion channels in cardiac myocytes. *Pflugers Arch.* 421:473–485.

Dale, B., L.J. De Felice, K. Kyozuka, L. Santella, and E. Tosti. 1994. Voltage clamp of the nuclear envelope. *Proc. R. Soc. Lond.* 255:119–124.

Eggena, P., J.H. Zhu, K. Clegg, and J.D. Berrett. 1993. Nuclear angiotensin receptor induce transcription of renin and angiotensiogen mRNA. *Hypertension (Dallas).* 22:496–501.

Gerasimenko, O.V., J.V. Gerasimenko, A.V. Tepikin, and O.H. Petersen. 1995. ATP-dependent accumulation and inositol trisphosphate- or cyclic ADP-ribose-mediated release of Ca^{2+} from the nuclear envelope. *Cell.* 80:439–444.

Greber, U.F., and L. Gerace. 1995. Depletion of calcium from the lumen of endoplasmic reticulum reversibly inhibits passive diffusion and signal-mediated transport into the nucleus. *J. Cell Biol.* 128:5–14.

Greber, U.F., A. Senior, and L. Gerace. 1990. A major glycoprotein of the nuclear pore complex is a membrane-spanning polypeptide with a large luminal domain and a small cytoplasmic tail. *EMBO J.* 9:1495–1502.

Goldfine, I.D., and G.J. Smith. 1976. Binding of insulin to isolated nuclei. *Proc. Natl. Acad. Sci. USA.* 73:1422–1431.

Hinshaw, J., B. Carragher, and R. Milligan. 1992. Architecture and design of the nuclear pore complex. *Cell.* 69:1133–1141.

Iino, M., and M. Endo. 1992. Calcium-dependent immediate feedback control of inositol 1,4,5-trisphosphate-induced Ca^{2+} release. *Nature.* 360:76–78.

Innocenti, B., and M. Mazzanti. 1993. Identification of a nucleo-cytoplasmic ionic pathway by osmotic shock in isolated mouse liver nuclei. *Memb. Biol.* 131:137–142.

Jain, S., K.M. Dolwick, J.V. Schmidt, and C.A. Bradfield. 1994. Potent transactivation domains of the Ah receptor and the Ah receptor nuclear translocation map to their carboxyl termini. *J. Biol. Chem.* 269:31518–31524.

Kume, S., A. Muto, J. Aruga, T. Nakagawa, T. Michikawa, T. Furuichi, S. Nakade, H. Okano, and K. Mikoshiba. 1993. The *Xenopus* IP$_3$ receptor: structure, function and localization in oocytes and eggs. *Cell.* 73:555–570.

Lange, I., M. Scholz, and R. Peters. 1986. Molecular mobility and nucleoplasmic flux in hepatoma cells. *J. Cell. Biol.* 102:1183–1190.

Lin, C., G. Hajnoczky, and A.P. Thomas. 1994. Propagation of cytosolic calcium waves into the nuclei of hepatocytes. *Cell Calcium.* 16:247–258.

Mak, D.O., and J.K. Foskett. 1994. Single-channel inositol 1,4,5-trisphosphate receptor currents revealed by patch-clamp of isolated *Xenopus* oocyte nuclei. *J. Biol. Chem.* 269:29375–29378.

Malviya, A.N., P. Rogue, and G. Vincendon. 1990. Stereospecific inositol 1,4,5-[^{32}P]trisphosphate binding to isolated trisphosphate receptor-mediated calcium release from the nucleus. *Proc. Natl. Acad. Sci. USA.* 87:9270–9274.

Malviya, A.N. 1994. The nuclear inositol 1,4,5-trisphosphate and inositol 1,3,4,5-tetrakisphosphate receptors. *Cell Calcium.* 16:301–313.

Matzke, A.J., T.M. Weiger, and M.A. Matzke. 1990. Detection of a large cation-selective channel in nuclear envelopes of avian erythrocytes. *FEBS Let.* 271:161–164.

Matzke, A.J., C. Behensky, T. Weiger, and M.A. Matzke. 1992. A large conductance ion channel in the nuclear envelope of a higher plant cell. *FEBS Let.* 302:81–85.

Mazzanti, M., L.J. DeFelice, J. Cohen, and H. Malter. 1990. Ion channels in the nuclear envelope. *Nature.* 343:764–767.

Mazzanti, M., L.J. DeFelice, and E.F. Smith. 1991. Ion channels in murine nuclei during early development and in fully differentiated adult cells. *J. Membrane Biol.* 121:189–198.

Mazzanti, M., B. Innocenti, and M. Rigatell. 1994. ATP-dependent ionic permeability on nuclear envelope in *in situ* nuclei of Xenopus oocytes. *FASEB J.* 8:231–236.

Parys, J.B., S.W. Sernett, S. DeLisle, P.M. Snyder, M.J. Welsh, and K.P. Campbell. 1992. Isolation, characterization, and localization of the inositol 1,4,5-trisphosphate receptor protein in *Xenopus laevis* oocytes. *J. Biol. Chem.* 267:18776–18782.

Prochnow, D., M. Thomson, H. Schroder, W. Muller, and P. Agutter. 1987. Efflux of RNA from resealed nuclear envelope ghosts. *Arch. Biochem. Biophys.* 312:579–587.

Riedel, N., and H. Fasold. 1987. Preparation and characterization of nuclear-envelope vesicles from rat liver nuclei. *Biochem. J.* 241:203–212.

Schlenstedt, G., E. Hurt, V. Doye, and P.A. Silver. 1993. Reconstitution of nuclear pore transport with semi-intact yeast cells. *J. Cell Biol.* 123:785–798.

Short, A.D., M.G. Klein, M.F. Schneider, and D.L. Gill. 1993. Inositol 1,4,5-trisphosphate-mediated quantal Ca^{2+} release maesured by high resolution imaging of Ca^{2+} within organelles. *J. Biol. Chem.* 268:25887–25893.

Silver, P.A. 1991. How proteins enter the nucleus. *Cell.* 64:489–497.

Stehno-Bittel, L., A. Luckhoff, and D.E. Clapham. 1995a. Calcium release from the nucleus by InsP$_3$ receptor channels. *Neuron.* 14:163–167.

Stehno-Bittel, L., C. Perez-Terzic, and D. Clapham. 1995*b*. Nuclear Ca^{2+} store regulates diffusion across the nuclear envelope. *Science. In press.*

Stern, M.D. 1992. Buffering of calcium in the vicinity of a channel pore. *Cell Calcium.* 3:183–192.

Sullivan, K.M.C., W.B. Busa, and K.L. Wilson. 1993. Calcium mobilization is required for nuclear vesicle fusion in vitro: implications for membrane traffic and IP$_3$ receptor function. *Cell.* 73:1411–1422.

Sullivan, K.M.C., and K.L. Wilson. 1994. A new role for IP$_3$ receptors: Ca^{2+} release during nuclear vesicle fusion. *Cell Calcium.* 16:314–421.

Tabares, L., M. Mazzanti, and D.E. Clapham. 1991. Chloride channels in the nuclear membrane. *J. Memb. Biol.* 123:49–54.

Watras, J., I. Bezprozvanny, and B.E. Ehrlich. 1991. Inositol 1,4,5-trisphosphate-gated channels in cerebellum: presence of multiple conductance states. *J. Neurosci.* 11:3229–3245.

Williams, D.A., K.E. Fogarty, R.Y. Tsien, and F.S. Fay. 1985. Calcium gradients in single smooth muscle cells revealed by the digital imaging microscope using Fura-2. *Nature.* 318:558–560.

Chapter 5

Secretion

Ion-Exchange Gel Regulates Neurotransmitter Release through the Exocytotic Fusion Pore

P. Marszalek, B. Farrell, and J.M. Fernandez

Department of Physiology and Biophysics, Mayo Clinic, Rochester, Minnesota 55905

Introduction

The majority of studies on regulated secretion have focused on the mechanisms of intracellular signaling (Gomperts, 1990) and the identification of effector proteins (Sudhoff, 1995). Less attention has been given to the actual storage and release of secretory products. The products are often implicitly assumed to be stored as a "cocktail" and released from the secretory vesicle by simple diffusion (Volknandt, 1995; Parsons et al., 1993; Stadler and Dowe, 1982). The development of techniques to probe exocytosis at the level of single vesicles (Neher and Marty, 1982; Leszczyszyn et al., 1990; Fig. 1 *a*) permits the examination of this hypothesis. These studies show that release has a complex time course (Fig. 1 *b*) where the bulk of release is typically delayed with respect to the onset of vesicle fusion (Chow et al., 1992; Alvarez de Toledo et al., 1993; Wightman et al., 1995). These observations suggest that secretion is regulated not only before, but also after the exocytotic fusion pore opens (Neher, 1993; Alvarez de Toledo et al., 1993; Wightman et al., 1995; Khanin et al., 1994).

The Exocytotic Fusion Pore

The fusion pore was first observed in degranulating mast cells by use of a combination of rapid freezing techniques and freeze-fracture electron microscopy (Chandler and Heuser, 1980). Patch-clamp capacitance techniques now permit direct measurements of the activity of single fusion pores in isolated cells undergoing exocytosis (Neher and Marty, 1982; Fernandez et al., 1984; Breckenridge and Almers, 1987; Zimmerberg et al., 1987). These measurements reveal that the exocytotic fusion pore opens abruptly and is initially small (1–2 nm diameter). It may then fluctuate in size and either close again completely (transient fusion, sometimes called *flicker*) or expand irreversibly (irreversible fusion) (Fig. 1 *b*).

The release of secretory products through the exocytotic fusion pore can be monitored by amperometry that measures the current produced when molecules are oxidized/reduced at an electrochemical detector, e.g., a carbon-fiber microelectrode surface (Leszczyszyn et al., 1990). Amperometric measurements in chromaffin cells (catecholamines) and in mast cells (serotonin) have shown that a single fusion event results in a spike-like amperometric current (Leszczyszyn et al., 1990; Tatham et al., 1991). A detailed analysis of catecholamine release indicated that the shape of the spikes could not be explained purely by diffusion from a point of in-

Organellar Ion Channels and Transporters © 1996 by The Rockefeller University Press

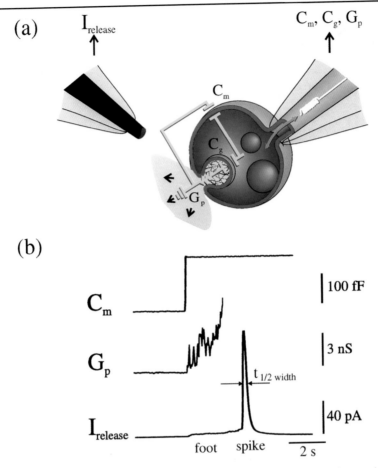

Figure 1. (*a*) Schematic of the experimental setup used to simultaneously monitor exocytotic fusion and the release of secretory products. A cell is patch clamped in the whole-cell configuration, and the plasma membrane capacitance (C_m), the secretory granule membrane capacitance (C_g) and the fusion-pore conductance (G_p) are determined from the measured admittance of the cell. Fusion of a secretory vesicle with the plasma membrane results in a characteristic stepwise increase in the capacitance (C_m) signal and an abrupt increase in the conductance (G_p). The release of secretory products is measured directly by amperometry ($I_{release}$) by use of a carbon fiber electrode, which is placed very close (~ 1 μm) to the cell. In mast cells we measure the oxidation of serotonin (at 650 mV). (*b*) Typical C_m, G_p, and $I_{release}$ signals observed during exocytosis in a mast cell (beige), where the main amperometric spike is preceded by a "foot" phase of release.

stantaneous release (Schroeder et al., 1992; Jankowski et al., 1993; Wightman et al., 1995). Furthermore, the spikes were frequently shown to be preceded by a slower phase of release that was called the *foot* of the spike (Fig. 1 *b*, Chow et al., 1992). These observations led to the proposal that catecholamine release was rate-limited by a small exocytotic fusion pore (Chow et al., 1992; Neher, 1993; Jankowski et al.,

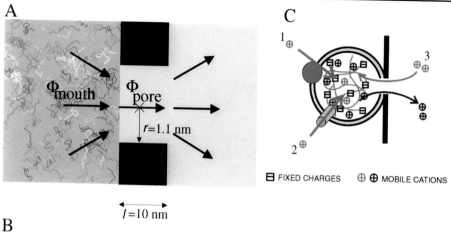

Fusion Pore	ρ (vesicle)	G$_{pore}$	D(vesicle)	Φ$_{mouth}$	Φ$_{pore}$
no hydrogel	100 Ohm·cm	326 pS	$1.0 \cdot 10^{-5}$ cm^2/s	$8.3 \cdot 10^{8}$ ions/s	$4.6 \cdot 10^{7}$ ions/s
with hydrogel	144 Ohm·cm	316 pS	$1.3 \cdot 10^{-8}$ cm^2/s	$1.0 \cdot 10^{6}$ ions/s	$4.6 \cdot 10^{7}$ ions/s

Figure 2. Effect of a gel matrix on the release of serotonin through a small fusion pore in mast cells. (*A*) Hypothetical fusion pore with a length of 10 nm and a radius 1.1 nm. The external mouth of the fusion pore faces the extracellular environment. The internal mouth of the pore faces the heparin proteoglycan gel that stores secretory products. (*B*) Comparison of the fluxes of serotonin at the mouth (Φ_{mouth}) and through the pore (Φ_{pore}) calculated with or without considering a charged hydrogel in the secretory vesicle. ρ, the resistivity of the vesicular medium; G_p, the pore conductance; and D, the diffusion coefficient of serotonin within the vesicle. The flux of serotonin molecules into the mouth of the pore, Φ_{mouth}, was calculated as $\Phi_{mouth} = 2\pi r D c$, and the flux through the pore (Φ_{pore}) was calculated as $\pi r^2 D c / l$ (Hille, 1984; 1994) using the pore dimension shown in *A* and assuming a concentration of serotonin in the granule of 2×10^{-4} moles/cm^3. We estimated gel resistivity (ρ_{gel}) from the current-voltage relationships measured in isolated granule matrices (Marszalek et al., 1995). G_p was calculated from $1/R_{pore}$ where:

$$R_{pore} = \frac{\rho}{\pi r^2}\left(1 + \frac{\pi r}{2}\right)$$

(Hille, 1984; 1994). (*C*) Schematic showing ion exchange as a mechanism for exocytotic release. The transmitters (positively charged) are stored in an anionic gel. After the formation of the fusion pore there is an influx of cations into the vesicle that exchanges with the cationic transmitters, which then leave through the exocytotic fusion pore. These exchanging cations can flow from the external electrolyte through the fusion pore and/or from the cytoplasm through the vesicular membrane. The flux of cations from the cytoplasm may be regulated by electrogenic pumps (*1*) or by ion channels (*2*). The flux of cations through the fusion pore (*3*) is regulated by the size of the pore and the properties of the granule matrix.

1993; Wightman et al., 1995). The significance of these findings is that they uncovered a new level of regulation for secretion. They suggest that the amount of transmitter released and the time course of secretion could be finely controlled by the size of the fusion pore.

Exocytotic Release through a Small Fusion Pore

We can calculate the flux (Φ) of a transmitter through a fusion pore using macroscopic laws (Hille, 1984; 1994):

$$\Phi = \frac{\pi r^2 D c}{l + \frac{\pi r}{2}} \qquad (1)$$

where D is the diffusion coefficient of the transmitter (assumed to be the same inside and outside of the pore); c is the concentration of the transmitter inside the vesicle (the concentration of the transmitter at the extracellular side of the pore is assumed to be zero); l and r are length and radius of the pore, respectively. (This equation takes into account the diffusional resistance at the mouth of the pore, that effectively increases the length of the pore by $\pi r/2$). The flux of a transmitter (serotonin) through a fusion pore (r: 1.1 nm; l: 10 nm, c: 0.2×10^{-3} moles/cm^3, and D: 10^{-5} cm^2/s; Fig. 2 A) is calculated to be 3.9×10^7 molecules/s. This fusion pore is not limited by the diffusion of molecules to the pore's mouth (Fig. 2 A). This is evident when the flux through the pore proper: $\Phi_{pore} = \pi r^2 D c/l$ is compared with the flux at the mouth of the pore: $\Phi_{mouth} = 2\pi r D c$ (Hille, 1994). For a pore of radius 1.1 nm Φ_{mouth} is 8.3×10^8 serotonin molecules/s, and this flux is 18 times higher than the flux sustained by the pore (Φ_{pore}, see Fig. 2 B). Under the above assumptions, this fusion pore ($r = 1.1$ nm; $l = 10$ nm; $D \sim 10^{-5}$ cm^2/s, Fig. 2 A) should limit the magnitude of the release of serotonin from the vesicle as proposed previously (Chow et al., 1992; Neher, 1993).

By combining patch-clamp measurements of the conductance of fusion pores with amperometric measurements of release, Alvarez de Toledo and colleagues (1993) tested the hypothesis that the size of the fusion pore limits the release of serotonin in mast cells. They found that the rate of release of serotonin was ~50 times smaller than that predicted by Eq. 1. One possible explanation for this surprising observation is that the diffusivity of serotonin was restricted by the secretory granule matrix and it is this matrix that ultimately regulates release through the fusion pore (Monck and Fernandez, 1994; Robinson and Fernandez, 1994).

The Secretory Granule Matrix

Uvnäs and colleagues showed that the secretory granules of mast and chromaffin cells and splenic nerve granule preparations contain a matrix that exhibits the properties of ion-exchange resins (Uvnäs and Åborg, 1983). Ion-exchange resins are often made of crosslinked charged polymers, where the fixed charges within the polymeric matrix are neutralized by mobile counterions. Charged secretory products could be stored within the matrix by electrostatically binding to the fixed charges and released from the matrix by ion exchange with the external electrolyte (Uvnäs and Åborg, 1989). If this hypothesis is correct, the time course of release of secretory products should be described by the kinetics of ion exchange.

The rate laws of ion exchange predict that the half time of release ($t_{1/2}$) for a spherical particle of radius r is given by: $t_{1/2} \approx 0.03\ r^2/D$ (Helfferich, 1962). To determine if this equation can describe the release of secretory products, we simplified the experimental model and examined the release of serotonin from intact secre-

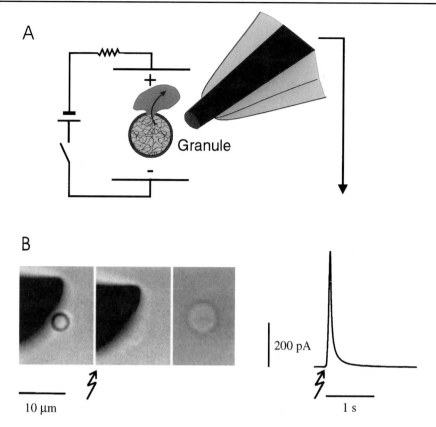

Figure 3. In vitro assay to measure the release of serotonin from single secretory granules isolated from a beige mast cell. The granules are isolated with their membranes intact and contain a condensed gel matrix that stores secretory products (e.g., serotonin and histamine). The release of transmitters, i.e., serotonin, is triggered by rapidly destroying the membrane by electroporation. This exposes the matrix to the external electrolyte (in this case a Ringer solution) and allows the exchange of transmitters by external cations. The serotonin that is released is detected amperometrically by a carbon fiber electrode. (*A*) In this assay an isolated intact granule is placed between two electrodes and positioned adjacent (distance ~ 1 μm) to a carbon fiber electrode. A short and high-intensity voltage pulse (e.g., 5 KV/cm for 30 μs) is delivered to the electrodes. This electric field generates a potential difference (ΔV) across the granular membrane that exceeds the threshold value ($\Delta V > \sim 1$ V) for its electric breakdown and causes extensive poration (Kinosita and Tsong, 1977). (*B*) Similar to what is observed in vivo, upon electroporation the granule matrix rapidly swells four-fold (compare leftmost with rightmost image) while simultaneously releasing serotonin with a spike-like time course (*right panel*).

tory granules isolated from the beige mast cell. We triggered the release by rapidly destroying the granule membrane by electroporation (Kinosita and Tsong, 1977) with a large electric field and measured release by amperometry with a carbon-fiber electrode that was positioned adjacent (<1 μm) to the granule (Fig. 3 *A*). We found that the amperometric current exhibited a spike-like time course (Fig. 3 *B*), where the half-time of release was well-described by a power law ($t_{1/2} \propto r^{1.9}$; see Fig. 4), which is close to that expected when the kinetics are limited by ion exchange within

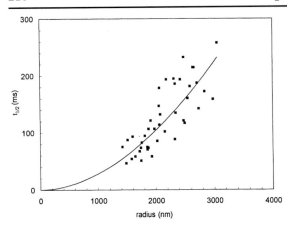

Figure 4. Half-time of release ($t_{1/2}$) of serotonin plotted against the granule radius. $t_{1/2}$ is the width of the amperometric spike at half of its amplitude. The granules were immersed in a Ringer solution and electroporated as described in Fig. 3. The solid line is a fit of $t_{1/2} \propto r^n$ to the data, where n was determined to be ~1.9, which is close to that expected when the kinetics is limited by ion-exchange within a vesicle. If we fit the data with $t_{1/2} \sim 0.03\ r^2/D$, which describes ion exchange that is limited by particle diffusion (Helfferich, 1962), we estimate a diffusion coefficient for serotonin of 1.3×10^{-8} cm²/s. This D is almost three orders of magnitude smaller than that in the bulk (~10^{-5} cm²/s), but reasonable for a charged molecule diffusing within an ion-exchanger (Helfferich, 1962). This low diffusion coefficient suggests that the gel matrix limits the release of serotonin during exocytosis.

the granule matrix. If we fit the data to the equation $t_{1/2} \sim 0.03\ r^2/D$, we estimate a diffusion coefficient for serotonin within the matrix to be 1.3×10^{-8} cm²/s, which is almost three orders of magnitude smaller than that in the bulk (~10^{-5} cm²/s), but reasonable for a charged molecule diffusing within an ion exchanger (Helfferich, 1962).

We use this diffusion coefficient (1.3×10^{-8} cm²/s) and calculate that only 1×10^6 molecules of serotonin/s can reach the mouth of a pore with a radius of 1.1 nm (see Fig. 2 *B*). Assuming that the diffusion coefficient for serotonin in the pore is similar to that in the bulk, we find that the pore can sustain a flux of ~4.6×10^7 molecules/s (Fig. 2 *B*). The number of molecules reaching the mouth of the pore

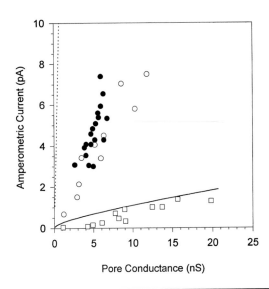

Figure 5. Plot of pore conductance (G_p) versus the serotonin (amperometric) current measured during the foot (I_{foot}) region. Different symbols represent different fusion events. The *dotted line* was calculated by use of Eq. 1, where D, C, and l were assumed to be 0.95×10^{-5} cm²sec⁻¹, 1.6×10^{-4} moles/cm³, and 10 nm, respectively. The *solid line* was calculated by use of equation $\Phi_{mouth} = 2\pi r D c$ where D is the measured diffusion coefficient of serotonin in the granule matrix (1.3×10^{-8} cm²sec⁻¹). The experimental data of this figure were extracted from Fig. 3 of Alvarez de Toledo et al. (1993).

per unit time is only $\sim$1/50 of the flux that the pore is capable of sustaining. Hence, release is limited by the flux of serotonin to the mouth of the pore ($\Phi_{mouth} = 2\pi rDc$) rather than the pore itself. This observation explains the surprisingly small amount of release observed through the fusion pore during its early stages (Alvarez de Toledo et al., 1993). If the fusion pore conductance is used to estimate the pore radius (assuming a pore length of 10 nm), the flux of serotonin through such a pore can be calculated by Eq. 1, predicting a nearly linear relationship between the flux and the pore conductance. However, this relationship fails to predict the experimental data that shows a much reduced slope (Fig. 5). In contrast, the flux of serotonin through a fusion pore limited by the number of molecules reaching the pore's mouth (ϕ_{mouth}) predicts a relationship between the pore conductance and serotonin release that more closely represents the experimental observations (Fig. 5).

Although the diffusion coefficient for charged molecules within a gel is smaller than in the bulk, gels are relatively good conductors because the lower mobility of ions is compensated by a high concentration of charge carriers. The effect of a gel matrix on the total resistance of a fusion pore would be to change the pore access resistance on the side of the vesicle lumen (see Fig. 2 *A*). The pore access resistance is given by $R_{pore-access} = \rho/4r$ (Hall, 1975), and from our measurements of gel resistance we calculated that the resistivity of the mast cell matrix is $\sim$144 ohm cm, which is similar to that of the extracellular electrolyte (100 ohm cm). Therefore the gel matrix should not significantly alter the total pore resistance (Fig. 2 *B*).

Exocytotic Release through a Large Fusion Pore

After the foot phase of release ends, a rapid expansion of the fusion pore is observed concomitant with an amperometric spike of release (i.e., see Fig. 1 *b*). The spike is proposed to represent the rapid emptying of a secretory vesicle when the fusion pore becomes large (Chow et al., 1992; Alvarez de Toledo, 1993).

In 1993 we presented evidence that the time course of release of secretory products from mast and chromaffin cells is related to the secretory vesicle radius (r) by a scaling law ($t_{1/2} \propto r^{1.5}$; Alvarez de Toledo et al., 1993), where $t_{1/2}$ is the width of the main spike of release at half of its amplitude. It was proposed that the time of release from other secretory vesicles including synaptic vesicles would follow the same scaling law. New measurements of the time course of release of 5-hydroxytryptamine (serotonin) from Retzius neurons (Bruns and Jahn, 1995) and catecholamines from rat superior ganglion neurons, rat chromaffin cells (Zhou and Misler, 1995), rat pheochromocytoma cells (PC12, Chen et al., 1994), and rabbit glomus cells (Ureña et al., 1994) support this hypothesis. The release from small synaptic vesicles (SSV), similar to that from nonneuronal cells, exhibits a characteristic spike-like time course that is resolved at the level of single vesicle exocytosis (Bruns and Jahn, 1995, and Zhou and Misler, 1995). As shown in Fig. 6, the same scaling law ($t_{1/2} \propto r^{1.5}$) holds for release of amines from beige mast cell secretory granules and small synaptic vesicles. This is striking and suggests that the mechanism regulating the time course of vesicular exocytotic release of amines is conserved.

An exponent of 3 ($t_{1/2} \propto$ vesicle volume) is expected when emptying through a fusion pore limits the release. According to this rule, a synaptic vesicle should release its contents $\sim$125,000 times faster than a beige mast cell granule. This is in disagreement with the experimental ratio of $\sim$1,000 and shows that this model cannot

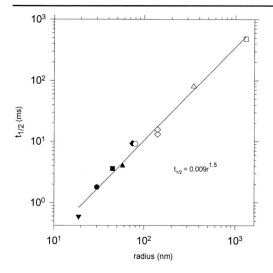

Figure 6. The time of exocytotic release of amines from different secretory vesicles follows a scaling law. The half-time of release ($t_{1/2}$) of transmitters is plotted against the vesicle radius of the secretory vesicle for different secretory cells. The cells were stimulated to exocytose, and the release of transmitter was recorded with amperometry. Exocytotic release was detected from single vesicles. The data points were obtained from Retzius neurons (serotonin); superior cervical ganglion neurons (catecholamines); mast cells (serotonin); chromaffin cells (epinephrine and norepinephrine); pheochromocytoma cells (dopamine and norepinephrine); and glomus cells (dopamine). ($\blacktriangledown$) Retzius (SSV), Bruns and Jahn (1995) ($t_{1/2}$) and Henderson et al. (1983) (radius); ($\bullet$) superior cervical ganglion (rat), Zhou and Misler (1995) ($t_{1/2}$) and Rees and Bunge (1974) (radius); ($\blacksquare$) retzius (LDCV), Bruns and Jahn (1995) ($t_{1/2}$) and Henderson et al. (1983) (radius); ($\blacktriangle$) glomus (rabbit), Ureña et al. (1994) ($t_{1/2}$) and Verna (1977) (radius); ($\blacklozenge$) PC12, Chen et al. (1994) ($t_{1/2}$) and Wagner (1985) (radius); ($\bigcirc$) chromaffin (rat), Zhou and Misler (1995) ($t_{1/2}$) and Unsicker and Chamley (1977) (radius); ($\diamondsuit$) chromaffin (bovine), Jankowski et al. (1993) ($t_{1/2}$) and Coupland (1968) (radius); ($\triangle$) mast (rat) and ($\square$) mast (mouse beige), Alvarez de Toledo et al. (1993) ($t_{1/2}$ and radius). The figure shows the average radii of the vesicles and average half time ($t_{1/2}$) of release except for $\bigcirc$ and $\bullet$, where the median value of the radii is plotted (average is not known), and for $\blacktriangle$, where the $t_{1/2}$ was obtained from one release spike. The *solid line* represents the best fit of the data to $t_{1/2} = Ar^n$ where $t_{1/2} = 0.009\ r^{1.5}$.

consistently explain the rate of release (Fig. 6). Kinetics of ion exchange may explain the scaling law of vesicular release. As discussed above, the calculated half-time of release for a spherical ion exchanger is given by $t_{1/2} \sim r^2$ which is close to $t_{1/2} \sim r^{1.5}$ obtained for exocytotic release. The difference between the exponents may be explained by: (*1*) differences in the geometry; $t_{1/2} \sim r^2$ is valid for release with spherical symmetry, whereas exocytotic release occurs through a single fusion pore; (*2*) diffusion at the boundary between the gel and the external electrolyte (called *film diffusion*; $t_{1/2} \sim r$) may also control the kinetics of ion exchange (Helfferich, 1962).

Ion Exchange Gel Regulates Exocytotic Release

By measuring the release of serotonin from isolated secretory granules of the beige mast cell, we found that the time course of release follows the kinetics of ion exchange. We determined that the diffusion coefficient of serotonin within the granule is $\sim 10^{-8}$ cm^2/s. This is almost three orders of magnitude lower than the bulk diffusivity and suggests that release of serotonin through the fusion pore is limited by diffusion within the granule matrix; this would explain the small amount of release observed during the foot phase of release, while the fusion pore is still small (Alvarez de Toledo et al., 1993; Fig. 5). Furthermore, it is unusual in biology to find cellu-lar responses that follow laws that hold true for a wide variety of cells; the scaling law of exocytotic release suggests that there is a common mechanism controlling the time course of release (Fig. 6). There is now ample evidence to suggest that sim-ple diffusion is not this mechanism (Alvarez de Toledo et al., 1993; Wightman et al., 1995) and growing evidence that release occurs by ion exchange as predicted origi-nally by Uvnäs and collaborators (i.e., Uvnäs and Åborg, 1983; 1989).

The kinetics of ion exchange could control the time course of release when charged secretory products neutralize the fixed charges of a vesicular matrix. For example, charges of the sulfate and carboxyl groups within the heparin proteogly-can matrix of mast cell granules are neutralized by serotonin and histamine. Upon exocytotic fusion the secretory products are released by exchange with an equiva-lent number of counterions to maintain bulk electroneutrality. The intracellular electrolyte bathing the secretory granule in an intact cell is different from the extra-cellular electrolyte, and both sources may supply counterions to allow the release of charged secretory products (see Fig. 2 *C*). The influx of intracellular counterions through the granule membrane could be regulated by ion transport mechanisms such as electrogenic ATPases and/or cation-selective ion channels located in the granule membrane, while the influx of extracellular counterions depends only on the state of the fusion pore. Secretory granules from many cells, including clear syn-aptic vesicles, contain charged proteoglycans (Carlson and Kelly, 1983; Volknandt, 1995); this suggests that an ion-exchange mechanism of release could be ubiquitous. For example, the neurotransmitter transporter SV2 is a keratan sulfate proteogly-can (Feany et al., 1992; Scranton et al., 1993), and the glycosyl domains from as few as 2–3 molecules would be sufficient to fill the vesicle volume. It is possible that these proteoglycans form a charged gel matrix that is similar to those found in the mast cell granules.

Different types of charged gels may be present in secretory vesicles from dif-ferent cells. Gels can be composed of many constituents, such as proteins (e.g., gel-atin), proteoglycans (heparin proteoglycans), or sugars (e.g., agar). The addition of charged groups to the gel matrix confers the gel ion-exchange properties. In con-trast to a "cocktail" of secretory products, charged gel matrices from secretory vesi-cles should be insoluble in water, exhibit elastic properties, and change their vol-ume under different ionic conditions. The giant secretory granules of the beige mouse mast cells have such properties. Curran and Brodwick first reported that the giant granule matrices of the beige mast cell swell when immersed in a saline solu-tion containing monovalent cations (Curran and Brodwick, 1985; 1991; Fernandez et al., 1991). Furthermore, they also showed that the granule matrix behaves as an elastic gel with a spring constant in the range $2–40 \times 10^6$ N/m^2, comparable to that of gelatin (Brodwick et al., 1992). These mechanical properties of secretory granule matrices, together with their ability to bind and exchange cations stoichiometrically (Uvnäs and Åborg, 1983; 1989) are typical characteristics of ion exchange resins (Helfferich, 1962).

Beige mouse mast cell granules have diameters of up to several micrometers and can be easily studied with the light microscope (Curran and Brodwick, 1991; Fernandez et al., 1991; Brodwick et al., 1992). Most secretory vesicles have diame-ters smaller than a micrometer (e.g., synaptic vesicles have diameters of ~40 nm; [Bruns and Jahn, 1995]) and cannot be studied with optical microscopes. Electron microscope studies require dehydration and fixation of the granules, procedures that destroy gel properties. Furthermore, some sugar-based gels cannot be made electron-dense and cannot be imaged with the electron microscope. These limitations have prevented a detailed characterization of the structure of the lumen of secretory vesicles. The recent development of atomic force microscopy may allow, for the first time, studies of the contents of the lumen of small synaptic vesicles. The atomic force microscope (AFM) has a resolution of $\sim$0.1 nm, can operate on samples in aqueous solutions, and can be used to study even the smallest secretory vesicles under physiologic conditions (Parpura, V., and J.M. Fernandez, manuscript submitted for publication).

Conclusions

The exocytotic release of secretory products has been oversimplified as the irreversible dumping of a "soluble cocktail" into the extracellular environment. From this perspective, regulation of secretion can only occur before exocytotic fusion. Direct observation of exocytotic events with patch-clamp and amperometric techniques allow, for the first time, a critical examination of the mechanisms of release. The emerging picture from the mast cell data is more complex and interesting than previously imagined. Fusion pores can undergo multiple rounds of opening/closing cycles, releasing small packets each time and leaving an intact vesicle. Furthermore, far from a simple diffusional mechanism, secretory product release appears to be regulated by an ion-exchange gel matrix. This regulation takes place after the fusion pore has opened and determines the time course of release of secretory products.

Regulation of exocytotic release can then exploit three different mechanisms that participate in different phases of exocytosis: (*1*) intracellular signaling and activation of effector proteins; (*2*) control of the opening and closure of the fusion pore; (*3*) ion exchange within the granule matrix. The great majority of studies of regulated secretion have examined the first mechanism (*1*) (i.e., Sudhof, 1995). We demonstrate that in mast cells there is regulation of release after exocytotic fusion (mechanisms (*2*) and (*3*)). A similar mechanism with fine control of release may regulate faster secretory events such as those that underlie synaptic transmission. It is possible that different time courses of neurotransmitter release (i.e., flicker, foot and spike, or spike alone; see Figs. 1 and 3) can generate very different post-synaptic responses. The regulation of release of secretory products after vesicle fusion may be an important regulatory mechanism of secretory systems.

References

Alvarez de Toledo, G., R. Fernandez-Chacon, and J.M. Fernandez. 1993. Release of secretory products during transient vesicle fusion. *Nature (Lond.).* 363:554–557.

Breckenridge, L.J., and W. Almers. 1987. Currents through the fusion pore that forms during exocytosis of a secretory vesicle. *Nature (Lond.).* 328:814–817.

Brodwick, M.S., M. Curran, and C. Edwards. 1992. Effects of osmotic stress on mast cell vesicles of the beige mouse. *J. Membr. Biol.* 126:159–169.

Bruns, D., and R. Jahn. 1995. Real-time measurement of transmitter release from single synaptic vesicles. *Nature (Lond.).* 377:62–65.

Carlson, S.S., and R.B. Kelly. 1983. A highly antigenic proteoglycan-like component of cholinergic synaptic vesicles. *J. Biol. Chem.* 258:11802–11091.

Chandler, D.E., and J.E. Heuser. 1980. Arrest of membrane fusion events in mast cells by quick-freezing. *J. Cell Biol.* 86:666–674.

Chen, T.K., G. Luo, and A.G. Ewing. 1994. Amperometric monitoring of stimulated catecholamine release from rat pheochromocytoma (PC12) cells at the zeptomole level. *Analyt. Chem.* 66:3031–3035.

Chow, R.H., L. von Ruden, and E. Neher. 1992. Delay in vesicle fusion revealed by electrochemical monitoring of single secretory events in adrenal chromaffin cells. *Nature (Lond.).* 356:60–63.

Coupland, R.E. 1968. Determining sizes and distributions of sizes of spherical bodies such as chromaffin granules in tissues sections. *Nature (Lond.).* 217:384–388.

Curran, M.J., and M.S. Brodwick. 1985. Mast cell exocytosis and the gel-swell of granules. *Biophys. J.* 47:172a. (Abstr.)

Curran, M.J., and M.S. Brodwick. 1991. Ionic control of the size of the vesicle matrix of beige mouse mast cells. *J. Gen. Physiol.* 98:771–790.

Feany, M.B., S. Lee, R.H. Edwards, and K.M. Buckley. 1992. The synaptic vesicle protein SV2 is a novel type of transmembrane transporter. *Cell.* 70:861–867.

Fernandez, J.M., E. Neher, and B.D. Gomperts. 1984. Capacitance measurements reveal stepwise fusion events in degranulating mast cells. *Nature (Lond.).* 312:453–455.

Fernandez, J.M., M. Villalon, and P. Verdugo. 1991. Reversible condensation of mast cell secretory products *in vitro. Biophys. J.* 59:1022–1027.

Gomperts, B.D. 1990. G_E: a GTP-binding protein mediating exocytosis. *Annu. Rev. Physiol.* 52:591–606.

Hall, J.E. 1975. Access resistance of a small circular pore. Letter to the Editor. *J. Gen. Physiol.* 66:531–532.

Helfferich, F. 1962. Ion Exchange. McGraw-Hill, New York, 624 pages.

Henderson, L.P., D.P. Kuffler, J. Nicholls, and R. Zhang. 1983. Structural and functional analysis of synaptic transmission between indentified leech neurons. *J. Physiol.* 340:347–358.

Hille, B., editor. 1984, 1994. Ionic Channels of Excitable Membranes. Sinauer Associates, Inc., Sunderland, MA. 1–426.

Jankowski, J.A., T.J. Schroeder, E.L. Ciolkowski, and R.M. Wightman. 1993. Temporal characteristics of quantal secretion of catecholamines from adrenal medullary cells. *J. Biol. Chem.* 268:14694–14700.

Khanin, R., H. Parnas, and L. Segel. 1994. Diffusion cannot govern the discharge of neurotransmitter in fast synapses. *Biophys. J.* 67:966–972.

Kinosita, K., Jr., and T.Y. Tsong. 1977. Voltage-induced pore formation and hemolysis of human erythrocytes. *Biochim. Biophys. Acta.* 471:227–242.

Leszczyszyn, D., J.A. Jankowski, H.O. Viveros, E.J. Diliberto, Jr., J.A. Near, and R.M. Wightman. 1990. Nicotinic receptor-mediated catecholamine secretion from individual chromaffin cells: chemical evidence for exocytosis. *J. Biol. Chem.* 265:14736–14737.

Marszalek, P.E., V.S. Markin, T. Tanaka, H. Kawaguchi, and J.M. Fernandez. 1995. The secretory granule matrix-electrolyte interface: a homologue of the p-n rectifying junction. *Biophys. J.* 69:1218–1229.

Monck, J.R., and J.M. Fernandez. 1994. The exocytotic fusion pore and neurotransmitter release. *Neuron.* 12:707–716.

Neher, E. 1993. Secretion without full fusion. *Nature (Lond.).* 363:497–498.

Neher, E., and A. Marty. 1982. Discrete changes of cell membrane capacitance observed under conditions of enhanced secretion in bovine adrenal chromaffin cells. *Proc. Natl. Acad. Sci. USA.* 79:6712–6716.

Parsons, S.M., C. Prior, and I.G. Marshall. 1993. Acetylcholine transport, storage, and release. *Int. Rev. Neurobiol.* 35:279–390.

Rees, R., and R.P. Bunge. 1974. Morphological and cytochemical studies of synapses formed in culture between isolated rat superior cervical ganglion neurons. *J. Comp. Neurol.* 157:1–12.

Robinson, I.M., and J.M. Fernandez. 1994. The fusion pore interface: a new biological frontier. *Curr. Opin. Neurobiol.* 4:330–336.

Schroeder, T.J., J.A. Jankowski, J. Senyshyn, R.W. Holz, and R.M. Wightman. 1992. Zones of exocytotic release on bovine adrenal medullary cells in culture. *J. Biol. Chem.* 269:17215–17220.

Scranton, T.W., M. Iwata, and S.S. Carlson. 1993. The SV2 protein of synaptic vesicles is a keratan sulfate proteoglycan. *J. Neurochem.* 61:29–44.

Stadler, H., and G.H.C. Dowe. 1982. Identification of a heparin sulphate containing proteoglycan as a specific core component of cholinergic synaptic vesicles from *Torpedo marmorata. Eur. Mol. Biol. J.* 1:1381–1384.

Sudhof, T.C. 1995. The synaptic vesicle cycle: a cascade of protein-protein interactions. *Nature (Lond.).* 375:645–653.

Tatham, P.E.R., M.R. Duchen, and J. Millar. 1991. Monitoring exocytosis from single mast cells by fast voltammetry. *Pflugers Arch.* 419:409–414.

Unsicker, K., and J.H. Charmley. 1977. Growth characteristics of postnatal rat adrenal medulla in culture. *Cell Tiss. Res.* 177:247–268.

Ureña, J., R. Fernandez-Chacón, A.R. Benot, G. Alvarez de Toledo, and J. López-Barneo. 1994. Hypoxia induces voltage-dependent Ca^{2+} entry and quantal dopamine secretion in carotid body glomus cells. *Proc. Natl. Acad. Sci. USA.* 91:10208–10211.

Uvnäs, B., and C.H. Åborg. 1983. Cation exchange - a common mechanism in the storage and release of biogenic amines stored in granules (vesicles)? *Acta Physiolgic. Scandinavica.* 119:225–234.

Uvnäs, B., and C.H. Åborg. 1989. Role of ion exchange in release of biogenic amines. *News Physiol. Sci.* 4:68–71.

Verna, A. 1977. Dense-cored vesicles and cell types in the rabbit carotid body. *In* Chemoreception in the Carotid Body. H. Acker et al., editors. Springer-Verlag, Berlin and New York. 216–220.

Volknandt, W. 1995. The synaptic vesicle and its targets. *Neurosci.* 64:277–300.

Wagner, J.A. 1985. Structure of catecholamine secretory vesicles from PC12 cells. *J. Neurochem.* 45:1244–1253.

Wightman, R.M., T.J. Schroeder, J.M. Finnegan, E.L. Ciolkowski, and K. Pihel. 1995. Timecourse of release of catecholamines from individual vesicles during exocytosis at adrenal medullary cells. *Biophys. J.* 68:383–390.

Zhou, Z., and S. Misler. 1995. Amperometric detection of stimulus-induced quantal release of catecholamines from cultured superior cervical ganglion neurons. *Proc. Natl. Acad. Sci. USA.* 92:6938–6942.

Zimmerberg, J., M. Curran, F.S. Cohen, and M. Brodwick. 1987. Simultaneous electrical and optical measurements show that membrane fusion precedes secretory granule swelling during exocytosis of beige mouse mast cells. *Proc. Natl. Acad. Sci. USA.* 84:1585–1589.

Membrane Fusion by the Influenza Hemagglutinin: The Fusion Pore

Judith M. White,* Tsafi Danieli,‡ Yoav I. Henis,‡ Grigory Melikyan,§ and Frederic S. Cohen§

*Department of Cell Biology, University of Virginia, Charlottesville, Virginia 22908;
‡Department of Neurobiochemistry, Tel Aviv University, 69978 Tel Aviv, Israel;
§Department of Molecular Biophysics and Physiology, Rush Medical College, Chicago, Illinois 60612

Introduction

A great deal of progress has been made in the unraveling of how viral glycoproteins mediate fusion between enveloped viruses and their host cells (Bentz, 1993). Two related principles appear to govern viral fusion reactions: (1) viral fusion proteins initially exist in the virus membrane in an inactive state; (2) viral fusion glycoproteins require a trigger to render them fusion competent. Different viruses use different fusion triggers. For many viruses (e.g., influenza and Semliki Forest virus), the trigger is exposure to low pH (Marsh and Helenius, 1989). For other viruses, (e.g., Rous sarcoma virus) the trigger appears to be binding to the primary host cell receptor (Gilbert et al., 1995). For other viruses (e.g., the human immunodeficiency virus), the fusion trigger appears to involve interaction with host cell accessory factors in addition to the primary virus receptor (Moore et al., 1993). Viruses that enter cells through the endocytic pathway are triggered by exposure to low pH. Viruses that do not require exposure to low pH and which appear to be able to fuse at the plasma membrane are triggered by binding to a primary virus receptor and/or other host cell factors. In all cases studied, the fusion triggers induce conformational changes in the fusion glycoprotein (Bullough et al., 1994; Gilbert et al., 1995; Sattentau and Moore, 1991).

Low-pH-Induced Conformational Changes in Viral Fusion Proteins

Among the low pH-triggered viral fusion proteins, there appear to be different types of fusion-activating conformational changes. The most extensively studied case is that of the influenza virus hemagglutinin (HA). When exposed to low pH, the organization of the HA oligomer, a homotrimer, is not altered. Instead there are dramatic conformational changes within the trimer. These conformational changes liberate (White and Wilson, 1987) and reposition (Bullough et al., 1994; Carr and Kim, 1993) the fusion peptide, and hence allow it to associate hydrophobically with the target membrane (Doms et al., 1985; Harter et al., 1989). In the case of the alphavirus Semliki Forest virus (SFV) exposure to low pH induces a dramatic rearrangement within the SFV spike oligomer. The native SFV spike is a trimer composed of three E1/E2 heterodimers. Upon exposure to low pH, the E1/E2 het-

Organellar Ion Channels and Transporters © 1996 by The Rockefeller University Press

erodimer dissociates and an E1 homotrimer, the fusogenic form, is produced (Bron et al., 1993; Fuller et al., 1995; Justman et al., 1993; Kenney et al., 1994; Wahlberg et al., 1992; Wahlberg and Garoff, 1992). During this process the hydrophobic fusion peptide (Levy-Mintz and Kielian, 1991) is presumably exposed for interaction with the target membrane.

A Model for Influenza Hemagglutinin-Mediated Membrane Fusion

For the remainder of this chapter, we will focus on the influenza virus HA because many aspects of its fusion mechanism have been probed in detail. The structure of HA is known at high resolution for its prefusogenic, pH-7 conformation (Wilson et al., 1981) and for its final low-pH form (Bullough et al., 1994; Hughson, 1995; Wharton et al., 1995). Intermediates along the pathway of the low-pH-induced conformational change in HA have been inferred from biochemical and immunologic studies (reviewed in Doms, 1993; White, 1994; White, 1996). Insights into the conformational change and the sequence requirements for the fusion peptide have been inferred by studies of selected or site-specific mutants in the HA protein (for a review, see Steinhauer et al., 1992).

The process of HA-mediated fusion has also been studied in detail by use of fluorescence technologies. Fluorescent lipid probes have been incorporated into the envelope of influenza virus particles or reconstituted virosomes containing the HA protein. In this manner, the kinetics of lipid mixing with various target membranes (as a function of pH, temperature, etc.) has been monitored, either as fluorescence dequenching or as fluorescence resonance energy transfer (for a review, see Duzgunes, 1993).

An informative system for probing the fusion mechanism of HA has been the study of fusion of red blood cells (RBCs) to fibroblasts engineered to express the HA protein (Doxsey et al., 1985; White et al., 1982). RBCs can be tagged with appropriate fluorescent probes to label either the outer RBC bilayer leaflet, the inner RBC bilayer leaflet, or the RBC cytoplasm (Kemble et al., 1994; Melikyan et al., 1995c; Morris et al., 1989; Sarkar et al., 1989; Tse et al., 1993; Zimmerberg et al., 1994). As evidence of fusion, transfer of the probes into the HA-expressing fibroblasts can be monitored by either fluorimetry or fluorescence microscopy. Experiments employing this basic methodology have revealed important features about HA-mediated fusion. In particular, the technology has been especially useful in (1) discernment of a lag phase before the onset of fusion (Morris et al., 1989; Stegmann et al., 1990; Danieli, unpublished data), (2) characterization of the relative dynamics of lipid and content transfer (Tse et al., 1993; Zimmerberg et al., 1994), and (3) detection of a hemifusion intermediate in fusion reactions mediated by a glycosylphosphatidyl-inositol (GPI)-anchored influenza HA (Kemble et al., 1994; Melikyan et al., 1995c).

Electrophysiologic studies have provided a powerful complement to fluorescent-based fusion studies. Two basic electrophysiologic methodologies have been employed. In the first, an HA-expressing fibroblast is subjected to patch-clamp analysis during fusion with an RBC (Spruce et al., 1991; Spruce et al., 1989; Tse et al., 1993; Zimmerberg et al., 1994). In the second, electrical measurements are made during fusion of HA-expressing fibroblasts with planar bilayers (Melikyan et al., 1993a; Melikyan et al., 1995a; Melikyan et al., 1993b; Melikyan et al., 1995b). Recent studies have combined electrophysiologic recordings with observations of fluorescent dye transfer (Melikyan et al., 1995c; Tse et al., 1993; Zimmerberg et al., 1994).

Fusion Pore Formation via a Hemifusion Intermediate

Results from both fluorescence and electrophysiologic studies of HA-mediated fusion have crystallized the concept of the fusion pore as a central structure in the fusion reaction. This is particularly satisfying, given the established role of fusion pores in exocytic fusion reactions (for review, see Almers et al., 1991; Monck and Fernandez, 1992).

The initial HA-fusion pore has a conductance of ~150pS. The pore often "flickers," that is, it opens and closes—sometimes repeatedly—before opening irreversibly. The pore can display semi-stable conductance states of ~500 pS before completing its growth phase (Spruce et al., 1991; Spruce et al., 1989). A detailed description of the stages and dynamics of HA-fusion pore formation can be found in (Melikyan et al., 1993a; Melikyan et al., 1995a; Melikyan et al., 1993b; Melikyan et al., 1995b).

A model for HA-fusion pore formation is shown in Fig. 1. A highly related model, which takes into account new structural information about the HA protein (Bullough et al., 1994; Hughson, 1995; Wharton et al., 1995), has recently been presented (White, 1996). The newer model differs only in terms of the conformational state of HA along the pathway. In both models, there are 4 critical steps: (1) close membrane contact, which is facilitated by the exposed fusion peptides; (2) formation of a hemifusion intermediate, which requires a small cluster of HA trimers; (3) reversible opening of a narrow fusion pore; and (4) irreversible dilation of the fusion pore. In our models, we depict the state of reversible pore opening (step 3) as the stage during which flickering occurs.

The central structure in the model (Fig. 1) is the hemifusion intermediate. *Hemifusion* is defined as a stage during which the outer, but not the inner, leaflets of two membranes have merged; during hemifusion, a membrane barrier to aqueous content mixing still exists. We recently showed, by use of fluorescent technology, that GPI-anchored HA promotes hemifusion but not full fusion (Kemble et al., 1994). Electrophysiologic studies have confirmed and extended this finding (Melikyan et al., 1995c). To date, hemifusion in a biologic system has only been shown for GPI-anchored HA. Our working hypothesis is, however, that fusion mediated by the wild-type HA protein proceeds via a hemifusion intermediate. Moreover, we postulate that all biologic fusion events proceed via hemifusion.

What is the structure surrounding the hemifusion intermediate and the nascent fusion pore? Our working model (Fig. 1) and those of others (Bentz et al., 1993; Guy et al., 1992; Stegmann et al., 1990) is that these structures are surrounded by a cluster of several conformationally altered HA trimers. Several lines of indirect evidence have supported the notion that, rather than a single HA trimer, a cluster of HA trimers is required to initiate fusion (Doms and Helenius, 1986; Ellens et al., 1990; Morris et al., 1989). It has also been reasoned that the lag phase observed before the onset of fusion (Fig. 1, *step 2*) encompasses time during which this macroassembly is formed. We have recently provided evidence for the implicit cooperativ-

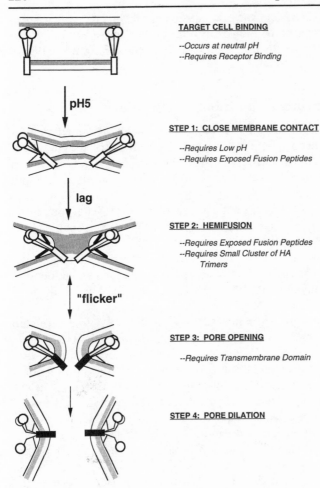

TARGET CELL BINDING

--Occurs at neutral pH
--Requires Receptor Binding

pH5

STEP 1: CLOSE MEMBRANE CONTACT

--Requires Low pH
--Requires Exposed Fusion Peptides

lag

STEP 2: HEMIFUSION

--Requires Exposed Fusion Peptides
--Requires Small Cluster of HA
  Trimers

"flicker"

STEP 3: PORE OPENING

--Requires Transmembrane Domain

STEP 4: PORE DILATION

Figure 1. Model for membrane fusion mediated by the influenza virus hemagglutinin. Reproduced with permission from White, 1994.

ity of HA-mediated fusion by demonstrating a sigmoidal relationship between the lag phase before the onset of fusion (as monitored by outer leaflet lipid mixing) and the density of HA trimers at the cell surface (Danieli et al., unpublished). Our results suggest that a minimum of 3–4 trimers is required. Hence, the nascent fusion pore is envisioned to be surrounded by, minimally, a ring of 3–4 HA trimers.

Conclusions and Perspectives

In conclusion, recent studies have provided strong support for a model in which HA-mediated fusion proceeds via a fusion pore. Evidence is mounting that a predecessor to the fusion pore is a hemifusion intermediate surrounded by a small cluster of HA trimers. In our model (Fig. 1; see also Fig. 4 in White, 1996), the hydrophobic fusion peptide plays its primary role during the initial stages of fusion (close membrane contact, hemifusion), whereas the other particularly hydrophobic region of HA, the transmembrane domain, plays its major role during the latter stages of fusion (fusion pore opening). Future work will address the sequence requirements and precise roles of the fusion peptide and the transmembrane domain and will elucidate additional details of fusion pore formation.

Acknowledgments

Work was supported by grants from the National Institutes of Health to J.M. White (AI22470) and F.S. Cohen (GM27367) and by a grant (91-00041) from the United States-Israel Binational Science Foundation (Jerusalem, Israel) to Y.I. Henis.

References

Almers, W., L.J. Breckenridge, A. Iwata, A.K. Lee, A.E. Spruce, and F.W. Tse. 1991. Millisecond studies of single membrane fusion events. *In* Calcium Entry and Action at the Presynaptic Nerve Terminal. E.F. Stanley, M.C. Nowycky, and D.J. Triggle, editors. New York Academy of Sciences, New York. 318–327.

Bentz, J., editor. 1993. Viral Fusion Mechanisms. CRC Press, Inc., Boca Raton, FL.

Bentz, J., H. Ellens, and D. Alford. 1993. Architecture of the influenza hemagglutinin fusion site. *In* Viral Fusion Mechanisms. J. Bentz, editor. CRC Press, Inc., Boca Raton, FL. 163–199.

Bron, R., J.M. Wahlberg, H. Garoff, and J. Wilschut. 1993. Membrane fusion of Semliki forest virus in a model system: correlation between fusion kinetics and structural changes in the envelope glycoprotein. *EMBO J.* 12:693–701.

Bullough, P.A., F.M. Hughson, J.J. Skehel, and D.C. Wiley. 1994. Structure of influenza haemagglutinin at the pH of membrane fusion. *Nature.* 371:37–43.

Carr, C.M., and P.S. Kim. 1993. A spring-loaded mechanism for the conformational change of influenza hemagglutinin. *Cell.* 73:823–832.

Doms, R.W. 1993. Protein conformational changes in virus-cell fusion. *Meth. Enzymol.* 221:61–82.

Doms, R.W., and A. Helenius. 1986. Quaternary structure of influenza virus hemagglutinin after acid treatment. *J. Virol.* 60:833–839.

Doms, R.W., A. Helenius, and J. White. 1985. Membrane fusion activity of the influenza virus hemagglutinin. *J. Biol. Chem.* 260:2973–2981.

Doxsey, S., J. Sambrook, A. Helenius, and J. White. 1985. An efficient method for introducing macromolecules into living cells. *J. Cell Biol.* 101:19–27.

Duzgunes, N. 1993. Membrane fusion techniques. *Meth. Enzymol.* 221:1–462.

Ellens, H., J. Bentz, D. Mason, F. Zhang, and J.M. White. 1990. Fusion of influenza hemagglutinin-expressing fibroblasts with glycophorin-bearing liposomes: Role of hemagglutinin surface density. *Biochemistry.* 29:9697–9707.

Fuller, S.D., J.A. Berriman, S.J. Butcher, and B.E. Gowen. 1995. Low pH induces swiveling of the glycoprotein heterodimers in the Semliki Forest Virus spike complex. *Cell.* 81:715–725.

Gilbert, J.M., L.D. Hernandez, J.W. Balliet, P. Bates, and J.M. White. 1995. Receptor-induced conformational changes in the subgroup A avian leukosis and sarcoma virus envelope glycoprotein. *J. Virol.* 69:7410–7415.

Guy, H.R., S.R. Durell, C. Schoch, and R. Blumenthal. 1992. Analyzing the fusion process of influenza hemagglutinin by mutagenesis and molecular modeling. *Biophys. J.* 62:95–97.

Harter, C., P. James, T. Bächi, G. Semenza, and J. Brunner. 1989. Hydrophobic binding of the ectodomain of influenza hemagglutinin to membranes occurs through the "fusion peptide." *J. Biol. Chem.* 264:6459–6464.

Hughson, F.M. 1995. Structural characterization of viral fusion proteins. *Curr. Biol.* 5:265–274.

Justman, J., M.R. Klimjack, and M. Kielian. 1993. Role of spike protein conformational changes in fusion of Semliki Forest virus. *J. Virol.* 67:7597–7607.

Kemble, G.W., T. Danieli, and J.M. White. 1994. Lipid-anchored influenza hemagglutinin promotes hemifusion, not complete fusion. *Cell.* 76:383–391.

Kenney, J.M., M. Sjoberg, H. Garoff, and S.D. Fuller. 1994. Visualization of fusion activation in the Semliki Forest virus spike. *Structure.* 2:823–832.

Levy-Mintz, P., and M. Kielian. 1991. Mutagenesis of the putative fusion domain of the Semliki Forest virus spike protein. *J. Virol.* 65:4292–4300.

Marsh, M., and A. Helenius. 1989. Virus entry into animal cells. *Adv. Vir. Res.* 36:107–151.

Melikyan, G.B., W.D. Niles, and F.S. Cohen. 1993a. Influenza virus hemagglutinin-induced cell-planar bilayer fusion: Quantitative dissection of fusion pore kinetics into stages. *J. Gen. Physiol.* 102:1131–1146.

Melikyan, G.B., W.D. Niles, and F.S. Cohen. 1995a. The fusion kinetics of influenza hemagglutinin expressing cells to planar bilayer membranes is affected by HA density and host cell surface. *J. Gen. Physiol.* 106:783–802.

Melikyan, G.B., W.D. Niles, M.E. Peeples, and F.S. Cohen. 1993b. Influenza hemagglutinin-mediated fusion pores connecting cells to planar membranes: Flickering to final expansion. *J. Gen. Physiol.* 102:1131–1149.

Melikyan, G.B., W.D. Niles, V.A. Ratinov, M. Karhanek, J. Zimmerberg, and F.S. Cohen. 1995b. Comparison of transient and successful fusion pores connecting influenza hemagglutinin expressing cells to planar membranes. *J. Gen. Physiol.* 106:803–819.

Melikyan, G.B., J.M. White, and F.S. Cohen. 1995c. GPI-anchored influenza hemagglutinin induces hemifusion to both red blood cell and planar bilayer membranes. *J. Cell Biol.* 131:679–691.

Monck, J.R., and J.M. Fernandez. 1992. The exocytotic fusion pore. *J. Cell Biol.* 119:1395–1404.

Moore, J.P., B.A. Jameson, R.A. Weiss, and Q. Sattentau. 1993. The HIV-cell fusion reaction. *In* Viral Fusion Mechanisms. J. Bentz, editor. CRC Press, Inc., Boca Raton, FL. 233–289.

Morris, S., D. Sarkar, J. White, and R. Blumenthal. 1989. Kinetics of pH-dependent fusion between 3T3 fibroblasts expressing influenza hemagglutinin and red blood cells. Measurement by dequenching of fluorescence. *J. Biol. Chem.* 264:3972–3978.

Sarkar, D.P., S.J. Morris, O. Eidelman, J. Zimmerberg, and R. Blumenthal. 1989. Initial stages of influenza hemagglutinin-induced cell fusion monitored simultaneously by two fluorescent events: Cytoplasmic continuity and membrane mixing. *J. Cell Biol.* 198:113–122.

Sattentau, Q.J., and J.P. Moore. 1991. Conformational changes induced in the human immunodeficiency virus envelope glycoprotein by soluble CD4 binding. *J. Exp. Med.* 174:407–415.

Spruce, A.E., A. Iwata, and W. Almers. 1991. The first milliseconds of the pore formed by a fusogenic viral envelope protein during membrane fusion. *Proc. Natl. Acad. Sci. USA.* 88:3623–3627.

Spruce, A.E., A. Iwata, J.M. White, and W. Almers. 1989. Patch clamp studies of single cell-fusion events mediated by a viral fusion protein. *Nature.* 342:555–558.

Stegmann, T., J.M. White, and A. Helenius. 1990. Intermediates in influenza-induced membrane fusion. *EMBO J.* 9:4231–4241.

Steinhauer, D.A., N.K. Sauter, J.J. Skehel, and D.C. Wiley, 1992. Receptor binding and cell entry by influenza viruses. *In* Seminars in Virology. A. Nomoto, editor. Saunders Scientific Publications. Academic Pres, London, U.K. 91–100.

Tse, F.W., A. Iwata, and W. Almers. 1993. Membrane flux through the pore formed by a fusogenic viral envelope protein during cell fusion. *J. Cell Biol.* 121:543–552.

Wahlberg, J.M., R. Bron, J. Wilschut, and H. Garoff. 1992. Membrane fusion of Semliki Forest virus involves homotrimers of the fusion protein. *J. Virol.* 66:7309–7318.

Wahlberg, J.M., and H. Garoff. 1992. Membrane fusion process of semliki forest virus I: Low pH-induced rearrangement in spike protein quaternary structure precedes virus penetration into cells. *J. Cell Biol.* 116:339–348.

Wharton, S.A., L.J. Calder, R.W. H. Ruigrok, J.J. Skehel, D.A. Steinhauer, and D.C. Wiley. 1995. Electron microscopy of antibody complexes of influenza virus haemagglutinin in the fusion pH conformation. *EMBO J.* 14:240–246.

White, J., A. Helenius, and M.J. Gething. 1982. Haemagglutinin of influenza virus expressed from a cloned gene promotes membrane fusion. *Nature.* 300:658–659.

White, J.M. 1994. Fusion of influenza virus in endosomes: Role of the hemagglutinin. *In* Cellular Receptors for Animal Viruses. E. Wimmer, editor. Cold Spring Harbor Laboratory Press, Cold Spring Harbor, NY. 281–301.

White, J.M. 1996. Membrane fusion: the influenza paradigm. *Cold Spring Harbor Symp. Quant. Biol.* In press.

White, J.M., and I.A. Wilson. 1987. Anti-peptide antibodies detect steps in a protein conformational change: Low-pH activation of the influenza virus hemagglutinin. *J. Cell Biol.* 105:2887–2896.

Wilson, I.A., J.J. Skehel, and D.C. Wiley. 1981. Structure of the haemagglutinin membrane glycoprotein of influenza virus at 3-Å resolution. *Nature.* 289:366–372.

Zimmerberg, J., R. Blumenthal, D.P. Sarkar, M. Curran, and S.J. Morris. 1994. Restricted movement of lipid and aqueous dyes through pores formed by influenza hemagglutinin during cell fusion. *J. Cell Biol.* 127:1885–1894.

Regulation of Store-operated Calcium Currents in Mast Cells

Anant B. Parekh and Reinhold Penner

Department of Membrane Biophysics, Max-Planck-Institute for Biophysical Chemistry, Am Fassberg, 37077 Göttingen, Germany

Introduction

In electrically non-excitable cells, activation of cell surface receptors that engage the phosphatidyl inositol pathway evoke a biphasic increase in cytosolic-free Ca^{2+}. The first transient component is mainly due to inositol 1,4,5-trisphosphate ($InsP_3$)-evoked Ca^{2+} release from internal stores, whereas the secondary plateau phase reflects Ca^{2+} influx into the cell (Berridge, 1993). This Ca^{2+} influx is important for refilling of the stores (Parekh et al., 1993), modification of the spatio-temporal pattern of Ca^{2+} signaling (Girard and Clapham, 1993), contribution to secretion (Parekh and Penner, 1995; Zhang and McCloskey, 1995), and regulation of enzymes like adenylate cyclase (Chiono et al., 1995).

The Ca^{2+} entry pathways are resistant to conventional organic Ca^{2+} channel blockers, which are powerful inhibitors of voltage-dependent Ca^{2+} channels, and are not voltage activated, because depolarization reduces Ca^{2+} influx rather than enhancing it (Penner et al., 1988). Hence the mechanisms underlying Ca^{2+} influx in excitable and non-excitable cells are rather different.

Although numerous Ca^{2+}-influx pathways have been proposed (reviewed by Tsien and Tsien, 1990), it is now widely accepted that the major Ca^{2+} entry pathway is capacitative Ca^{2+} influx, originally introduced by Putney in 1986. In this scheme, the Ca^{2+} content of the $InsP_3$ stores controls a plasmalemmal Ca^{2+}-influx pathway. Depletion of the stores activates Ca^{2+} entry. Direct support for this scheme was provided by patch–clamp experiments in mast cells, in which three very different procedures for depletion of stores activated, in all cases, a selective Ca^{2+} current termed I_{CRAC} (Ca^{2+} release-activated Ca^{2+} current; Hoth and Penner, 1992). Since then, similar store-operated currents (SOC) have been observed in several other non-excitable cells (reviewed in Penner et al., 1993; Fasolato et al., 1994).

In this review, we will describe how SOCs can be activated, their biophysical properties, their regulation, and some properties of the activation mechanism. The discussion will be restricted to I_{CRAC} in mast cells and the tumor-derived rat basophilic leukemia cells, model cells for the study of secretion, since our laboratory has focused intensively on them.

Store Depletion Activates I_{CRAC}

Fig. 1 illustrates a whole-cell recording experiment designed to demonstrate I_{CRAC} in a rat basophilic leukemia (RBL-2H3) cell. Store depletion was induced by dialysis of the cell with 20 μM InsP$_3$ while the intracellular Ca^{2+} concentration ([Ca^{2+}]$_i$) was effectively buffered to very low levels with 10 mM EGTA. The extracellular bath solution contained 10 mM Ca^{2+} to maximize the current amplitude. The cell was kept under voltage clamp at a holding potential of 0 mV, and brief voltage ramps of 50-ms duration and spanning a range of −100 to +100 mV were periodically applied to obtain the current–voltage relationship of I$_{CRAC}$. Under these conditions, an inwardly rectifying conductance develops over a time course of several tens of seconds. It is characterized by a short delay of a few seconds, during which InsP$_3$ releases Ca^{2+} from intracellular stores and the depletion of these stores generates a signal that activates I$_{CRAC}$ in the plasma membrane (for details on kinetic aspects of I$_{CRAC}$ see Hoth and Penner, 1993).

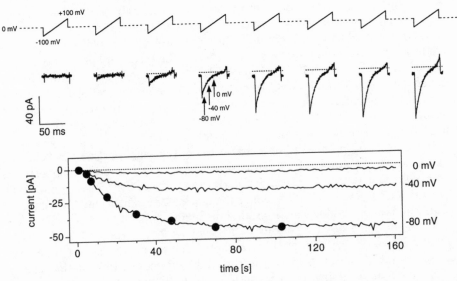

Figure 1. Activation of I$_{CRAC}$ by store depletion. The Ca^{2+} current was activated by depletion of stores with 20 μM InsP$_3$. EGTA (10 mM) was included in the pipette solution to clamp cytosolic Ca^{2+} to very low values. The Ca^{2+} current was monitored by voltage ramps spanning −100 to +100 mV in 50 ms. Raw data of ramps (corrected by subtracting the very first ramp trace) measured at various times during the activation of I$_{CRAC}$ (indicated by the filled circles in the lower graph). The arrows indicate the times at which a certain voltage is applied by the voltage ramp, and the lower graph superimposes the current amplitudes measured at these voltages from each voltage ramp applied at 2-s intervals.

The activation of I$_{CRAC}$ does not require InsP$_3$ per se, although this second messenger acts as the physiologic stimulus following activation of receptors that signal through the phospatidyl inositol cascade. One can induce store depletion experimentally by numerous procedures independent of InsP$_3$ generation (Hoth and Penner, 1992, 1993). Fig. 2 illustrates various mechanisms that effectively deplete Ca^{2+} stores by either actively translocating Ca^{2+} across the store membrane (e.g., antigen, InsP$_3$, and ionomycin) or passively by interfering with the refilling of the stores (e.g., EGTA and thapsigargin). The latter stimuli rely on an as yet unidentified leak pathway that constitutively releases Ca^{2+} from the storage organelles and

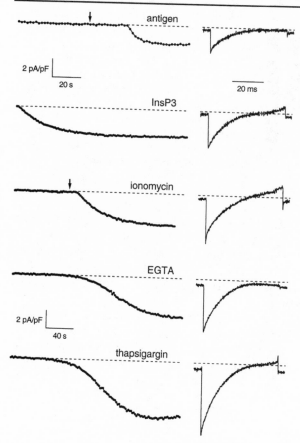

Figure 2. Activation of I_{CRAC} by active and passive store depletion. All experiments were carried out in Cs-glutamate–based internal solutions supplemented with 2 mM ATP and buffered to about 70 nM free $[Ca^{2+}]_i$ by 10 mM EGTA and appropiate additions of Ca^{2+}. When I_{CRAC} was activated by EGTA, no Ca^{2+} was added. $InsP_3$ (40 μM) or thapsigargin (1 μM) were included in the pipette solution, whereas ionomycin (14 μM) or antigen (200 ng/ml) were applied locally through an external application pipette at the times indicated. The Ca^{2+} current was monitored by voltage ramps (*right*) spanning -100 to $+100$ mV in 50 ms at intervals of 1 or 2 s. From these ramps, amplitudes of currents measured at -80 mV are plotted versus time (*left*).

which will gradually empty the stores when preventing replenishment by blocking SERCA ATPases or buffering $[Ca^{2+}]_i$ to very low levels. As a result, the activation of I_{CRAC} by passive store depletion is characterized by a longer delay and a slightly slower time course (Fig. 2). But in any case, the biophysical characteristics of the current are identical regardless of the mode of activation and no additivity is observed when various combinations of the stimuli are used. These observations suggest that their common action is depletion of stores.

Permeation Properties of I_{CRAC}

The permeation properties of I_{CRAC} share some similarities with voltage-dependent Ca^{2+} channels, such as anomalous mole fraction behavior, permeation of monovalent ions in the absence of divalent ions, and inhibition by other divalent ions such as Cd^{2+}, Co^{2+}, and Mn^{2+} (Hoth and Penner, 1993). The blocking efficacies of various inorganic cations on I_{CRAC} are illustrated in Fig. 3. Although I_{CRAC} is clearly blocked by Mn^{2+}, it appears to have some small Mn^{2+} permeability. This property is often used as an indicator for Ca^{2+} influx in fura-2 quenching assays in intact cells; however, it is shared by other cationic channels as well (Fasolato et al., 1993) and is

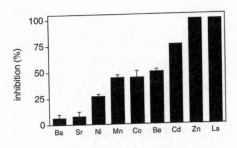

Figure 3. Blocking efficacy of various divalent ions: ranking order of the inhibition of I_{CRAC} by 1 mM of various divalent ions and the trivalent ion La^{3+}. I_{CRAC} was activated by $InsP_3$ in 10 mM extracellular Ca^{2+} and the desired test concentrations of blocking ions were applied from a puffer pipette. Values represent means $\pm$SEM of three to seven determinations and correspond to the inhibition of current amplitudes at -40 mV. (Data taken from Hoth and Penner, 1993.)

not an unequivocal identifier of I_{CRAC}. It is noteworthy, and might be currently considered a hallmark property of I_{CRAC}, that in contrast to voltage-dependent Ca^{2+} channels, divalent ions such as Ba^{2+} and Sr^{2+} are much less effective charge carriers through I_{CRAC} (Hoth and Penner, 1993; Hoth, 1995). In fact, they can even block permeation of Ca^{2+} through I_{CRAC}. In this respect, Ba^{2+}, Sr^{2+}, and Mn^{2+} might be considered permeation blockers of I_{CRAC}.

I_{CRAC} is a highly selective Ca^{2+} current (Hoth and Penner, 1992, 1993) and is barely detectable under physiologic conditions of unbuffered $[Ca^{2+}]_i$ and 1–2 mM $[Ca^{2+}]_o$ (Penner et al., 1988). The dependence of I_{CRAC} on $[Ca^{2+}]_o$ in rat peritoneal mast cells is shown in Fig. 4 *a*, which yields an apparent k_D for $[Ca^{2+}]_o$ of about 3 mM (Hoth and Penner, 1993).

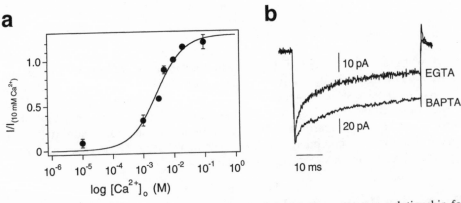

Figure 4. Dependence of I_{CRAC} on $[Ca^{2+}]_o$ and $[Ca^{2+}]_i$. (*a*) Dose-response relationship for extracellular Ca^{2+} concentration. I_{CRAC} was activated by $InsP_3$ and EGTA in 10 mM extracellular Ca^{2+}, and the desired test concentrations were applied from a puffer pipette. Data points correspond to the ratio of current amplitudes at -40 mV at various extracellular Ca^{2+} concentrations with respect to the standard Ca^{2+} concentration of 10 mM. (*b*) After full activation of I_{CRAC} by 10 μM $InsP_3$, large inward currents through I_{CRAC} were elicited by hyperpolarizing voltage steps to -100 mV in the presence of EGTA and BAPTA, respectively. This caused a $[Ca^{2+}]_i$-dependent inactivation of I_{CRAC}. For comparison, the current sweep obtained with EGTA in the pipette was scaled to match the larger amplitude of the current under BAPTA. (Data taken from Hoth and Penner, 1993.)

The magnitude of I_{CRAC} is not only dependent on external Ca^{2+}, but it is also tightly regulated by $[Ca^{2+}]_i$. Since I_{CRAC} constitutes a persistent and highly Ca^{2+}-selective influx pathway, its unregulated activation would impose a serious threat to the cell as a potentially cytotoxic event. While under certain circumstances this might be a desired function (e.g., in apoptotic signaling), the physiologic role of I_{CRAC} in agonist-mediated signaling calls for tight regulation of this conductance; in its simplest form this could be an auto-feedback inhibition. This is indeed provided by $[Ca^{2+}]_i$-induced inactivation of I_{CRAC}, a phenomenon that is also observed in voltage-dependent Ca^{2+} channels (Eckert and Chad, 1984). Fig. 4 *b* illustrates the basic phenomenon of $[Ca^{2+}]_i$-induced inactivation of I_{CRAC} as revealed by the differential effects of a slow Ca^{2+} buffer (EGTA) and a fast buffer (BAPTA). It shows that the amount of current through I_{CRAC} is reduced by inactivation in both cases but less so with the faster Ca^{2+} chelator BAPTA (Hoth and Penner, 1993). A detailed quantitative assessment of $[Ca^{2+}]_i$-induced inactivation based on similar experiments determined that the putative Ca^{2+} binding site is likely to reside on the channel itself (Zweifach and Lewis, 1995).

Inactivation of I_{CRAC} by Protein Kinases

While Ca^{2+}-induced inactivation of I_{CRAC} will immediately provide feedback inhibition, there may be additional mechanisms that modulate the influx of Ca^{2+} through these channels. Since phosphorylation of ion channels is a widespread mechanism of modulation, it is not surprising that this regulation is also found in I_{CRAC} (Parekh and Penner, 1995). When RBL cells were dialyzed with an internal solution that lacked ATP, I_{CRAC} inactivated only slightly with time (Fig. 5, *a* and *b*). However, in the presence of 2 mM ATP, inactivation of I_{CRAC} could be observed. The nonhydrolyzable ATP analogue ATPγS increased the extent of inactivation (Fig. 5, *a* and *b*). This analogue is readily used by protein kinases, but the reaction results in irreversible phosphorylation since phosphatases cannot dephosphorylate the phosphorothiolate moiety. 5'-Adenylimidodiphosphate, which is also a nonhydrolyzable analogue of ATP, but one that is not used by kinases, did not mimic the effects of ATP and ATPγS on inactivation.

Because these experiments were carried out in the presence of 10 mM EGTA (where resting Ca^{2+} is subnanomolar) and because ATPγS is not used by Ca^{2+} ATPases, the observed inactivation is unlikely to reflect refilling of the Ca^{2+} stores. Instead, the results suggest that a kinase inactivates either I_{CRAC} or the mechanism of sustaining the current, once it is activated. To determine which kinase was responsible for this inactivation, we tested various activators and inhibitors of known kinases. Neither the calmodulin inhibitor calmidazolium (50 μM) nor dialysis of cells with either cAMP or cGMP (both at 100 μM) changed the rate or extent of inactivation. The nonspecific kinase inhibitor staurosporine (2 μM) and the selective protein kinase C inhibitor bisindolylmaleimide (500 nM) both prevented inactivation (Fig. 5, *c* and *d*); these observations suggest that protein kinase C was responsible for the inactivation. Consistent with this was the finding that direct activation of kinase C with phorbol ester accelerated the inactivation of I_{CRAC} (Fig. 5, *c* and *d*). Although one must always exert caution in interpreting the effects of drugs, the pharmacologic profile of the kinase is compatible with protein kinase C.

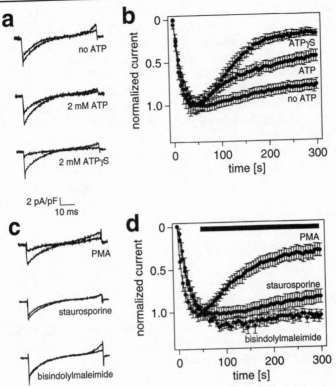

Figure 5. Protein kinase inactivates I_{CRAC}. The Ca^{2+} current was activated by depletion of stores with 40 μM InsP$_3$. EGTA (10 mM) was included in the pipette solution to clamp cytosolic Ca^{2+} to very low values. The Ca^{2+} current was monitored by voltage ramps spanning −100 to +100 mV in 50 ms. (*a*) Raw data of ramps measured at 50 s (when I_{CRAC} had peaked) and at 250 s in the presence of the indicated adenine nucleotides. (*b*) Pooled data from all the cells analyzed (20 cells for 0 mM ATP, 15 cells for 2 mM ATP, and 11 cells for 2 mM ATPγS). Ramps (50 and 250 s, as in *a*) obtained in the presence of pharmacologic agents that interact with protein kinase C. (*d*) Pooled data of these agents (six cells for 100 nM phorbol 12-myristate 13-acetate [PMA], seven cells for 2 μM staurosporine, and five cells for 500 nM bisindolylmaleimide). Drugs were applied at 50 s, when I_{CRAC} had peaked, and were maintained throughout. (Data taken from Parekh and Penner, 1995.)

Role of Kinase in Activation of I_{CRAC}

Results of the previous experiments suggest that staurosporine, when applied after full activation of I_{CRAC}, maintains Ca^{2+} influx by prevention of kinase-mediated inhibition. Interestingly, when cells were pretreated with staurosporine (2 μM), the ability of ionomycin to activate I_{CRAC} was substantially reduced. Fig. 6 shows the average response of four cells that were incubated in staurosporine before the onset of whole-cell recording and four cells from the same preparation that were incubated in DMSO, the solvent for staurosporine. In four other cells, ionomycin activation of I_{CRAC} was virtually abolished by staurosporine pretreatment. In two out of two cells, activation of I_{CRAC} by dialysis of cells with InsP$_3$ was also substantially re-

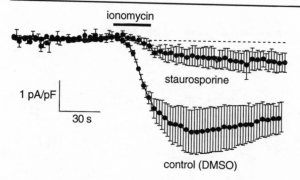

Figure 6. Staurosporine prevents activation of I_{CRAC}. Cells were incubated in either 2 µM staurosporine or DMSO (the solvent) for 30 min before patching the cells. Ionomycin was applied as indicated. The Ca^{2+} concentration of the pipette solution was clamped at 90 nM by varying the ratio of EGTA to CaEGTA. This was done to prevent the spontaneous activation of I_{CRAC} that occurs when cells are subjected to dialysis with high concentrations of Ca^{2+} chelators in the absence of added Ca^{2+}.

duced after staurosporine incubation. The inhibitory effects of staurosporine on the activation of I_{CRAC} were not mimicked by bisindolylmaleimide (500 nM, three of three cells), an observation suggesting that if staurosporine works through blocking a kinase then the kinase is not protein kinase C. Another conclusion from these experiments is that I_{CRAC}, once activated, appears to become independent of its initial activation mechanism, because staurosporine cannot inhibit I_{CRAC} after it has been turned on.

Conclusions

I_{CRAC} is a major source of Ca^{2+} influx in mast and RBL cells. It is highly selective for Ca^{2+} and is not voltage gated. Instead, Ca^{2+} permeation through I_{CRAC} increases as the membrane potential is hyperpolarized, a procedure that increases the electrical driving force for Ca^{2+} entry and thus gives rise to the marked inward rectification of the current. Like voltage-operated Ca^{2+} channels, I_{CRAC} is blocked by divalent cations, exhibits anomalous mole fraction behavior, becomes permeable to monovalent cations in the absence of divalent cations in the external solution, and exhibits fast Ca^{2+}-dependent inactivation from the cytosolic side. Noise analysis estimates a single-channel conductance of <1 pS (Hoth and Penner, 1993; Zweifach and Lewis, 1993), which is at least an order of magnitude smaller than that of voltage-operated Ca^{2+} channels.

The signal emanating from depleted stores that activates I_{CRAC} is still unresolved. Several obvious candidates, like $InsP_3$, $InsP_4$, Ca^{2+}, and cyclic nucleotides can be ruled out. A protein kinase might be involved since staurosporine, a nonspecific kinase inhibitor, substantially reduced the activation of I_{CRAC} but, importantly, it did not reduce the current once it had been activated (in fact it prevented inactivation). This latter result argues against a pharmacologic action of staurosporine on the CRAC channels. Table I summarizes numerous pharmacologic treatments and their effects on activation and inactivation of I_{CRAC}.

I_{CRAC} is clearly inactivated by a protein kinase with a pharmacologic profile compatible with kinase C. This is of physiologic significance since kinase C will be activated concomitantly with $InsP_3$ production after receptor activation of phos-

TABLE I

Summary of Effects of Various Compounds on Activation and Inactivation of I_{CRAC}

Compound	Activation	Inactivation	Concentration
InsP$_3$	Yes (active)	—	10 μM
Ionomycin	Yes (active)	Partial (↑ [Ca^{2+}]$_i$)	10 μM
Antigen	Yes (active)	Partial (↑ PKC)	200 ng/ml
EGTA	Yes (passive)	—	10 mM
BAPTA	Yes (passive)	Block (PKC?)	10 mM
Thapsigargin	Yes (passive)	—	1 μM
[Ca^{2+}]$_i$	—	Partial (↑ [Ca^{2+}]$_i$)	1 μM
InsP$_4$ (± [Ca^{2+}]$_i$)	—	—	50 μM
cGMP (PKG)	—	—	100 μM
cAMP (PKA)	—	—	100 μM
PMA (PKC)	—	Yes (↑ PKC)	0.1 μM
ATP	—	Partial (↑ PKC)	2 mM
ATPγS	—	Yes (↑ PKC)	2 mM
GDPβS	—	—	300 μM
GTPγS	Block	—	100 μM
Na-fluoride	Yes (↑ IP$_3$)	Yes (↑ PKC?)	50 μM
arf, cdc-42, rab-3a/b, rac, ras, rho	—	—	20 μg/ml
Genistein (tyrosine kinases)	Variable effects	—	100 μM
Calmidazolium (CK II)	—	—	50 μM
Bisindolylmaleimide (PKC)	—	Block (PKC)	0.5 μM
Staurosporine	Block	Block (PKC)	2 μM

Dashes (—) mean that no significant effect was observed. All effects were verified in RBL-2H3 cells in at least three determinations.

phatidyl inositol-4,5bisphosphate hydrolysis. Indeed, the ability of a receptor to evoke Ca^{2+} influx is critically dependent on kinase C activity. Simply blocking kinase C can convert an adenosine receptor (A$_3$ type) agonist that evokes virtually no I$_{CRAC}$ and small Ca^{2+} influx into one that triggers large I$_{CRAC}$ and prominent Ca^{2+} influx (Parekh and Penner, 1995). Because Ca^{2+} entry through I$_{CRAC}$ is an important source of Ca^{2+} for secretion (Zhang and McCloskey, 1995), regulation by kinases will have important consequences on cell functioning.

References

Berridge, M.J. 1993. Inositol trisphosphate and calcium signalling. *Nature (Lond.).* 361:315–325.

Chiono, M., R. Mahey, G. Tate, and D.M. Cooper. 1995. Capacitative Ca^{2+} entry exclusively inhibits cAMP synthesis in C6-2B glioma cells. *J. Biol. Chem.* 270:1149–1155.

Eckert, R., and J.E. Chad. 1984. Inactivation of calcium channels. *Progr. Biophys. Mol. Biol.* 44:215–267.

Fasolato, C., M. Hoth, and R. Penner. 1993. Multiple mechanisms of manganese-induced quenching of fura-2 fluorescence in rat mast cells. *Pflüger's Arch.* 423:225–231.

Fasolato, C., B. Innocenti, and T. Pozzan. 1994. Receptor-activated Ca^{2+} influx: how many mechanisms for how many channels. *Trends Pharmacol. Sci.* 15:73–83.

Girard, S., and D.E. Clapham. 1993. Acceleration of intracellular calcium waves in Xenopus oocytes by calcium influx. *Science (Wash. DC)*. 260:229–232.

Hoth, M. 1995. Calcium and barium permeation through calcium release-activated calcium (CRAC) channels. *Pflüger's Arch.* 430:315–322.

Hoth, M., and R. Penner. 1992. Depletion of intracellular calcium stores activates a calcium current in mast cells. *Nature (Lond.)*. 355:353–355.

Hoth, M., and R. Penner. 1993. Calcium release-activated calcium current in rat mast cells. *J. Physiol.* 465:359–386.

Parekh, A.B., and R. Penner. 1995. Depletion-activated calcium current is inhibited by protein kinase in RBL cells. *Proc. Natl. Acad. Sci. USA.* 92:7907–7911.

Parekh, A.B., M. Foguet, H. Lübbert, and W. Stühmer. 1993. Calcium oscillations and calcium influx in Xenopus oocytes expressing a novel 5-hydroxytryptamine receptor. *J. Physiol.* 469:653–671.

Penner, R., C. Fasolato, and M. Hoth. 1993. Calcium influx and its control by calcium release. *Curr. Opin. Neurobiol.* 3:368–374.

Penner, R., G. Matthews, and E. Neher. 1988. Regulation of calcium influx by second messengers in rat mast cells. *Nature (Lond.)*. 334:499–504.

Putney, J.W. 1986. A model for receptor-regulated calcium entry. *Cell Cal.* 7:1–12.

Tsien, R.Y., and R.W. Tsien. 1990. Calcium channels, stores and oscillations. *Annu. Rev. Cell Biol.* 6:715–760.

Zhang, L., and M. McCloskey. 1995. Immunoglobulin E receptor-activated calcium conductance in rat mast cells. *J. Physiol.* 483:59–67.

Zweifach, A., and R.S. Lewis. 1993. Mitogen-regulated Ca^{2+} current of T lymphocytes is activated by depletion of intracellular stores. *Proc. Natl. Acad. Sci. USA.* 105:6295–6299.

Zweifach, A., and R.S. Lewis. 1995. Rapid inactivation of depletion-activated calcium current (I_{CRAC}) due to local calcium feedback. *J. Gen. Physiol.* 105:209–226.

Positive and Negative Regulation of Depletion-activated Calcium Channels by Calcium

Richard S. Lewis, Ricardo E. Dolmetsch, and Adam Zweifach

Department of Molecular and Cellular Physiology, Stanford University School of Medicine, Stanford, California 94305

Introduction

In many cell types, the depletion of intracellular Ca^{2+} stores by inositol 1,4,5-tris-phosphate (IP_3) triggers Ca^{2+} influx through store-operated channels (SOCs) in the plasma membrane, a process referred to as capacitative Ca^{2+} entry (Putney and Bird, 1993; Fasolato et al., 1994). An important function of these channels is to promote sustained increases in intracellular Ca^{2+} concentration ($[Ca^{2+}]_i$) in response to maintained stimulation through phosphoinositide-linked receptors. Recent work indicates that SOCs play an essential role in the activation of T lymphocytes by antigen, the process by which quiescent T cells are induced to enter the cell cycle, proliferate, and differentiate to become immunologically active effector cells. The binding of antigen by the T-cell receptor complex (TCR) leads to the generation of IP_3, which releases Ca^{2+} from stores and stimulates Ca^{2+} influx across the plasma membrane. Because of the finite capacity of the intracellular stores, influx is required to sustain the $[Ca^{2+}]_i$ rise for durations of >30 min that are needed to help commit the cells to a program of gene expression that leads to T-cell activation (Crabtree, 1989; Negulescu et al., 1994). The central importance of depletion-activated Ca^{2+} influx to the immune system has been dramatically demonstrated by several recent cases of severe immunodeficiency that have been traced to a failure of store depletion to activate Ca^{2+} influx in human T cells (Partiseti et al., 1994).

Much recent evidence indicates that Ca^{2+} influx in T cells occurs through depletion-activated Ca^{2+} channels (for a review, see Lewis and Cahalan, 1995). These channels display a number of distinctive characteristics, including a high selectivity for Ca^{2+} over monovalent cations and a low steady-state conductance for Ba^{2+} or Sr^{2+}, voltage-independent gating, an inwardly rectifying current-voltage relation, inactivation by intracellular Ca^{2+}, and an extremely small unitary conductance of 10–30 fS (Lewis and Cahalan, 1989; Hoth and Penner, 1992; 1993; Zweifach and Lewis, 1993; Partiseti et al., 1994; Premack, et al., 1994). We refer to these channels as CRAC (for Ca^{2+} release-activated Ca^{2+}) channels because of their close similarities to the Ca^{2+} channels in mast cells for which the name was originally proposed (Hoth and Penner, 1992). T lymphocytes are uniquely suited in several respects for detailed studies of CRAC channels. First, CRAC channels are likely to be the sole pathway for Ca^{2+} entry in T cells, as Ca^{2+} currents activated by thapsigargin (TG) or through the TCR share the same characteristic properties (Zweifach and Lewis, 1993; Partiseti et al., 1994; Premack et al., 1994), and mutant T cells selected for a defect in depletion-activated Ca^{2+} entry also lack TCR-stimulated entry and I_{CRAC} (Fanger et al., 1995). Second, the electrophysiologic properties of T cells have been

Organellar Ion Channels and Transporters © 1996 by The Rockefeller University Press

described extensively; thus, it is possible to isolate I_{CRAC} from other contaminating currents, even to the extent that current noise from CRAC channels can be detected at the fA level in whole-cell recordings (Zweifach and Lewis, 1993). Finally, the link between Ca^{2+} influx through CRAC channels and gene expression in T cells is becoming clear (Negulescu et al., 1994; Fanger et al., 1995), and this provides a physiologic context for biophysical studies. For these reasons, we have studied the basic properties of CRAC channels in T cells with the ultimate goal of understanding the ways in which they influence T-cell behavior.

The mechanisms that control CRAC channel activity are not well understood. The activation signal generated by store depletion remains elusive despite a multitude of proposals, including diffusible messengers, kinases and phosphatases, vesicle insertion, and conformational coupling between proteins in the ER and plasma membranes (Putney and Bird, 1993; Fasolato et al., 1994). Moreover, gating of the channels appears to be complex. In an early study of Ca^{2+} signaling in Jurkat T cells, we found that the Ca^{2+} current could oscillate under voltage-clamp conditions to generate pronounced oscillations of $[Ca^{2+}]_i$ (Lewis and Cahalan, 1989). These results strongly suggested the existence of positive and negative feedback involved in CRAC channel regulation. The studies summarized in this chapter describe our attempts to understand some of the processes that regulate CRAC channel gating and contribute to the generation of dynamic Ca^{2+} signals in T cells. Rather than simply being opened and closed by a store-dependent signal, we have found that CRAC channels are regulated in four distinct ways by Ca^{2+} and that these actions are modulated by the membrane potential. Several of these Ca^{2+}-dependent processes may contribute to the generation of $[Ca^{2+}]_i$ oscillations.

Methods

The Ca^{2+} imaging experiments shown in Fig. 1 were conducted with intact human peripheral blood T cells loaded with fura-2 as described (Dolmetsch and Lewis, 1994). All other results shown were obtained by conventional whole-cell recording from Jurkat E6-1 cells, a human leukemic T cell line. For whole-cell recording, the pipette solution contained: 140 mM Cs aspartate, 2 mM free Mg^{2+}, 5 nM free Ca^{2+}, 1.2 or 12 mM EGTA, and 10 mM Cs-HEPES (pH 7.2). Cells were bathed in a Ringer's solution containing; 155 mM NaCl, 4.5 mM KCl, 1 mM $MgCl_2$, 2 mM or 22 mM $CaCl_2$, 10 mM D-glucose, and 5 mM Na-HEPES (pH 7.4). Complete experimental details are given elsewhere (Zweifach and Lewis, 1993; Zweifach and Lewis, 1995*a*; *b*).

Results and Discussion
Calcium Oscillations in T Lymphocytes

Stimulation through the TCR by antigen or polyclonal mitogens (anti-CD3 antibodies, phytohemagglutinin [PHA]) evokes a smooth sigmoidal rise in the average $[Ca^{2+}]_i$ of T-cell populations. However, parallel measurements in single T cells reveal a variety of dynamic responses, including periodic $[Ca^{2+}]_i$ oscillations (Lewis and Cahalan, 1989; Donnadieu et al., 1992*a*; *b*; Hess et al., 1993). $[Ca^{2+}]_i$ oscillations in T cells are unlike those seen in many other nonexcitable cells, in that they appear

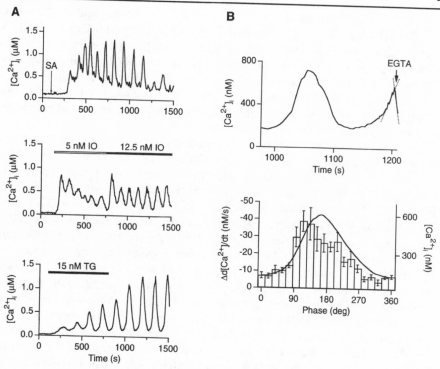

Figure 1. $[Ca^{2+}]_i$ oscillations in T cells. (*A*) $[Ca^{2+}]_i$ oscillations are elicited in single human T cells by conditions that enhance Ca^{2+} release from the ER. Single cells were stimulated with 20 μg/ml biotinylated anti-CD3 at time=0 followed by 4 μg/ml streptavidin (*arrow; top*), or 5–12.5 nM ionomycin (*middle*), or 15 nM TG (*bottom*). The oscillations evoked by anti-CD3 and by ionomycin occur at a frequency of 9.3 mHz, significantly faster than those elicited by TG (6.6 mHz). (*B*) Ca^{2+} influx fluctuates during $[Ca^{2+}]_i$ oscillations. In the *upper graph*, 1 mM EGTA was applied during oscillations induced by 10 nM TG (*arrow*), and the change in slope ($\Delta d[Ca^{2+}]/dt$) indicates a relative measure of Ca^{2+} influx at the time EGTA was added. In the *lower graph*, each *bar* indicates the mean and SEM of $\Delta d[Ca^{2+}]/dt$ for a population of cells, while the *smooth curve* shows the average $[Ca^{2+}]_i$ during the immediately preceding oscillation normalized for phase. The rate of Ca^{2+} influx oscillates, peaking when $[Ca^{2+}]_i$ is rising at its maximum rate. Adapted from Dolmetsch and Lewis, 1994.

to be absolutely dependent on periodic Ca^{2+} influx across the plasma membrane rather than on repetitive release from stores. This conclusion is based primarily on the observation that rapid removal of extracellular Ca^{2+} (Ca_o^{2+}) immediately terminates all oscillatory activity (Lewis and Cahalan, 1989; Donnadieu et al., 1992; Hess et al., 1993; Dolmetsch and Lewis, 1994).

Further studies have shown that partial depletion of stores with agents that operate independently of the IP_3 cascade can also evoke $[Ca^{2+}]_i$ oscillations (Donnadieu et al., 1992a; Dolmetsch and Lewis, 1994). Fig. 1 *A* illustrates the responses of single human T cells to antibodies against the CD3 component of the TCR as well as to low doses of ionomycin or TG. Because ionomycin and TG do not significantly alter resting levels of IP_3, the basic oscillation mechanism appears to be independent of periodic IP_3 generation. Instead, we have proposed that the oscillations are generated by the interaction between internal Ca^{2+} stores and depletion-activated Ca^{2+} channels in the plasma membrane (Dolmetsch and Lewis, 1994). According to this model, low levels of ionomycin, TG, or IP_3 (generated by TCR stimulation) partially deplete the stores, thereby activating CRAC channels. Increased Ca^{2+} influx across the plasma membrane causes $[Ca^{2+}]_i$ to rise; this enhances Ca^{2+} reuptake by the stores. Finally, store repletion is assumed to close the CRAC channels and cause a decline in $[Ca^{2+}]_i$ that enhances Ca^{2+} leakage from the endoplasmic reticulum (ER) and starts the next cycle.

Several lines of evidence support the model. First, Ca^{2+} influx and store content appear to fluctuate during $[Ca^{2+}]_i$ oscillations (Dolmetsch and Lewis, 1994). Ca^{2+} influx was measured in a population of oscillating cells by rapid chelation of extracellular Ca^{2+} with EGTA (Fig. 1 *B*, *top*). Because the rate at which $[Ca^{2+}]_i$ changes ($d[Ca^{2+}]_i/dt$) is proportional to the sum of Ca^{2+} fluxes into and out of the cytosol, the change in rate ($\Delta d[Ca^{2+}]_i/dt$) immediately after removal of Ca^{2+}_o reflects the ongoing rate of influx (Friel and Tsien, 1992). As shown in Fig. 1 *B* (*bottom*), Ca^{2+} influx oscillates by ~4-fold, with a maximum occurring near the time when $[Ca^{2+}]_i$ is increasing most rapidly. A second piece of evidence supporting the model is that abrupt termination of Ca^{2+} influx at different points in the oscillation cycle fails to unmask any measurable contribution to $[Ca^{2+}]_i$ from store release itself (Dolmetsch and Lewis, 1994). Thus, the stores appear to serve more of a time-keeping function, controlling the periodic changes in I_{CRAC}, rather than being a major source of Ca^{2+} themselves. This notion is consistent with the observation that oscillation frequency depends on the rate at which calcium can equilibrate across the store membrane. Ionomycin and IP_3, which increase the Ca^{2+} permeability of the stores, elicit faster oscillations than TG, which inhibits Ca^{2+} reuptake (Fig. 1 *A*).

Two important assumptions implicit in our model are that I_{CRAC} activation is graded according to store content and that time lags exist between changes in store content and I_{CRAC} (Dolmetsch and Lewis, 1994). The first assumption is supported by the observation that the speed with which I_{CRAC} develops depends on the rate at which stores are emptied. The time needed for the current to increase from 10% to 90% of its maximal amplitude was 131 ± 45 s (mean $\pm$ SD, $n = 16$) after treatment with TG, which releases Ca^{2+} relatively slowly, but only 41 ± 14 s (mean $\pm$ SD, $n = 11$) after stimulation with PHA, which releases it rapidly (Zweifach and Lewis, 1993). Thus, activation of I_{CRAC} appears to be graded with store content, a conclusion reached previously for endothelial cells on the basis of results from a Mn^{2+} quench assay (Jacob, 1990). The assumption of time lags in the system prompted us to search for time-dependent calcium feedback mechanisms that may be involved in generating oscillations in intact cells.

Regulation of I_{CRAC} by Calcium

To examine the mechanisms by which Ca^{2+} regulates CRAC channels, we have measured the changes in I_{CRAC} induced by abrupt increases in the driving force for Ca^{2+} entry. Several distinct effects of Ca^{2+} are summarized in the experiment of Fig. 2. In this experiment, the stores were depleted passively by incubating the cell in Ca^{2+}-free Ringer's solution for 3 min while dialyzing its interior with a pipette solution containing 5 nM buffered Ca^{2+}. Current was monitored during 200-ms pulses from -12 mV (the holding potential) to -132 mV every 2 s. Following store depletion, exposure of the cell to 22 mM Ca^{2+} elicits a biphasic change in I_{CRAC}, consisting of a slow increase in current over $\sim$10 s followed by a slow decline over the next 60 s (Fig. 2 *A*). As described below, we believe that this behavior results from a potentiation of CRAC channel opening by extracellular Ca^{2+}, followed by slow inactivation of the channels driven by a global rise in $[Ca^{2+}]_i$ (Zweifach and Lewis, 1995*b*). In addition, I_{CRAC} elicited during each hyperpolarizing pulse declines as a result of a fast inactivation process (Fig. 2 *B*) (Zweifach and Lewis, 1995*a*). To-

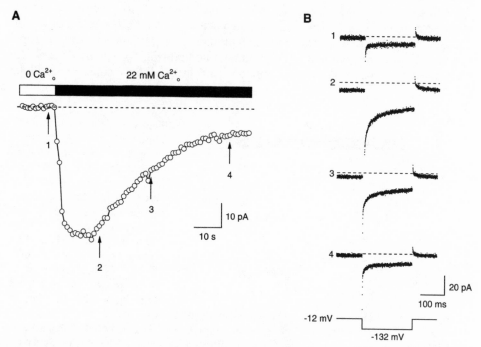

Figure 2. An increase in the driving force for Ca^{2+} entry reveals several modes by which Ca^{2+} regulates I_{CRAC}. Stores were depleted passively by cell incubation in Ca^{2+}-free Ringer's for 3 min while the cell interior was dialyzed with 1.2 mM EGTA (5 nM free Ca^{2+}). (*A*) Each point represents the peak current evoked by a hyperpolarizing voltage pulse; numbers refer to the responses shown in *B*. After the cell was exposed to 22 mM Ca^{2+} as indicated, the current increased over $\sim$10 s to a peak (Ca^{2+}-dependent potentiation), followed by a slow decline over the next 60 s (slow inactivation). (*B*) Hyperpolarizations from -12 to -132 mV cause an immediate increase in I_{CRAC} due to the increased driving force for Ca^{2+}, followed by a rapid decline due to fast inactivation. *A* and *B* are adapted from Zweifach and Lewis, 1995*b*.

gether, the complex response of the current to changes in Ca^{2+} and membrane potential reveals a remarkable complexity in the CRAC channel gating mechanism.

Calcium-dependent Potentiation

In its simplest form, the capacitative Ca^{2+} entry hypothesis assumes that CRAC channels are opened solely by a signal generated by store depletion (Putney, 1990). Thus, the hypothesis would predict that the application of Ca^{2+} to cells with depleted stores would cause an immediate increase of I_{CRAC} to a maximal amplitude. We were surprised to find that this prediction does not hold. In the experiment shown in Fig. 3, I_{CRAC} was monitored during brief hyperpolarizing pulses to -80 mV delivered from a holding potential of -50 or $+50$ mV as the cell was exposed to 2 mM Ca^{2+}. I_{CRAC} appeared in two phases when the holding potential was -50 mV. The initial phase was complete within 1 s, the time needed for solution exchange. The second phase consisted of a several-fold exponential increase in current amplitude with a time constant of 7.5 s. This effect of extracellular Ca^{2+} is voltage-dependent; in the same cell held at $+50$ mV between pulses, I_{CRAC} increased only by about 75%, while it increased by 230% when held at -50 mV. The effect of voltage appears to require Ca^{2+}_o, because the magnitude of I_{CRAC} immediately after exposure to Ca^{2+} was independent of the holding potential (Fig. 3). The binding site for Ca^{2+}-dependent potentiation is probably not intracellular, since intracellular

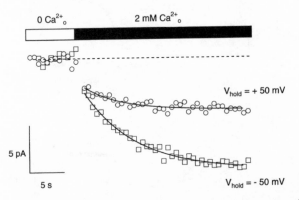

Figure 3. Ca^{2+}-dependent potentiation of I_{CRAC}. Stores were depleted in the absence of Ca^{2+}_o as in Fig. 2, and each point represents I_{CRAC} measured during brief (100-ms) hyperpolarizing pulses to -75 mV before and after addition of 2 mM Ca^{2+} to the bath. At a holding potential of -50 mV, CRAC channel activity increases in two phases: a rapid phase limited by the solution exchange time ($\sim$1 s), followed by an additional exponential increase of 230%. The slow potentiation of I_{CRAC} is reduced to $\sim$75% at the more positive holding potential of $+50$ mV, although the initial amplitude of the current is not affected. Exponential curves with time constants of 5.2 s ($\bigcirc$) and 7.5 s ($\square$) have been fitted to the data.

BAPTA or EGTA do not inhibit the process and extracellular Ni^{2+}, a blocker of CRAC channels, can substitute for Ca^{2+} (Zweifach and Lewis, 1996; Christian et al., 1996). It is of interest that Ba^{2+}, a permeant ion, does not appear to support potentiation. We interpret these results to suggest that Ca^{2+} slowly enhances the opening of CRAC channels by binding to a site within the pore or possibly to a voltage-dependent site on the extracellular surface of the channel.

The existence of Ca^{2+}-dependent potentiation forces a reexamination of several widely assumed, fundamental characteristics of CRAC channels. First, it indicates that at physiologic potentials, the depletion signal by itself accounts for only a small fraction ($\sim$20%) of the total activity of CRAC channels. Second, the voltage dependence of this process confers a slow voltage dependence to CRAC channel gating. Third, because Ba^{2+} fails to support potentiation, comparisons of steady-state Ca^{2+} and Ba^{2+} currents presumably reflect not only differences in permeation but in channel activity as well. Thus, the real permeability of CRAC channels to Ba^{2+} may be significantly higher than has been reported on the basis of steady-state measurements, and hence more similar to that of voltage-gated Ca^{2+} channels. Recent experiments on I_{CRAC} permeation in mast cells, RBL cells, and Jurkat cells support this conclusion (Hoth, 1995). Finally, potentiation may limit the rate at which CRAC channels open fully and may thereby generate a time lag between store depletion and I_{CRAC} activation that contributes to oscillatory behavior.

Fast Inactivation Results from Intracellular Calcium Binding Near the Pore

Fig. 4 *A* illustrates the rapid inactivation of I_{CRAC} caused by brief hyperpolarization. The time course of inactivation is biexponential with time constants in the range of 8–30 ms and 50–150 ms (Zweifach and Lewis, 1995*a*). This process is several orders of magnitude faster than the changes in I_{CRAC} that occur during $[Ca^{2+}]_i$ oscillations and is therefore unlikely to participate directly in the oscillation mechanism. Because its rate and extent increase with hyperpolarization below −50 mV, fast inacti-

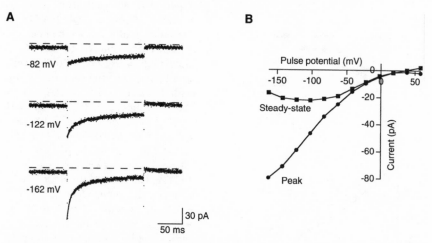

Figure 4. Fast inactivation of I_{CRAC}. (*A*) Fast inactivation during hyperpolarizing pulses from −12 mV to the potentials indicated. (*B*) Fast inactivation reduces the apparent voltage dependence of I_{CRAC} at potentials below −50 mV. Peak and steady-state current-voltage relations are shown from the experiment shown in *A*. The experiment was conducted in the presence of 22 mM Ca_o^{2+} (Zweifach and Lewis, 1995*a*).

vation has the overall effect of reducing the voltage dependence of I_{CRAC} at these hyperpolarized voltages (Fig. 4 *B*).

Fast inactivation is not intrinsically voltage-dependent but rather depends upon Ca^{2+} flux through single channels. This conclusion is supported by the observation that the total driving force for Ca^{2+} entry, and not the membrane potential or $[Ca^{2+}]_o$ alone, determines the rate and extent of inactivation (Zweifach and Lewis, 1995*a*). Several lines of evidence argue that the site for inactivation is located in close proximity to the intracellular mouth of the pore. First, inactivation is dependent on the single-channel current level but independent of the number of activated CRAC channels in the cell; this indicates that Ca^{2+} entering through one channel is unable to affect inactivation of its neighbors (Zweifach and Lewis, 1995*a*). Second, inactivation is slowed by intracellular BAPTA, a rapid chelator, but not by the slower buffer EGTA (Fig. 5 *A*; see also Hoth and Penner, 1993). A simple model describing Ca^{2+} diffusion from a point source in the presence of an excess of highly mobile buffer (Neher, 1986) predicts a gradient of [Ca^{2+}]$_i$ near each open channel. The gradient is expected to be steeper with BAPTA$_i$ than with EGTA$_i$ because of BAPTA's more rapid Ca^{2+} binding kinetics (Fig. 5 *B*). Thus, for any two values of the single-channel current that produce equal levels of inactivation with BAPTA$_i$ and EGTA$_i$, the model predicts a unique location at which [Ca^{2+}]$_i$ will be equal in the presence of the two buffers (Fig. 5 *B*). Fig. 5 *C* shows that at a distance of 3 nm from the mouth of the channel, inactivation in the presence of BAPTA and EGTA shows the same dependence on estimated [Ca^{2+}]$_i$, consistent with a binding site at this location. Furthermore, the Hill equation with a coefficient of two provides the best fit to the data, implying that inactivation is driven by Ca^{2+} binding to

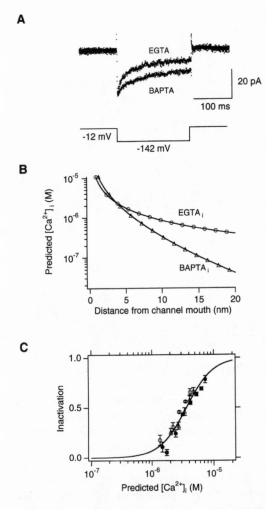

Figure 5. Fast inactivation is due to local binding of Ca^{2+}. (*A*) BAPTA, a rapid Ca^{2+} buffer, slows the inactivation process relative to EGTA, a slower buffer. Responses of two cells to a hyperpolarizing step are shown, with 12 mM EGTA or BAPTA in the recording pipette and 22 mM Ca$_o^{2+}$. (*B*) A simple Ca^{2+} diffusion model predicts that the [Ca^{2+}]$_i$ gradient declines more steeply near the channel with BAPTA$_i$ than with EGTA$_i$. Curves are drawn for 12 mM EGTA$_i$ with single-channel i_{CRAC} = −3.3 fA, and for 12 mM BAPTA$_i$ with i_{CRAC} = −5.5 fA. The fact that these conditions produce roughly equal amounts of inactivation implies that the Ca^{2+}-binding site lies near the intersection of the two curves (i.e., ∼4 nm). (*C*) Fast inactivation involves at least two Ca^{2+} binding sites located ∼3 nm from the intracellular mouth of the pore. The extent of inactivation during 200-ms pulses was measured as shown in Fig. 4 for a range of potentials with 12 mM BAPTA$_i$ and 22 mM Ca$_o^{2+}$ (△) or with 12 mM EGTA$_i$ and 22 mM (●) or 2 mM (○) Ca$_o^{2+}$. These inactivation values are plotted against the values of [Ca^{2+}]$_i$ 3 nm from the mouth of the pore as predicted from the estimated single-channel currents. An equation of the form $I = ([Ca^{2+}]^n/(K_d^n + [Ca^{2+}]^n)$ has been fitted to the data, where I is the measured extent of inactivation, n = 2.04, and K_d = 3.6 μM. Adapted from Zweifach and Lewis, 1995a.

at least two sites positioned several nanometers from the mouth of the channel, possibly residing on the channel itself.

Two Mechanisms of Slow Inactivation by Calcium

A basic tenet of the capacitative Ca^{2+} entry model is that store refilling should turn off the influx of Ca^{2+}. For this reason, we examined slow inactivation of I_{CRAC} by Ca^{2+} while monitoring $[Ca^{2+}]_i$ in the same cell using indo-1 (Zweifach and Lewis, 1995b). After stores are depleted with a low concentration of EGTA (1.2 mM) in the recording pipette, readmission of Ca_o^{2+} causes an increase in I_{CRAC}, followed by a rise in $[Ca^{2+}]_i$ as Ca^{2+} influx exceeds the effective buffering capacity of the EGTA (Fig. 6 A). As $[Ca^{2+}]_i$ rises, I_{CRAC} begins to decline, leading ultimately to a decline of $[Ca^{2+}]_i$. The fall in the level of I_{CRAC} over a period of $\sim$100 s appears to be driven by the global increase in cytosolic Ca^{2+}, since I_{CRAC} is much more sustained in the presence of 12 mM EGTA$_i$, which confines $[Ca^{2+}]_i$ to <100 nM (Fig. 6 B).

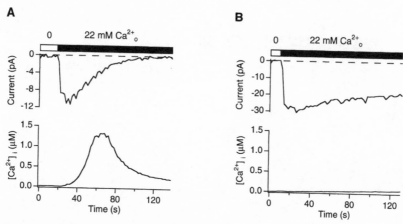

Figure 6. Slow inactivation of I_{CRAC} is dependent on global intracellular $[Ca^{2+}]$. Passive store depletion and measurement of I_{CRAC} is as described in Fig. 2. (*A*) In the presence of 1.2 mM EGTA$_i$, exposure to 22 mM Ca_o^{2+} causes a rise and slow decline of I_{CRAC} (*top*) that is associated with a delayed rise and fall of $[Ca^{2+}]_i$ (*bottom*). (*B*) 12 mM EGTA$_i$ clamps $[Ca^{2+}]_i$ to <100 nM, largely preventing the inactivation of I_{CRAC}. From Zweifach and Lewis, 1995b.

These results are consistent with the notion that store refilling due to the elevation of $[Ca^{2+}]_i$ leads to the closing of CRAC channels in the plasma membrane. We tested this idea by repeating the experiment in the added presence of 1 μM TG $\pm$ 20 μM intracellular IP$_3$ to prevent Ca^{2+} reuptake and maintain the store in the empty state. Surprisingly, under these conditions the current still inactivates with approximately the same time course, though not to the same extent as when store refilling is permitted (Fig. 7 A). Thus, a store-independent mechanism of inactivation by Ca^{2+} operates in parallel with the store-dependent one.

The underlying mechanism of store-independent (TG-insensitive) inactivation is unclear. It is inhibited by okadaic acid (100 nM) as well as by a pharmacologic dose of cyclosporin A (1.7 μM), but the effects of 1-norokadaone, calyculin A, and FK506 are not consistent with a role for protein phosphatases 1, 2A, 2B, 2C, or 3

A

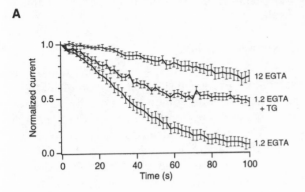

B

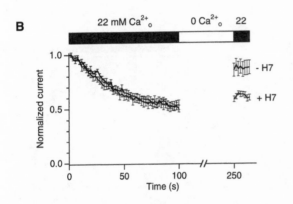

Figure 7. Store-dependent and store-independent forms of slow inactivation. (*A*) Thapsigargin distinguishes two types of slow inactivation. Current amplitude is normalized to the maximum reached in each experiment after exposure to 22 mM Ca_0^{2+}, and time is plotted from this point onward. In cells dialyzed with 1.2 mM $EGTA_i$, the addition of 1 μM TG to prevent refilling of stores prevents only about half of the inactivation. Therefore, store-dependent and -independent mechanisms operate in parallel to inhibit I_{CRAC}. Adapted from Zweifach and Lewis, 1995*b*. (*B*) The kinase inibitor H-7 (100 μM) inhibits recovery from store-independent slow inactivation without affecting its development. Where indicated, H-7 was continuously present from the start of the experiment (3 min prior to the first addition of Ca^{2+}). In *A* and *B*, plotted values are the mean ± SE of 10–20 cells.

(Zweifach and Lewis, 1995*b*). On the other hand, an attempt to promote promiscuous phosphorylation via protein kinases A and C with intracellular ATPγS (4 mM) and cAMP (100 μM) together with extracellular phorbol 12,13-dibutyrate (50 nM) inhibited the inactivation (data not shown). In addition, the broad-spectrum protein kinase inhibitor H-7 inhibited recovery from inactivation. As illustrated in Fig. 7 *B*, I_{CRAC} slowly inactivated by ∼50% in the presence of TG, and this could be reversed by a 150-s incubation in Ca^{2+}-free Ringer's. The added presence of 100 μM H-7 had no effect on the current or its inactivation, but did inhibit the recovery from inactivation. These results suggest that the H-7-sensitive protein kinases A, C, and G are not directly involved in either I_{CRAC} activation or inactivation, but that a kinase may be required for recovery from the inactivated state.

What is the possible utility of multiple modes of slow inactivation by Ca^{2+}? The answer to this question is not clear; however, it is noteworthy that the relative contributions of each mechanism to the feedback inhibition of I_{CRAC} may vary with the degree to which stores are able to refill. Under conditions of weak stimulation, when IP_3 levels are relatively low, stores may refill efficiently, enabling the store-dependent mechanism to dominate. In contrast, strong stimulation may elevate IP_3 to high enough levels to keep stores empty for a longer period, during which the store-independent inactivation mechanism may provide the required feedback control of the magnitude of Ca^{2+} influx. For example, in parotid acinar cells that have been treated with a high dose of TG, Ca^{2+} influx and $[Ca^{2+}]_i$ oscillate despite the fact that stores are continuously depleted, an observation suggesting that oscillations can arise from periodic store-independent inactivation of CRAC channels by Ca^{2+} (Foskett and Wong, 1994). In T cells, the slow kinetics of both types of inactivation are consistent with a role in generating $[Ca^{2+}]_i$ oscillations by creating a lag between the rise in $[Ca^{2+}]_i$ and the consequent decline in Ca^{2+} influx. Modeling studies may provide additional insights into the special functions of these two modes of inactivation.

Conclusions

As originally proposed, our simple model for $[Ca^{2+}]_i$ oscillations in T cells was based on delayed feedback between store content and the activity of CRAC channels. In principle, this feedback could be provided by the dependence of I_{CRAC} on store content that lies at the heart of the capacitative Ca^{2+} entry hypothesis. However, upon investigating this simple hypothesis, we discovered a remarkable diversity of mechanisms by which Ca^{2+} regulates the activity of CRAC channels. As summarized in Table I, three modes of negative feedback by intracellular Ca^{2+} can be distinguished by their speed, location, and sensitivity to experimental reagents.

TABLE I
Calcium-dependent Regulation of CRAC Channels

Type	Speed	Location	Inhibitors
Potentiation	5–10 s	In pore?	
Inactivation	10–200 ms	Intracellular $\sim$3 nm from pore	BAPTA$_i$
Inactivation (store-dependent)	$\sim$30 s	Intracellular stores (refilling)	Thapsigargin, EGTA$_i$
Inactivation (store-independent)	$\sim$30 s $\sim$30 s	Intracellular >100 nm from pore	Okadaic acid, 1-norokadaone, cyclosporin A, EGTA$_i$

Speed is expressed as an exponential time constant for potentiation and fast inactivation, and as $t_{1/2}$ for slow inactivation. The location of store-independent inactivation is inferred from a calculated mean free path length of 129 nm for Ca^{2+} diffusing in the presence of 12 mM EGTA (Zweifach and Lewis, 1995a).

Furthermore, extracellular Ca^{2+} significantly potentiates the activity of CRAC channels.

The kinetics of potentiation and slow inactivation of I_{CRAC} by Ca^{2+} are compatible with a role in generating slow oscillations in T cells. However, additional contributions from voltage oscillations driven by Ca^{2+}-activated and voltage-activated K^+ channels should not be excluded (Dolmetsch and Lewis, 1994; Verheugen and Vijverberg, 1995). A critical unknown is the relation of store content to the kinetics and magnitude of I_{CRAC}; thus far, the technical difficulties involved in measuring and manipulating Ca^{2+} levels in the ER have thwarted attempts to measure this basic relation directly. A close integration of experimental data and quantitative modeling will be needed to unravel the oscillation mechanism.

While significant progress has been made in the determination of how $[Ca^{2+}]_i$ oscillations in T cells are generated, their downstream consequences are as yet unclear. Do they enhance the fidelity or efficiency of antigen detection, or do they perhaps serve a more instructive role, selecting among a number of downstream Ca^{2+}-sensitive pathways? The ability to create defined patterns of $[Ca^{2+}]_i$ elevation by manipulating influx through depletion-activated Ca^{2+} channels, together with the ability to monitor Ca^{2+}-dependent gene expression in single cells by use of reporter genes, may provide a powerful approach to these questions.

Ultimately, a full understanding of CRAC channel regulation and the mechanisms of Ca^{2+} oscillations at the molecular level will require the isolation and manipulation of the channel gene. Thus far, progress in this area has been hampered by the channel's ubiquitous expression and unique properties and by a lack of high-affinity blockers. However, the outlook is improving; recent evidence suggests that the *Drosophila trp* gene encodes a depletion-activated Ca^{2+} channel (Vaca et al., 1994), and human *trp* homologs have been isolated (Wes et al., 1995). In addition, mutant T-cell lines defective for I_{CRAC} have been generated that may serve as useful expression systems (Fanger et al., 1995; Serafini et al., 1995). The identification of the channel may constitute a crucial first step towards identifying and isolating other molecules in the depletion-activated Ca^{2+}-influx pathway.

Acknowledgments

The authors would like to thank Dr. Markus Hoth for comments on the manuscript and Supriya Kelkar for technical assistance. This work was supported by National Institutes of Health (NIH) postdoctoral fellowship AI08568 to A. Zweifach, American Heart Association California Affiliate predoctoral fellowship 93-407 to R.E. Dolmetsch, and NIH grant GM47354 to R.S. Lewis.

References

Christian, E.P., K.T. Spence, J.A. Togo, P.G. Dargis, and J. Patel. 1996. Calcium-dependent enhancement of depletion-activated calcium current in Jurkat T lymphocytes. *J. Membr. Biol.* 150:63–71.

Crabtree, G.R. 1989. Contingent genetic regulatory events in T lymphocyte activation. *Science.* 243:355–361.

Dolmetsch, R., and R.S. Lewis. 1994. Signaling between intracellular Ca^{2+} stores and depletion-activated Ca^{2+} channels generates $[Ca^{2+}]_i$ oscillations in T lymphocytes. *J. Gen. Physiol.* 103:365–388.

Donnadieu, E., G. Bismuth, and A. Trautmann. 1992a. Calcium fluxes in T lymphocytes. *J. Biol. Chem.* 267:25864–25872.

Donnadieu, E., D. Cefai, Y.P. Tan, G. Paresys, G. Bismuth, and A. Trautmann. 1992b. Imaging early steps of human T cell activation by antigen-presenting cells. *J. Immunol.* 148:2643–2653.

Fanger, C.M., M. Hoth, G.R. Crabtree, and R.S. Lewis. 1995. Characterization of T cell mutants with defects in capacitative calcium entry: Genetic evidence for the physiological roles of CRAC channels. *J. Cell Biol.* 131:655–667.

Fasolato, C., B. Innocenti, and T. Pozzan. 1994. Receptor-activated Ca^{2+} influx: How many mechanisms for how many channels? *Trends Pharm. Sci.* 15:77–83.

Foskett, J.K., and D.C.P. Wong. 1994. $[Ca^{2+}]_i$ inhibition of Ca^{2+} release-activated Ca^{2+} influx underlies agonist- and thapsigargin-induced $[Ca^{2+}]_i$ oscillations in salivary acinar cells. *J. Biol. Chem.* 269:31525–31532.

Friel, D.D., and R.W. Tsien. 1992. Phase-dependent contributions from Ca^{2+} entry and Ca^{2+} release to caffeine-induced $[Ca^{2+}]_i$ oscillations in bullfrog sympathetic neurons. *Neuron.* 8:1109–1125.

Hess, S.D., M. Oortgiesen, and M.D. Cahalan. 1993. Calcium oscillations in human T and natural killer cells depend upon membrane potential and calcium influx. *J. Immunol.* 150:2620–2633.

Hoth, M. 1995. Calcium and barium permeation through calcium release-activated calcium (CRAC) channels. *Pflüg. Arch.* 430:315–322.

Hoth, M., and R. Penner. 1992. Depletion of intracellular calcium stores activates a calcium current in mast cells. *Nature.* 355:353–356.

Hoth, M., and R. Penner. 1993. Calcium release-activated calcium current in mast cells. *J. Physiol. (Lond.).* 465:359–386.

Jacob, R. 1990. Agonist-stimulated divalent cation entry into single cultured human umbilical vein endothelial cells. *J. Physiol. (Lond.).* 421:55–77.

Lewis, R.S., and M.D. Cahalan. 1989. Mitogen-induced oscillations of cytosolic Ca^{2+} and transmembrane Ca^{2+} current in human leukemic T cells. *Cell Regul.* 1:99–112.

Lewis, R.S., and M.D. Cahalan. 1995. Potassium and calcium channels in lymphocytes. *Annu. Rev. Immunol.* 13:623–653.

Negulescu, P.A., N. Shastri, and M.D. Cahalan. 1994. Intracellular calcium dependence of gene expression in single T lymphocytes. *Proc. Nat. Acad. Sci. USA.* 91:2873–2877.

Neher, E. 1986. Concentration profiles of intracellular calcium in the presence of a diffusible chelator. *Exp. Brain Res. Series.* 14:80–96.

Partiseti, M., F. Le Diest, C. Hivroz, A. Fischer, H. Korn, and D. Choquet. 1994. The calcium current activated by T cell receptor and store depletion in human lymphocytes is absent in a primary immunodeficiency. *J. Biol. Chem.* 51:32327–32335.

Premack, B.A., T.V. McDonald, and P. Gardner. 1994. Activation of Ca^{2+} current in Jurkat T cells following the depletion of Ca^{2+} stores by microsomal Ca^{2+}-ATPase inhibitors. *J. Immunol.* 152:5226–5240.

Putney, J.W., Jr. 1990. Capacitative calcium entry revisted. *Cell Cal.* 11:611–624.

Putney, J.W., Jr., and G.S.J. Bird. 1993. The inositol phosphate-calcium signaling system in nonexcitable cells. *Endocr. Rev.* 14:610–631.

Serafini, A.T., R.S. Lewis, N.A. Clipstone, R.J. Bram, C.M. Fanger, S. Fiering, L.A. Herzenberg, and G.R. Crabtree. 1995. Isolation of mutant T lymphocytes with defects in capacitative calcium entry. *Immunity.* 3:239–250.

Vaca, L., W.G. Sinkins, Y. Hu, D.L. Kunze, and W.P. Schilling. 1994. Activation of recombinant *trp* by thapsigargin in Sf9 insect cells. *Am. J. Physiol.* 267:C1501–C1505.

Verheugen, A.H., and H.P.M. Vijverberg. 1995. Intracellular Ca^{2+} oscillations and membrane potential fluctuations in intact human T lymphocytes: Role of K^+ channels in Ca^{2+} signaling. *Cell Cal.* 17:287–300.

Wes, P.D., J. Chevisch, A. Jeromin, C. Rosenberg, G. Stetten, and C. Montell. 1995. TRPC1, a human homolog of a *Drosophila* store-operated channel. *Proc. Nat. Acad. Sci. USA.* 92:9652–9656.

Zweifach, A., and R.S. Lewis. 1993. Mitogen-regulated Ca^{2+} current of T lymphocytes is activated by depletion of intracellular Ca^{2+} stores. *Proc. Nat. Acad. Sci. USA.* 90:6295–6299.

Zweifach, A., and R.S. Lewis. 1995*a*. Rapid inactivation of depletion-activated calcium current (I_{CRAC}) due to local calcium feedback. *J. Gen. Physiol.* 105:209–226.

Zweifach, A., and R.S. Lewis. 1995*b*. Slow calcium-dependent inactivation of depletion-activated calcium current. Store-dependent and -independent mechanisms. *J. Biol. Chem.* 270:14445–14451.

Zweifach, A., and R.S. Lewis. 1996. Calcium-dependent potentiation of store-operated calcium channels in T lymphocytes. *J. Gen. Physiol.* 107:597–610.

Sarcoplasmic Reticulum Calcium Release in Frog Cut Muscle Fibers in the Presence of a Large Concentration of EGTA

De-Shien Jong,* Paul C. Pape,* John Geibel,*‡ and W. Knox Chandler*

*Departments of *Cellular and Molecular Physiology and ‡Surgery, Yale University School of Medicine, New Haven, Connecticut 06510-8026*

Introduction

In frog skeletal muscle, contraction is normally activated by an action potential as it propagates along the surface of a fiber and spreads inward along the transverse tubular system. In response to the change in potential across the membranes of the transverse tubular system, Ca is released from the sarcoplasmic reticulum (SR) into the myoplasm, where it can bind to the Ca-regulatory sites on troponin so that contraction can occur. Two proteins that are closely apposed at the triadic junction (Block et al., 1988) play important roles in this process: the dihydropyridine receptor (DHPR), which forms the voltage sensor in the tubular membrane (Ríos and Brum, 1987; Tanabe et al., 1988), and the ryanodine receptor (RyR), which forms the Ca channel in the SR membrane (Imagawa et al., 1987; Hymel et al., 1988; Lai et al., 1988).

During the past few years, we have studied some of the properties of SR Ca release and its regulation by membrane potential and by myoplasmic Ca. In these investigations, frog cut fibers have been equilibrated with solutions that contain 20 mM EGTA, 0–1.76 mM Ca, and 0.63 mM phenol red. At the values of myoplasmic pH encountered in these experiments, almost all of the Ca-free and Ca-bound EGTA is expected to exist as H_2EGTA^{2-} and $CaEGTA^{2-}$, respectively. Hence, the net reaction between Ca and EGTA can be represented by the scheme

$$Ca^{2+} + H_2EGTA^{2-} \rightleftharpoons CaEGTA^{2-} + 2H^+. \qquad (1)$$

According to the stopped-flow studies of Smith et al. (1984), reaction sequence 1 consists of two steps: the combination of Ca^{2+} and H_2EGTA^{2-} to form CaH_2EGTA and the rapid dissociation of CaH_2EGTA to form $CaEGTA^{2-}$ and two H^+. The released protons lower the value of myoplasmic pH according to the relation

$$\Delta[CaEGTA] = -\beta/2 \Delta pH. \qquad (2)$$

Δ signifies the change of a variable with respect to its resting value, and β represents the buffering power of myoplasm, which is $\sim$22 mM/pH unit under the condi-

Dr. Jong's current address is Department of Animal Science, National Taiwan University, Taipei, Taiwan, R. O. C.

Dr. Pape's current address is Département de Physiologie et Biophysique, Faculté de Médecine, Université de Sherbrooke, Sherbrooke (Québec), Canada J1H5N4

tions of our experiments; here and below, [EGTA] and [CaEGTA] represent the total concentrations of Ca-free and Ca-bound EGTA, respectively. ΔpH is measured optically by monitoring the absorbance of the pH indicator phenol red. Additional information about the EGTA-phenol red method is given in Pape et al. (1995).

The EGTA-Phenol Red Method Can Be Used to Measure SR Ca Release and SR Ca Content

With the concentration of EGTA used in our experiments, EGTA would be expected to complex almost all (>99.9%) of the Ca released from the SR if there were no intrinsic Ca buffers such as troponin and parvalbumin present. Even with troponin and parvalbumin in the fiber, however, it seems likely that almost all ($\sim$96%) of the Ca released by an action potential is complexed by EGTA. Consequently, the total amount of Ca released from the SR, $\Delta[Ca_T]$, is approximately equal to $\Delta[CaEGTA]$, which can be estimated from ΔpH with Eq. 2. In addition, the complexation of Ca by EGTA is expected to occur rapidly, within <0.1 ms (the time constant of Ca complexation by EGTA is given approximately by $(k_1[EGTA]_R)^{-1}$, in which k_1 is the apparent forward rate constant for reaction 1 and $[EGTA]_R$ is the resting value of Ca-free [EGTA]).

Fig. 1 *A* shows records from a cut fiber that was mounted in a double Vaseline-gap chamber and stimulated to produce an action potential, as shown in the top trace. The second trace shows $\Delta[Ca_T]$. Within a few milliseconds of stimulation, the signal rapidly increased and reached a plateau value of 366 μM. The duration of Ca release was brief, as shown by the third trace: the peak value of $d\Delta[Ca_T]/dt$ was 132

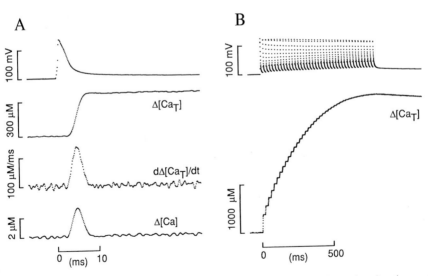

Figure 1. Ca signals associated with a single action potential (*A*) and a train of action potentials (*B*). The internal solution contained 45 mM K-glutamate, 20 mM K_2EGTA plus 1.76 mM Ca, 0.63 mM phenol red, 6.8 mM $MgSO_4$, 5.5 mM Na_2-ATP, 20 mM K_2-creatine phosphate, 5 mM K_3-phospho(enol)pyruvate, and 5 mM 3-[*N*-morpholino]-propanesulfonic acid (MOPS); pH = 7.0, free [Ca] = 0.036 μM, and free [Mg] = 1 mM. The external solution was Ringer's, 14°C. From Pape et al. (1995).

µM/ms and its half-width was 2.7 ms (half-width is the interval of time between the half-peak on the rising phase and the half-peak on the falling phase). The bottom trace shows $\Delta[Ca]$, the change in spatially averaged free [Ca] in the myoplasmic solution. This signal, which has a time course that is similar to that of $d\Delta[Ca_T]/dt$, was estimated from the time courses of [EGTA], [CaEGTA], k_1, and k_{-1} (the apparent backward rate constant for reaction 1), as described in Pape et al. (1995).

Fig. 1 *B* shows the response to a train of 40 action potentials at 50 Hz. Since it was necessary to increase the interval of time between experimental points from 0.12 ms in Fig. 1 *A* to 0.48 ms in Fig. 1 *B*, the time course of the individual action potentials in Fig. 1 *B* cannot be resolved reliably. During the first part of the train, the $\Delta[Ca_T]$ signal showed abrupt increases after each action potential. At later times, $\Delta[Ca_T]$ reached an almost steady value, consistent with the idea that almost all of the readily releasable Ca had moved from the SR into the myoplasm. The final value of $\Delta[Ca_T]$, 2,777 µM, is taken to represent the prestimulus value of the readily releasable SR Ca content (expressed in terms of myoplasmic concentration), which is denoted by $[Ca_{SR}]_R$. In this experiment, the value of $\Delta[Ca_T]$ after the first action potential was 369 µM, indicating that $369/2,777 = 0.13$ of the SR Ca content had been released.

This and other similar experiments show that the EGTA-phenol red method can be used to measure SR Ca release and, with a depleting stimulation, SR Ca content. This method offers several advantages over methods that estimate release from the free [Ca] transient: (*a*) the measurement is direct and rapid and does not depend on the Ca-binding properties of the intrinsic Ca buffers; (*b*) the rate of Ca resequestration by the SR is slow so that Ca release can be studied with little interference from Ca reuptake; (*c*) mechanical activation and the associated movement artifacts are reduced; (*d*) the method is extremely sensitive so that small rates of SR Ca release can be measured (see Fig. 6). One of the disadvantages of the EGTA-phenol red method is that EGTA, by lowering free [Ca], is able to perturb the release process, for example, by reducing Ca inactivation of Ca release (Jong et al., 1995*a*). Additional information about the EGTA-phenol red method is given in Pape et al. (1995).

The Q_γ Component of Intramembranous Charge Movement Is Present After the SR Has Been Depleted of Its Readily Releasable Ca

When the DHPRs in the tubular membrane perform their function as voltage sensors, they undergo a movement that can be detected as a small current (Schneider and Chandler, 1973). Adrian and Peres (1977; 1979) showed that, after a step depolarization, this intramembranous charge movement current, I_{cm}, consists of two components, which they called I_β and I_γ. I_β increases rapidly and then decays with an approximately exponential time course. If the depolarization is near or past the mechanical threshold, I_γ is observed; it has a delayed time course that resembles a hump. In addition to I_β and I_γ having different time courses, the underlying charges Q_β and Q_γ ($Q_\beta = \int I_\beta dt$ and $Q_\gamma = \int I_\gamma dt$) have different dependences on voltage: the Q_γ vs. *V* relation is steeper than the Q_β vs. *V* relation. The finding that Q_γ first appears near threshold and has a steep voltage dependence has led several investigators, beginning with Almers (1978), to suggest that Q_γ is the component of intramembranous charge that controls SR Ca release, at least in frog skeletal muscle.

A recent series of experiments on frog cut muscle fibers has shown that SR Ca content or release or some related event is able to alter the time course of I_{cm} (Csernoch et al., 1991; García et al., 1991; Szucs et al., 1991; Pizarro et al., 1991). Pizarro et al. (1991) developed an explanation for these kinetic changes based on the idea that I_γ is the result, not the cause, of SR Ca release. According to their idea, frog skeletal muscle has only one kind of intramembranous charged particle that is involved in excitation-contraction coupling, Q_β. After depolarization, when a small amount of Q_β moves and activates Ca flux from the SR into the myoplasm, Ca binds to the sarcoplasmic surface of the tubular membrane and produces a change in surface potential. In a voltage-clamped fiber, an equal but opposite change in potential occurs across the tubular membrane that favors the movement of additional Q_β charge. Since this additional component of I_β does not occur until the SR begins to release Ca, it has a delayed time course. According to Pizarro et al. (1991), this delayed component of I_β is the component of I_{cm} that has been identified as I_γ.

This idea about the origin of I_γ can be tested by depletion of the SR of Ca and then measurement of I_{cm}. If I_{cm} consists of only I_β, support would be given for the proposal of Pizarro et al. (1991). On the other hand, if I_{cm} contains both I_β and I_γ components, support would be given for the idea that Q_β and Q_γ represent either two distinct species of charge or two transitions with different properties of a single species of charge.

I_β has three main identifiable properties: (*a*) the time course of ON I_β is approximately exponential at all potentials and does not show humps; (*b*) the time course of OFF I_β is also exponential and the time constant is independent of both the potential of the pulse and its duration; (*c*) the charge (Q_β) vs. V relation obeys the Boltzmann distribution function,

$$Q = \frac{Q_{max}}{1 + \exp[-(V - \overline{V})/k]},$$
(3)

with a value of k, the voltage steepness factor, that is appropriate for Q_β, 11–15 mV. V represents the voltage measured between the internal and external solutions (which is equal to the sum of the potential across the tubular membrane and the surface potentials on both sides of the membrane), $\overline{V}$ is the value of V at which the amount of equilibrium charge in the resting and activating states is the same, and Q_{max} represents the maximal amount of charge.

Experiments were carried out on Ca-depleted fibers to find out whether I_{cm} had these three properties. Frog cut muscle fibers were equilibrated with a Ca-free internal solution that contained 20 mM EGTA and an external solution that was also Ca-free. After an equilibration period of at least one hour, successive step depolarizations were used to deplete the SR of any remaining Ca. After 30–40 such depolarizations, the amount of readily releasable Ca inside the SR was usually <10 μM. The success of this procedure depends on the elimination of Ca from both the internal and external solutions and the use of a large concentration of EGTA in the internal solution.

Fig. 2 *A* shows six traces of I_{cm} recorded at voltages between -60 and -20 mV, as indicated. The ON I_{cm} during the depolarization to -60 mV shows only the early I_β component. When the potential was increased to -50 mV, I_β was followed by a small, prolonged I_γ component. As the potential was made progressively more positive, the amplitude of I_γ increased and its time course became briefer. Prominent I_γ humps are apparent in the traces to -40 to -20 mV. The time course of ON I_{cm} in this experiment does not satisfy property a of I_β.

After repolarization to -90 mV, the time course of the OFF I_{cm} was relatively brief after the depolarization to -60 mV. As the pulse potential was made more positive, the time course became progressively longer. The nonexponential behavior of OFF I_{cm} and the dependence of its time course on pulse potential does not satisfy property b of I_β.

Fig. 2 B shows the values of Q_{cm} plotted as a function of pulse potential, V_1. The curve shows a least-squares fit of a single Boltzmann distribution function, Eq. 3, calculated to include the currents from the different pathways in a double Vaseline-gap experiment, as described by Hui and Chandler (1990). These gap corrections produce a foot in the curve at potentials less than -60 mV and a slight negative slope at potentials greater than -20 mV. The best fit parameters are $\bar{V} = -48.1$ mV, $k = 6.1$ mV, and $q_{max}/c_m = 29.7$ nC/μF. In nine experiments of this type, $\bar{V} = -48.3$ mV (SEM, 0.7 mV), $k = 7.2$ mV (SEM, 0.3 mV), and $q_{max}/c_m = 33.5$ nC/μF (SEM, 1.5 nC/μF). The small value of k shows that Q_{cm} was strongly voltage dependent, similar to the situation in intact fibers that have not been Ca depleted (see Table VII in Hui and Chandler, 1990). Since the value of k is clearly smaller than that associated with Q_β, 11–15 mV (which was used in theoretical calculations by Pizarro et al., 1991), property c of I_β is not satisfied.

These and other results, which are described in Jong et al. (1995*b*), are inconsistent with the idea that there is one type of charge, Q_β, and that I_γ is a movement

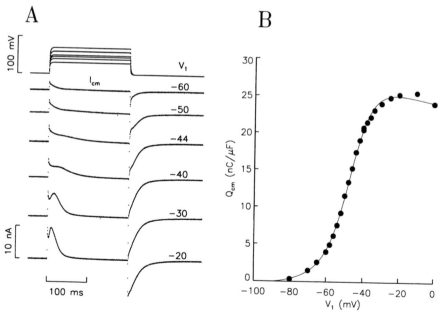

Figure 2. Traces of I_{cm} during different voltage steps (*A*) and the Q_{cm} vs. *V* relation (*B*) after SR Ca depletion. The internal solution was the same as that used in Fig. 1 except that Ca, Na, and K were replaced with Cs. The Ca-free external solution contained 110 mM TEA-gluconate, 10 mM MgSO$_4$, 1 μM tetrodotoxin, and 10 mM MOPS; pH $= 7.1$. Temperature, 14°C. From Jong et al. (1995*b*).

of Q_β caused by SR Ca release, as proposed by Pizarro et al. (1991). Rather, our results imply that Q_β and Q_γ represent either two distinct species of charge or two
transitions with different properties of a single species of charge.

Experiments described by Jong et al. (1995b) and by Pape et al. (1996) show
that SR Ca content or release or some related event alters the kinetics, but not the
amount, of Q_γ. For this reason, measurements of intramembranous charge movement in Ca-depleted fibers provide an opportunity for comparison of experimental
results, unaltered by any effects of SR Ca, with predictions from theoretical models
of charge movement. Jong et al. (1995b) show that many of the properties of Q_γ, as
well as the voltage dependence of the rate of SR Ca release for small depolarizations, are consistent with a simple model in which the voltage sensor for SR Ca release consists of four interacting charge movement particles, presumably DHPRs.

EGTA Can Be Used to Confine the Increase in Free [Ca] to Distances Near the SR Release Sites

Since, in frog muscle, the RyR Ca channels are located at the Z-line, it is reasonable
to suppose that SR Ca release occurs only in this region. If this is the case, after
stimulation the concentration of free Ca would be expected to increase first at the
Z-line and then, because of diffusional delays, later at more distant locations along
the sarcomere. To test this idea, Escobar et al. (1994) used a confocal spot detection
system to measure changes in fluorescence in frog cut muscle fibers equilibrated
with a fluorescent Ca indicator. After an action potential, the indicator's fluorescence changed in a manner consistent with Ca complexation. The amplitude of the
fluorescence change was slightly larger at the Z-line than at the M-line (which is situated midway between two Z-lines), and the rising phase of the signal was faster.
These and other observations are consistent with the idea that the delay between
the action potential and the onset of the fluorescence change was the same at the
Z-line and the M-line; this raised the possibility that Ca entry into the myoplasm
may not have been restricted to the Z-line.

In the experiments of Escobar et al. (1994), the local changes in myoplasmic
free [Ca] were influenced both by the location of the Ca-release sites and by the
presence of intrinsic myoplasmic Ca buffers, which are expected to have different
concentrations at the Z-line and the M-line. More direct information about the location of the release sites per se can be obtained with a high concentration of Ca
buffer such as EGTA used in combination with a small concentration of a rapidly
reacting fluorescent Ca indicator. The EGTA confines the increase in free [Ca] to
distances close to the release sites. The fluorescent indicator reacts with Ca within
this region, and the spatial profile of Ca-complexed indicator can be monitored
with confocal spot detection. In our experiments, the Ca indicator was fluo-3
(Minta et al., 1989), which is appreciably fluorescent only when complexed with Ca.

Fig. 3 shows a line-scan image of a fiber that was stimulated to give six action
potentials. A standard laser scanning confocal microscope was used to scan the fluorescence intensity at 512 pixel locations along a 40-μm line positioned parallel to
the long axis of the fiber. Each scan took 1.4 ms to complete. Horizontal lines from
1,024 successive scans are shown in chronologic order from top to bottom. The increases in [Cafluo-3] that were elicited by the six action potentials, which were
spaced 0.18 s apart, appear as brightened horizontal bands.

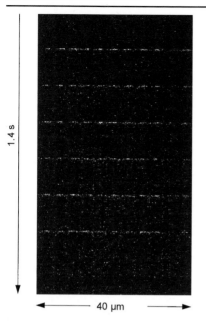

1.4 s

◄——— 40 μm ———►

Figure 3. Line scan of Cafluo-3 fluorescence along the fiber axis during action-potential stimulation. A standard LSM 410 Zeiss laser scanning confocal microscope was used with an objective with 40× magnification, 1.3 NA. An argon laser provided 488 nm light for excitation and fluo-3 fluorescence was measured at 515–565 nm. The internal and external solutions were the same as those used in Fig. 1 except that the internal solution contained 50 μM fluo-3 instead of 0.63 mM phenol red. Temperature, 21°C.

The signal-to-noise ratio of the spatial variation of fluorescence intensity within these bands was improved in three ways. First, for each of the 512 pixel locations, the prestimulus baselines were subtracted from each of the six action–potential stimulated responses and the signals were averaged. Second, the five bands with the maximal increases in intensity (which covered the time range 4–11 ms after stimulation) were averaged to give one value of intensity for each pixel location. Third, the resulting relation between intensity and pixel location was spatially filtered with a digital Gaussian filter (Colquhoun and Sigworth, 1983).

The final result is shown in Fig. 4, where the increase in fluorescence intensity (in arbitrary units) is plotted as a function of distance along a 30-μm path parallel to the long axis of the fiber. The increase in intensity varies periodically with distance with a period of 3.5 μm, which corresponds to the striation spacing of the fiber determined with transmitted light. The fluorescence intensity of the prestimulus baseline showed little, if any, discernible spatial variation in this experiment but did in experiments that were carried out with ≥100 μM fluo-3 in the internal solution.

In the experiment in Fig. 4, EGTA is expected to have captured almost all of the Ca that was released from the SR into the myoplasm (Pape et al., 1995). As a result, the spatial variation of fluorescence intensity is expected to have been little affected by any spatial variation of the intrinsic Ca buffers such as troponin, which is associated with the thin filaments. Consequently, the spatial variation of intensity is most likely due to spatial variation of Ca release along the sarcomere.

Estimates were made of the values of the 9 maxima and 8 minima in intensity in Fig. 4, from which 8 values of the minimum-to-maximum ratio were obtained. The mean value is 0.339 with a standard deviation of 0.085. This suggests that the rate of Ca release varied at least three-fold along a sarcomere. The actual variation is expected to have been greater than this, however, because the spatial variation of Δ[Cafluo-3] is expected to be broader than that of Δ[Ca]: After Ca-free fluo-3 (which is weakly fluorescent) complexes Ca near the release sites, Cafluo-3 (which

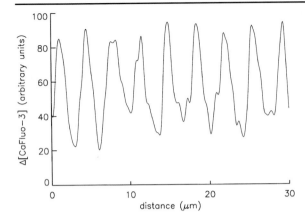

Figure 4. Spatial variation of Cafluo-3 fluorescence after action-potential stimulation. From the experiment in Fig. 3.

is highly fluorescent) has a chance to diffuse away from the sites before it dissociates into Ca and fluo-3.

Although the exact spatial location of the maxima of the fluorescence signals was not determined in these experiments, the peaks are expected to have occurred at the Z-line, where the RyR Ca channels are located. If the release sites are uniformly distributed in the plane of the Z-line, the spatial variation of $\Delta[Ca]$ in the presence of a large concentration of EGTA can be analyzed in terms of the usual one-dimensional diffusion equation. If x represents the distance along a sarcomere with $x = 0$ corresponding to the location of the Z-line, then

$$\Delta[Ca](x) \cong \Delta[\overline{Ca}]\left[\frac{l}{\lambda_{Ca}} \cdot \exp(-x/\lambda_{Ca})\right] \tag{4}$$

(Pape et al., 1995). In this equation, $\Delta[Ca](x)$ represents the value of the change in myoplasmic free [Ca] at x and $\Delta[\overline{Ca}]$ represents the spatially averaged value of $\Delta[Ca]$ (which is denoted simply by $\Delta[Ca]$ in Fig. 1). l is one-half the sarcomere length. λ_{Ca} is the characteristic distance associated with the diffusion of Ca before capture by EGTA,

$$\lambda_{Ca} = \sqrt{\frac{D_{Ca}}{k_1[EGTA]_R}}, \tag{5}$$

in which D_{Ca} is the diffusion constant of Ca in myoplasm (Neher, 1986; Pape et al., 1995). $\Delta[Ca]_0$, the value of $\Delta[Ca](x)$ at $x = 0$, is equal to $\Delta[\overline{Ca}]\cdot(l/\lambda_{Ca})$. Since, under the conditions of these experiments, the value of $\Delta[\overline{Ca}]$ is expected to be proportional to the rate of SR Ca release (Pape et al., 1995), the value of $\Delta[Ca](x)$ is also expected to be proportional to the rate of release.

The curve labeled $\Delta[Ca]/\Delta[Ca]_0$ in Fig. 5 was calculated from Eq. 4 with $l = 1.75$ μm (corresponding to a sarcomere spacing of 3.5 μm) and $\lambda_{Ca} = 81$ nm (calculated from Eq. 5 with $D_{Ca} = 3.0 \times 10^{-6}$ cm^2/s and $k_1[EGTA]_R = 45,600$ s^{-1}, Pape et al., 1995).

The spatial variation of $\Delta[Cafluo-3]$ was calculated from the one-dimensional steady-state equation that relates the diffusion of Cafluo-3 and the reaction between Ca and fluo-3,

$$D_{fluo}d^2y/dx^2 = k_2\Delta[Ca](y-1) + k_{-2}y. \tag{6}$$

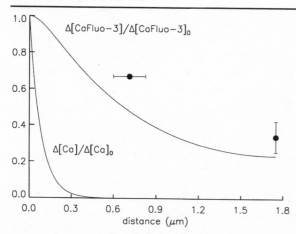

Figure 5. Ratio of minimum-to-maximum Cafluo-3 fluorescence and halfway distance, from Fig. 4. The $\Delta[\text{Cafluo-3}]/\Delta[\text{Cafluo-3}]_0$ curve was calculated by numerical integration of Eq. 6 with $D_{\text{fluo}} = 0.20 \times 10^{-6}$ cm^2/s, $k_2 = 1.31 \times 10^7$ M^{-1}s^{-1}, and $k_{-2} = 33.5$ s^{-1}. For the integration and the $\Delta[\text{Ca}]/\Delta[\text{Ca}]_0$ curve, $\Delta[\text{Ca}]$ was calculated from Eq. 4 with $l = 1.75$ μm, $\lambda_{\text{Ca}} = 81$ nm, and $\Delta[\overline{\text{Ca}}] = 3.3$ μM.

y represents the fraction of fluo-3 that is complexed with Ca, D_{fluo} represents the apparent myoplasmic diffusion constant of Cafluo-3, and k_2 and k_{-2} represent the forward and backward rate constants, respectively, for the reaction between Ca and fluo-3. Eq. 6 was derived with the assumptions that the myoplasmic diffusion constant of Cafluo-3 is the same as that of fluo-3 and that the sum of the concentrations of Cafluo-3 and fluo-3 is constant.

The curve labeled $\Delta[\text{Cafluo-3}]/\Delta[\text{Cafluo-3}]_0$ in Fig. 5 was calculated by numerical integration of Eq. 6. The values of D_{fluo}, k_2, and k_{-2} were assumed to be the same as those measured by Harkins et al. (1993) in intact fibers at 16–17°C: $D_{\text{fluo}} = 0.20 \times 10^{-6}$ cm^2/s, $k_2 = 1.31 \times 10^7$ M^{-1}s^{-1}, and $k_{-2} = 33.5$ s^{-1}. The value of $\Delta[\text{Ca}]$ was calculated from Eq. 4 with $l = 1.75$ μm and $\lambda_{\text{Ca}} = 81$ nm (see above) and with $\Delta[\overline{\text{Ca}}] = 3.3$ μM, the mean peak value determined by Pape et al. (1995) in fibers equilibrated with the same solutions used in Figs. 3–5 (except that phenol red was used instead of fluo-3). The $\Delta[\text{Cafluo-3}]/\Delta[\text{Cafluo-3}]_0$ curve is broader than the $\Delta[\text{Ca}]/\Delta[\text{Ca}]_0$ curve, as expected, and its minimal value at $x = 1.75$ μm, 0.175, is larger than $\sim$0. These differences depend on the distance that Cafluo-3 is able to diffuse before it dissociates into Ca and fluo-3. They would be reduced if the value of D_{fluo} were reduced or the value of k_{-2} were increased.

The filled circle at $x = 1.75$ μm gives the mean value of the minimum-to-maximum ratio, 0.339, with ± 1 standard deviation indicated (see above). The other filled circle marks the mean value of x, with ± 1 standard deviation indicated, for which $\Delta[\text{Cafluo-3}]/\Delta[\text{Cafluo-3}]_0$ is halfway between maximum and minimum values. Both experimental points lie somewhat above the theoretical curve.

Several factors should be considered in the comparison of the experimental points in Fig. 5 with the theoretical $\Delta[\text{Cafluo-3}]/\Delta[\text{Cafluo-3}]_0$ curve. The spatial limitations of the confocal detection system and the spatial filtering of the data would be expected to increase the values of both points; for example, the digital Gaussian filter increased the value of the minimum-to-maximum ratio of the theoretical $\Delta[\text{Cafluo-3}]/\Delta[\text{Cafluo-3}]_0$ curve by 16% (not shown). Another source of uncertainty is the selection of the values of D_{fluo}, k_2, and k_{-2} for the theoretical curve; they were determined from experiments on intact fibers at 16–17°C, whereas our experiments were carried out on cut fibers at $\sim$21°C. In addition, the theoretical curve applies to the steady state whereas the experimental points were obtained during the first 4–11 ms after stimulation. With these considerations in mind, it seems safe to conclude that most of the SR Ca-release sites have a spatial location that has the same periodicity as the sarcomeres (for example, the Z-line). Although it is not possible to state with certainty that all of the release occurs at this location, our data are probably consistent with this possibility.

With Low Levels of Release, EGTA Can Shield an Open SR Ca Channel from the Increases in Free [Ca] Produced by Neighboring Open Channels

According to Eq. 4 and the $\Delta[Ca]/\Delta[Ca]_0$ curve in Fig. 5, 20 mM EGTA is able to shield the SR Ca sites in one Z-line from increases in free [Ca] that might arise from Ca movements through open sites in adjacent Z-lines. At extremely low levels of activation, however, EGTA can shield each open site in a particular Z-line from Ca from neighboring open sites in the same Z-line. In this situation, the activation of any particular open site could not have been influenced by Ca from other open sites. Since extremely small rates of SR Ca release can be measured with the EGTA-phenol red method, the voltage dependence of Ca release can be assessed in the absence of any positive feedback effects of Ca. For the purposes of this article, an SR Ca-release site consists of a single SR Ca channel or a collection of channels that function as a singly gated unit (for example, a single voltage-gated channel and neighboring channel(s) that are slaved to it).

Fig. 6 shows the results of an experiment in which SR Ca release was elicited by small step depolarizations to different voltages. The upper trace in panel A shows a representative voltage record and the lower superimposed traces show seven $\Delta[Ca_T]$ signals obtained at the indicated voltages (in mV). In this experiment, each 400-ms depolarization was followed by a 500-ms repolarization to the holding potential, -90 mV, after which a 600-ms pulse to -35 mV was given to deplete the SR of any remaining Ca. A recovery period of five minutes was used before each trial so that the SR would be able to reaccumulate almost all of the Ca released by the preceding pulse; as a result, the value of $[Ca_{SR}]_R$ changed little during the experiment, from 2,594 to 2,447 μM.

A sloping straight line was least-squares fitted to the rising phase of each trace in Fig. 6 A and of two additional traces from the same experiment. The filled circles in Fig. 6 B show the values of the slopes of these lines, $d\Delta[Ca_T]/dt$, plotted on a semilogarithmic scale as a function of pulse potential. The straight line that was least-squares fitted to the points, obtained from -80 to -57 mV, provides a good fit. At potentials more positive than -57 mV, the experimental values of $d\Delta[Ca_T]/dt$ lie below the extrapolated line (not shown). The slope of the line corresponds to an e-fold increase in $d\Delta[Ca_T]/dt$ every 3.7 mV. In four experiments of this type, the mean e-fold factor was 3.5 mV (SEM, 0.2 mV).

In Fig. 6, the rate of SR Ca release was steeply voltage dependent even when its value was as small as 0.01 μM/ms. This is four orders of magnitude smaller than the peak rate of release, $\sim$100 μM/ms, that was observed in this fiber with strong depolarizations (not shown). Since the rate of release with all of the SR Ca channels open would be expected to be $>$100 μM/ms, because of Ca inactivation of Ca release, the results in Fig. 6 B show that SR Ca release is steeply voltage-dependent under conditions in which only one SR Ca channel in $\geqslant$10^4 is open.

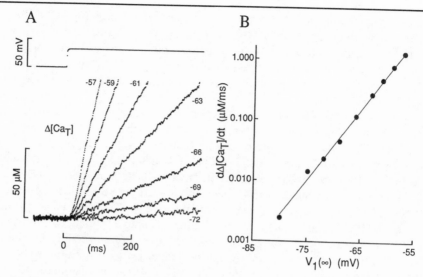

Figure 6. Voltage dependence of the rate of SR Ca release for small depolarizations. The internal solution was the same as that used in Fig. 2 except that it contained 1.76 mM Ca. The Ca-free external solution was the same as that used in Fig. 2. Temperature, 14°C. From Pape et al. (1995).

On the assumption that the concentration of SR Ca channels is the same as that of the foot structures described by Franzini-Armstrong (1975), Pape et al. (1992) estimated the concentration of channels in the myoplasmic solution to be 0.27 μM. In a frog fiber with a sarcomere length of 3.6 μm, which is typical of our EGTA-phenol red experiments, a channel concentration of 0.27 μM corresponds to about 600 channels per μm² of cross-sectional area in the plane of the Z-line, where the channels are expected to be located. If only one channel in ≥10⁴ is open, the density of open channels, ρ, is ≤0.06 channels per μm².

If the Ca-releasing activity of an SR Ca channel is approximated by a point source of strength φ (in units of moles per second) immersed in an infinite isotropic medium, the steady state value of Δ[Ca] at a distance r from the source is given by the well known equation

$$\Delta[\text{Ca}] = \frac{\phi}{4\pi D_{\text{Ca}}r}. \tag{7}$$

In this equation, Δ[Ca] refers to the value of free [Ca] at r minus that at $r \to \infty$. Neher (1986) showed that the effect of EGTA is to reduce the steady state value of Δ[Ca] by the factor $\exp(-r/\lambda_{\text{Ca}})$, so that

$$\Delta[\text{Ca}] = \frac{\phi}{4\pi D_{\text{Ca}}r}\exp(-r/\lambda_{\text{Ca}}). \tag{8}$$

To apply Eq. 8 to the experiment in Fig. 6, first consider the case that the measured peak value of $d\Delta[\text{Ca}_\text{T}]/dt$, ~100 μM/ms, corresponds to all of the SR Ca channels being open. The ratio of the value of $d\Delta[\text{Ca}_\text{T}]/dt$ to the concentration of SR Ca channels (0.27 μM, given above) gives a value of φ that corresponds to a flux rate of 3.7×10^5 ions/s. Since ρ = 0.06 channels per μm² (see above), the mean distance between an open channel and its nearest open neighbor, given by $(4\rho)^{-1/2}$ if the open channels are distributed randomly, is equal to 2 μm. At $r = 2$ μm, Eq. 8 gives $\Delta[Ca] = 1.5 \times 10^{-18}$ M, which is too small to be expected to exert any influence on channel gating. On the other hand, if the peak release rate of $\sim$100 μM/ms is supported by less than 100% of the channels being open, the same set of calculations gives $\Delta[Ca] < 1.5 \times 10^{-18}$ M.

Pape et al. (1995) used these and other considerations to conclude that, if open Ca channels or, more generally, Ca-release sites are distributed randomly in the plane of the Z-line, the open state of any particular site in the experiment in Fig. 6 could not have been influenced by Ca from another open site, at least during the smallest rates of release. For this reason, the steep voltage dependence of SR Ca release would not be expected to have been influenced by SR Ca release—such as might occur by Ca-induced Ca release, by the positive feedback model proposed by Pizarró et al. (1991), or by some other mechanism. A similar conclusion is expected to apply to the entire voltage range illustrated in Fig. 6 B because all of the data are well-fitted by the same straight line. At larger depolarizations, the points lay below the extrapolated line; this indicates that the voltage steepness of release never exceeded that observed with small rates of release (such as might occur if a positive feedback effect of Ca became pronounced). Since the voltage steepness of release in these fibers equilibrated with 20 mM EGTA is similar to that determined in fibers with unmodified [Ca] transients (Baylor et al., 1983; Maylie et al., 1987), it seems reasonable to conclude that the voltage dependence of Ca release recorded under normal physiologic conditions with unmodified [Ca] transients directly reflects the voltage dependence of activation of single SR release sites by their voltage sensors in the membranes of the transverse tubular system.

Conclusions

The experiments described in this chapter were carried out on frog cut twitch fibers that had been equilibrated with an internal solution that contained 20 mM EGTA and 0–1.76 mM Ca. After stimulation, almost all of the Ca that is released from the SR is expected to be complexed rapidly by EGTA and exchanged for protons with a 1:2 stoichiometry. A reliable estimate of SR Ca release can be obtained from measurements of ΔpH. One advantage of this method is that the estimate of SR Ca release does not depend on the properties of the various intrinsic myoplasmic Ca buffers. Experiments with Ca-depleted fibers show that intramembranous charge movement consists of both Q_β and Q_γ components, even when the SR does not release Ca. Two findings are consistent with the idea that the voltage steepness of SR Ca release is an intrinsic function of the voltage sensor in the membranes of the transverse tubular system and does not require positive feedback from Ca release. The first finding is that the voltage dependence of the Q_{cm} vs. V relation in Ca-depleted fibers is similar to that obtained from fibers with Ca inside their SR. The second finding is that the rate of SR Ca release elicited by small depolarizations is steeply voltage-dependent under conditions in which EGTA is expected to shield each open channel (or site) from any significant increase in free [Ca] produced by Ca flux through a neighboring open site. Experiments with confocal microscopy show that SR Ca release is localized along the sarcomere, presumably at the Z-line, consistent with the idea that the voltage control of release occurs at the triadic junction, where both the DHPRs and the RyRs are located.

Acknowledgments

We thank Drs. Ariel Escobar and Julio Vergara for help with the design of the experimental chamber. We also thank Drs. Steve Baylor and Stephen Hollingworth for reading the manuscript.

This work was supported by U.S. Public Health Service grant AM-37643.

References

Adrian, R.H., and A. Peres. 1977. A "gating" signal for the potassium channel? *Nature.* 267:800–804.

Adrian, R.H., and A. Peres. 1979. Charge movement and membrane capacity in frog muscle. *J. Physiol.* 289:83–97.

Almers, W. 1978. Gating currents and charge movements in excitable membranes. *Rev. Physiol. Biochem. Pharmacol.* 82:96–190.

Baylor, S.M., W.K. Chandler, and M.W. Marshall. 1983. Sarcoplasmic reticulum calcium release in frog skeletal muscle fibres estimated from arsenazo III calcium transients. *J. Physiol.* 344:625–666.

Block, B.A., T. Imagawa, K.P. Campbell, and C. Franzini-Armstrong. 1988. Structural evidence for direct interaction between the molecular components of the transverse tubule/sarcoplasmic reticulum junction in skeletal muscle. *J. Cell Biol.* 107:2587–2600.

Colquhoun, D., and F.J. Sigworth. 1983. Fitting and statistical analysis of single-channel records. *In* Single-Channel Recording. B. Sakmann and E. Neher, editors. Plenum Press, New York. 191–263.

Csernoch, L., G. Pizarro, I. Uribe, M. Rodriguez, and E. Ríos. 1991. Interfering with calcium release suppresses Iγ, the "hump" component of intramembranous charge movement in skeletal muscle. *J. Gen. Physiol.* 97:845–884.

Escobar, A.L., J.R. Monck, J.M. Fernandez, and J.L. Vergara. 1994. Localization of the site of Ca^{2+} release at the level of a single sarcomere in skeletal muscle fibres. *Nature.* 367:739–741.

Franzini-Armstrong, C. 1975. Membrane particles and transmission at the triad. *Fed. Proc.* 34:1382–1389.

Garcia, J., G. Pizarro, E. Ríos, and E. Stefani. 1991. Effect of the calcium buffer EGTA on the "hump" component of charge movement in skeletal muscle. *J. Gen. Physiol.* 97:885–896.

Harkins, A.B., N. Kurebayashi, and S.M. Baylor. 1993. Resting myoplasmic free calcium in frog skeletal muscle fibers estimated with fluo-3. *Biophys. J.* 65:865–881.

Hui, C.S., and W.K. Chandler. 1990. Intramembranous charge movement in frog cut twitch fibers mounted in a double Vaseline-gap chamber. *J. Gen. Physiol.* 96:257–297.

Hymel, L., M. Inui, S. Fleischer, and H. Schindler. 1988. Purified ryanodine receptor of skeletal muscle sarcoplasmic reticulum forms Ca^{2+}-activated oligomeric Ca^{2+} channels in planar bilayers. *Proc. Natl. Acad. Sci. USA.* 85:441–445.

Imagawa, T., J.S. Smith, R. Coronado, and K.P. Campbell. 1987. Purified ryanodine receptor from skeletal muscle sarcoplasmic reticulum is the Ca^{2+} permeable pore of the calcium release channel. *J. Biol. Chem.* 262:16636–16643.

Jong, D.-S., P.C. Pape, S.M. Baylor, and W.K. Chandler. 1995a. Calcium inactivation of calcium release in frog cut muscle fibers that contain millimolar EGTA or fura-2. *J. Gen. Physiol.* 106:337–388.

Jong, D.-S., P.C. Pape, and W.K. Chandler. 1995b. Effect of sarcoplasmic reticulum calcium depletion on intramembranous charge movement in frog cut muscle fibers. *J. Gen. Physiol.* 106:659–704.

Lai, F.A., H.P. Erickson, E. Rousseau, Q.-Y. Liu, and G. Meissner. 1988. Purification and reconstruction of the calcium release channel from skeletal muscle. *Nature.* 331:315–319.

Maylie, J., M. Irving, N.L. Sizto, and W.K. Chandler. 1987. Calcium signals recorded from cut frog twitch fibers containing antipyrylazo III. *J. Gen. Physiol.* 89:83–143.

Minta, A., J.P.Y. Kao, and R.Y. Tsien. 1989. Fluorescent indicators for cytosolic calcium based on rhodamine and fluorescein chromophores. *J. Biol. Chem.* 264:8171–8178.

Neher, E. 1986. Concentration profiles of intracellular calcium in the presence of a diffusible chelator. *In* Calcium Electrogenesis and Neuronal Functioning. U. Heinemann, M. Klee, E. Neher, and W. Singer, editors. Springer-Verlag, Berlin Heidelberg. 80–96.

Pape, P.C., D.-S. Jong, and W.K. Chandler. 1995. Calcium release and its voltage dependence in frog cut muscle fibers equilibrated with 20 mM EGTA. *J. Gen. Physiol.* 106:259–336.

Pape, P.C., D.-S. Jong, and W.K. Chandler. 1996. A slow component of intramembranous charge movement during sarcoplasmic reticulum calcium release in frog cut muscle fibers. *J. Gen. Physiol.* 107:79–101.

Pape, P.C., M. Konishi, and S.M. Baylor. 1992. Valinomycin and excitation-contraction coupling in skeletal muscle fibres of the frog. *J. Physiol.* 449:219–235.

Pizarro, G., L. Csernoch, I. Uribe, M. Rodriguez, and E. Ríos. 1991. The relationship between Q_γ and Ca release from the sarcoplasmic reticulum in skeletal muscle. *J. Gen. Physiol.* 97:913–947.

Ríos, E., and G. Brum. 1987. Involvement of dihydropyridine receptors in excitation-contraction coupling in skeletal muscle. *Nature.* 325:717–720.

Schneider, M.F., and W.K. Chandler. 1973. Voltage dependent charge movement in skeletal muscle: A possible step in excitation-contraction coupling. *Nature.* 242:244–246.

Smith, P.D., G.W. Liesegang, R.L. Berger, G. Czerlinski, and R.J. Podolsky. 1984. A stopped-flow investigation of calcium ion binding by ethylene elycol eis(β-aminoethyl ether)-N,N'-tetraacetic acid. *Anal. Biochem.* 143:188–195.

Szucs, G., L. Csernoch, J. Magyar, and L. Kovacs. 1991. Contraction threshold and the "hump" component of charge movement in frog skeletal muscle. *J. Gen. Physiol.* 97:897–911.

Tanabe, T., K.G. Beam, J.A. Powell, and S. Numa. 1988. Restoration of excitation-contraction coupling and slow calcium current in dysgenic muscle by dihydropyridine receptor complementary DNA. *Nature.* 336:134–139.

List of Contributors

Cristina Ballarin, Dipartimento di Chimica Biologica, Università di Padova, 35121 Padova, Italy

Alessandro Bertoli, Dipartimento di Chimica Biologica, Università di Padova, 35121 Padova, Italy

Ilya Bezprozvanny, Department of Molecular and Cellular Physiology, Beckman Center, Stanford University Medical Center, Stanford, California 94305

Elizabeth Blachly-Dyson, Vollum Institute of Advanced Biomedical Research, Oregon Health Sciences University, Portland, Oregon 97201

Barbara A. Block, Department of Biological Sciences, Hopkins Marine Station, Stanford University, Pacific Grove, California 93950

Paul Blount, Laboratory of Molecular Biology and Department of Genetics, University of Wisconsin, Madison, Wisconsin 53706

G. Brandolin, Laboratoire de Biochimie, Unité de Recherche Associée 1130 du Centre National de la Recherche Scientifique, Département de Biologie Moléculaire et Structurale, CEA/Grenoble, France

Anne-Marie B. Brillantes, Cardiovascular Institute, Department of Medicine, and Brookdale Center for Molecular Biology, Mount Sinai School of Medicine, New York 10029

W. Knox Chandler, Department of Cellular and Molecular Physiology, Yale University School of Medicine, New Haven, Connecticut 06510-8026

David E. Clapham, Department of Pharmacology, Mayo Foundation, Rochester, Minnesota 55905

Frederic S. Cohen, Department of Molecular Biophysics and Physiology, Rush Medical College, Chicago, Illinois 60612

Marco Colombini, Department of Zoology, University of Maryland, College Park, Maryland 27402

Tsafi Danieli, Department of Neurobiochemistry, Tel Aviv University, 69978 Tel Aviv, Israel

A.C. Dianoux, Laboratoire de Biochimie, Unité de Recherche Associée 1130 du Centre National de la Recherche Scientifique, Département de Biologie Moléculaire et Structurale, CEA/Grenoble, France

Ricardo E. Dolmetsch, Department of Molecular and Cellular Physiology, Stanford University School of Medicine, Stanford, California 94305

Barbara E. Ehrlich, Departments of Medicine and Physiology, University of Connecticut, Farmington, Connecticut 06030

B. Farrell, Department of Physiology and Biophysics, Mayo Clinic, Rochester, Minnesota 55905

J.M. Fernandez, Department of Physiology and Biophysics, Mayo Clinic, Rochester, Minnesota 55905

C. Fiore, Laboratoire de Biochimie, Unité de Recherche Associée 1130 du Centre National de la Recherche Scientifique, Département de Biologie Moléculaire et Structurale, CEA/Grenoble, France

Michael Forgac, Department of Cellular and Molecular Physiology, Tufts University School of Medicine, Boston, Massachusetts 02111

Michael Forte, Vollum Institute of Advanced Biomedical Research, Oregon Health Sciences University, Portland, Oregon 97201

Jens Franck, Department of Biological Sciences, Hopkins Marine Station, Stanford University, Pacific Grove, California 93950

Clara Franzini-Armstrong, Department of Cell and Developmental Biology, University of Pennsylvania School of Medicine, Philadelphia, Pennsylvania 19104-6058

John Geibel, Departments of Cellular and Molecular Physiology and Surgery, Yale University School of Medicine, New Haven, Connecticut 06510-8026

H. Robert Guy, Laboratory of Mathematical Biology, National Cancer Institute, National Institutes of Health, Bethesda, Maryland 20892

Yoav I. Henis, Department of Neurobiochemistry, Tel Aviv University, 69978 Tel Aviv, Israel

Carlos B. Hirschberg, Department of Biochemistry and Molecular Biology, University of Massachusetts Medical School, Worcester, Massachusetts 01655

Masamitsu Iino, Department of Pharmacology, Faculty of Medicine, The University of Tokyo, Bunkyo-ku, Tokyo 113, Japan

De-Shien Jong, Department of Animal Science, National Taiwan University, Taipei, Taiwan, Republic of China

Ching Kung, Laboratory of Molecular Biology and Department of Genetics, University of Wisconsin, Madison, Wisconsin 53706

G.J.M. Lauquin, Laboratoire de Physiologie Moléculaire et Cellulaire, Institut de Biochimie et Génétique Cellulaires, Unité Propre de Recherche 9026 du Centre National de la Recherche Scientifique, Bordeaux, France

A. Le Saux, Laboratoire de Physiologie Moléculaire et Cellulaire, Institut de Biochimie et Génétique Cellulaires, Unité Propre de Recherche 9026 du Centre National de la Recherche Scientifique, Bordeaux, France

Richard S. Lewis, Department of Molecular and Cellular Physiology, Stanford University School of Medicine, Stanford, California 94305

Andreas Luckhoff, Institute of Pharmacology, Berlin D-14195, Germany

David H. MacLennan, Banting and Best Department of Medical Research, University of Toronto, Charles H. Best Institute, Toronto, Ontario, Canada M5G1L6

Andrew Marks, Cardiovascular Institute, Department of Medicine, and Brookdale Center for Molecular Biology, Mount Sinai School of Medicine, New York 10029

P. Marszalek, Department of Physiology and Biophysics, Mayo Clinic, Rochester, Minnesota 55905

Boris Martinac, Department of Pharmacology, The University of Western Australia, Nedlands, Western Australia 6907

Grigory Melikyan, Department of Molecular Biophysics and Physiology, Rush Medical College, Chicago, Illinois 60612

John O'Brien, Department of Ophthalmology and Visual Sciences, University of Illinois, Chicago, Illinois 60612

Karol Ondrias, Cardiovascular Institute, Department of Medicine, and Brookdale Center for Molecular Biology, Mount Sinai School of Medicine, New York 10029

Paul C. Pape, Département de Physiologie et Biophysique, Faculté de Médecine, Université de Sherbrooke, Sherbrooke, Québec, Canada J1H5N4

Anant B. Parekh, Department of Membrane Biophysics, Max-Planck Institute for Biophysical Chemistry, Am Fassberg, 37077 Göttingen, Germany

Reinhold Penner, Department of Membrane Biophysics, Max-Planck Institute for Biophysical Chemistry, Am Fassberg, 37077 Göttingen, Germany

Carmen Perez-Terzic, Department of Pharmacology, Mayo Foundation, Rochester, Minnesota 55905

P. Roux, Laboratoire de Biochimie, Unité de Recherche Associée 1130 du Centre National de la Recherche Scientifique, Département de Biologie Moléculaire et Structurale, CEA/Grenoble, France

C. Schwimmer, Laboratoire de Physiologie Moléculaire et Cellulaire, Institut de Biochimie et Génétique Cellulaires, Unité Propre de Recherche 9026 du Centre National de la Recherche Scientifique, Bordeaux, France

Andrew Scott, Cardiovascular Institute, Department of Medicine, and Brookdale Center for Molecular Biology, Mount Sinai School of Medicine, New York 10029

M. Catia Sorgato, Dipartimento di Chimica Biologica, Università di Padova, 35121 Padova, Italy

Lisa Stehno-Bittel, Department of Physical Therapy, University of Kansas Medical Center, Kansas City, Kansas 66160-7601

Sergei I. Sukharev, Laboratory of Molecular Biology and Department of Genetics, University of Wisconsin, Madison, Wisconsin 53706

Kathleen M.C. Sullivan, Department of Cell Biology and Anatomy, The Johns Hopkins University School of Medicine, Baltimore, Maryland 21205

Toshihiko Toyofuku, Banting and Best Department of Medical Research, University of Toronto, Charles H. Best Institute, Toronto, Ontario, Canada M5G1L6

V. Trezeguet, Laboratoire de Physiologie Moléculaire et Cellulaire, Institut de Biochimie et Génétique Cellulaires, Unité Propre de Recherche 9026 du Centre National de la Recherche Scientifique, Bordeaux, France

P.V. Vignais, Laboratoire de Biochimie, Unité de Recherche Associée 1130 du Centre National de la Recherche Scientifique, Département de Biologie Moléculaire et Structurale, CEA/Grenoble, France

Judith M. White, Department of Cell Biology, University of Virginia, Charlottesville, Virginia 22908

Christiane Wiese, Department of Cell Biology and Anatomy, The Johns Hopkins University School of Medicine, Baltimore, Maryland 21205

Katherine L. Wilson, Department of Cell Biology and Anatomy, The Johns Hopkins University School of Medicine, Baltimore, Maryland 21205

Grazyna Wojcik, Dipartimento di Chimica Biologica, Università di Padova, 35121 Padova, Italy

Adam Zweifach, Department of Molecular and Cellular Physiology, Stanford University School of Medicine, Stanford, California 94305

Subject Index